The
Essential Oils

BY

ERNEST GUENTHER, Ph.D.

Vice President and Technical Director
Fritzsche Brothers, Inc., New York, N. Y.

VOLUME SIX

INDIVIDUAL ESSENTIAL OILS
OF THE PLANT FAMILIES

ERICACEAE, BETULACEAE, VALERIANACEAE, VERBENA-CEAE, CISTACEAE, CRUCIFERAE, LILIACEAE, IRIDACEAE, ARACEAE, PALMAE, CYPERACEAE, MORACEAE, ARISTOLO-CHIACEAE, CHENOPODIACEAE, RANUNCULACEAE, EU-PHORBIACEAE, MALVACEAE, USNEACEAE, PODOCARPA-CEAE, PINACEAE, TAXODIACEAE, AND CUPRESSACEAE

1952

D. VAN NOSTRAND COMPANY, Inc.

TORONTO   NEW YORK   LONDON

NEW YORK

D. Van Nostrand Company, Inc., 250 Fourth Avenue, New York 3

TORONTO

D. Van Nostrand Company (Canada), Ltd., 228 Bloor Street, Toronto

LONDON

Macmillan & Company, Ltd., St. Martin's Street, London, W.C. 2

PRINTED IN THE UNITED STATES OF AMERICA

PREFACE

The present volume—the sixth—completes this series on "The Essential Oils." Like the third, fourth, and fifth, it is composed of monographs describing individual oils. Many of these will be of particular interest to the pharmaceutical, flavor and perfume industries: wintergreen, sweet birch, valerian, mustard, onion, hops, wormseed, juniper, labdanum and oak moss—to name only a few. A large section of the volume is devoted to the pine oils, so valuable to manufacturers of soaps, disinfectants, sprays, bath and other scented technical preparations. An authoritative and detailed chapter, by Dr. Leo Goldblatt, deals with the turpentine and related oils of the American Naval Stores Industries.

As was pointed out in the Prefaces to previous volumes, the monographs on individual essential oils are not arranged according to any complete taxonomic system, but follow a sequence considered more convenient for practical use. However, to satisfy the botanist, a table showing the taxonomic classification of all the essential oils described in these six volumes has been included at the end of the present volume.

In addition to the oils treated in this series there are many more that have been produced on a purely experimental scale during the last fifty or hundred years. However, much of the information on such oils, particularly that relating to plant origin, is confused and contradictory. No purpose would have been served by including these little-known and often ill-defined oils in this work, in which emphasis has been placed upon oils of technical and scientific importance, and upon reliability of data. Any reader interested in oils of such secondary rank will find the literature on them in the third (German) edition of Gildemeister and Hoffmann's "Die Ätherischen Öle" (1928–31); for later information Chemical Abstracts should be consulted.

The completion of "The Essential Oils" has required more than twenty years of field investigations throughout the oil-producing regions of the world, and ten years of literature research, editing and writing. Much effort and toil have been expended on a task made difficult not only by the continuing rapid progress of chemistry, but also by the profound economic changes that have taken place recently in the essential industry throughout the world. A work originally planned to comprise no more than three volumes has now grown to six—an enterprise of some magnitude for one private concern to have undertaken, particularly in a time of economic and political uncertainty. Mounting costs of research and publication—most unfortunately for science and technology—may deter any future attempt to publish a comparable work in so relatively limited a field. It seems not unlikely that in the future comprehensive scientific and technical works on the scale of "The Essential Oils" will have to be compiled by foundations supported financially in a large measure by the particular industry concerned. This should by no means be taken to imply that the present series is the accomplishment of only one individual. It represents a joint effort; as such may it be accepted as a sincere endeavor to present the complete story of those interesting, widely important, and often highly romantic products—the essential oils.

ERNEST GUENTHER

New York, N. Y.
March, 1952

NOTE

All temperatures given in this work are expressed in degrees Centigrade unless otherwise specified in the text.

ACKNOWLEDGMENT

The author wishes to express his sincere gratitude to those collaborators and correspondents whose advice concerning special features and developments in the essential oil industry—scientific as well as technical—has been so valuable in the compilation of this volume. Some of these contributors have been personal friends for many years; all are experts in their respective fields:

Mr. Ramon Bordas, Destilaciones Bordas Chinchurreta, S. A., Sevilla, Spain.

Mr. Pierre Chauvet, Pierre Chauvet & Co., Seillans, Var, France.

Dr. Yves-René Naves, Research Laboratories of Givaudan & Cie., Geneva, Switzerland.

Dr. H. Schinz, Research Laboratories of Firmenich et Cie., Successeurs de Chuit, Naef et Cie., Geneva, Switzerland.

Messrs. Unterweger, Erste Tiroler Latschenöl-Brennerei, Thal-Assling (Eastern Tyrol), Austria.

The Staffs of the New York Public Library, the Library of the Chemists' Club, New York, and of the Bronx Botanical Gardens have been most courteous and helpful on innumerable occasions. To the last of these the author is particularly indebted.

Dr. Leo A. Goldblatt, In Charge, Fundamental Section, Naval Stores Research Division, Bureau of Agricultural and Industrial Chemistry, United States Department of Agriculture, Olustee, Florida, wrote the comprehensive chapter on the American Turpentines. In his task Dr. Goldblatt was advised by E. L. Patton, Head of the Naval Stores Research Division, by Mr. R. V. Lawrence, in charge of the Technological Section of the Division, by Dr. J. P. Bain of the Glidden Company, and by Mr. R. C. Palmer of Newport Industries, Inc.

Dr. Theodor Philipp Haas, Philadelphia College of Pharmacy and Science, Pennsylvania, contributed the plant taxonomic tables at the end of the volume, and frequently assisted the author in problems of botanical nomenclature that arose in the course of this work.

Dr. Teikichi Hiraizumi, Takasago Perfumery Co., Ltd., Tokyo, Japan, gave valuable information about several Japanese and Formosan essential oils, previously little known in the Occident.

Mr. A. R. Penfold, Director of the Museum of Applied Arts and Sciences, Sydney, Australia, and Mr. F. R. Morrison, Economic Chemist of the same Institution, lent their wide experience regarding certain Australian oils.

Mr. Edward E. Langenau, Director of Analytical Laboratories, Fritzsche Brothers, Inc., New York, not only assembled and edited the physicochemical properties of essential oils examined by that firm over a period of many years, but throughout this entire series has been one of the author's most constant and trusted consultants.

Mr. William P. Leidy, Chief Librarian of Fritzsche Brothers, Inc., most ably assisted the author in many phases of the entire series, particularly those related to problems of bibliography and indexing.

The author's deepest appreciation and highest praise should go to his very conscientious and cooperative secretaries, Mrs. Ann Blake Hencken and Miss Catherine McGuire, who, in a decade of exacting, tedious work, have never faltered in their devotion and interest, and through trying, at times discouraging, years, have constantly been a source of inspiration toward final accomplishment.

Ernest Guenther

New York, N. Y.
March, 1952

CONTENTS

ILLUSTRATIONS

CHAPTER I

ESSENTIAL OILS OF THE PLANT FAMILY *ERICACEAE*

OIL OF WINTERGREEN

Essence de Gaultheria   Aceite Esencial Wintergreen (Gualteria)
Wintergrünöl   Oleum Gaultheriae

Wintergreen is one of the oldest and best-known American flavors. Its strong, characteristic taste was familiar to the Indians, who chewed the leaves for their agreeable odor and flavor. Early French explorers, following the course of the great central rivers in Indian canoes, probably learned from the American aborigenes how to employ wintergreen in hot infusions. As a result of such use, the leaf came to be known as "Thé du Canada." It is recorded that during the American War of Independence, leaves of wintergreen were often substituted for Chinese tea.

Botany.—*Gaultheria procumbens* L. (fam. *Ericaceae*), is an aromatic evergreen plant, with an underground or creeping stem that produces branches not exceeding 6 in. in height, the lower part smooth and naked, while near the ends are borne crowded clusters of evergreen leaves. These are alternate, short (1 to 1½ in. long), of varying width, shiny dark green above and lighter in color on the under side. Solitary white flowers appear in July and August. The red, spicy, globular berries ripen in the fall, and sometimes remain on the plant until the spring. All parts of the plant, but particularly the leaves, are aromatic.

Wintergreen prefers sandy soil, in cool, damp woods, and thrives in the shade of shrubs and evergreen trees. It grows in large beds on mountainous tracts, as well as on dry, barren plains. The wild plant invades abandoned farmland, remaining on the borders for as many as twenty years. Wintergreen occurs in Canada and the northeastern United States. Its range extends from Newfoundland, Manitoba, and Minnesota to Georgia and Alabama. The chief producing area lies in eastern Pennsylvania, particularly Carbon County.

Collection of Plant Material.—The plant is collected by hand, a very tedious task. Kneeling on the ground, the harvesters "clean" the soil of foreign matter—fallen leaves, branchlets, etc.—with a small, wooden rake, until a patch of wintergreen stands free. The leaves are then picked and collected in sacks. It is not easy to obtain the labor necessary for such tiring tasks, which entail stooping and crawling for hours through the woods.

At the end of a year, the plant has developed new leaves, which can be gathered again. Collection of the leaves stops with the coming of winter, when the plant is dormant, and contains little essential oil. Besides, the cold, frost, and snow make that type of work impossible in northern forests. The best time for harvesting is from June to September, when the leaves give the highest yield of oil. This period also coincides with school vacations, so that young labor is available for the work. The low prices for leaf material do not as a rule attract male labor, except, perhaps, for the fact that a harvester can work as he pleases. When prices are low, distillers may have difficulty procuring sufficient plant material.

Distillation.—At one time, many small distilleries were distributed throughout the producing areas; lately, however, the picture has changed considerably, and only a few distilleries remain. Competition from synthetic methyl salicylate, low prices for the natural oil, and the shortage of labor, have all operated to discourage many distillers.

Most of the stills are surprisingly primitive, only a few being of more modern construtcion. All are heated by a direct wood fire. The stills are charged with plant material through a manhole on top. The bottom of the retort being enclosed in the fire hearth, the exhausted material must be forked out through the top manhole, which makes operations awkward, and consumes a good deal of time.

Sacks of fresh leaf material are weighed immediately after arrival, in order to settle questions of payment with the collectors. The leaves should be distilled as fresh as possible. They may, however, be stored as long as two weeks, provided they are carefully spread out to dry. Wet leaf material tends to ferment; it may spoil, or give a low yield of oil, which obviously must be avoided.

For a special reason, however, it is necessary to submit the leaf material to *intentional* fermentation, by maceration in warm water, shortly before distillation. Such fermentation causes splitting of the primeveroside of methyl salicylate (also known as monotropitin or monotropitoside) and frees the methyl salicylate, chief constituent of oil of wintergreen. Methyl salicylate does not occur in the plant in free form, but as glycoside.[1] Actually the plant contains very little volatile oil, and only after splitting of the glycoside under the influence of the enzyme primeverosidase can appreciable yields of oil be obtained. A simple test will demonstrate this fact: a wintergreen leaf is almost odorless, but on chewing (action of enzyme on the glycoside!) the characteristic odor and flavor of wintergreen (methyl salicylate) will be noticed. The reaction that takes place may be illustrated as follows:

$$\text{Monotropitin} \xrightarrow{\text{Enzyme}} \text{Methyl salicylate} + \text{Primeverose}$$

Distillers charge the plant material into the still, cover it with warm water of about 120° F., keep the mass at this temperature overnight, and

[1] Cf. the monograph on "Oil of Sweet Birch," in the present volume, p. 11.

start distillation the following morning. Distillation of one batch takes 5 or 6 hr. The distillate separates in a Florentine flask into a layer of essential oil, heavier than water, and a lighter layer of milky distillation water, which is returned into the still for cohobation. As the operation proceeds, the distillation water becomes increasingly clear, so that finally it contains no more suspended oil; this indicates the end of one operation. Distillation is then discontinued, the manhole on the still head opened, the exhausted leaf material forked out, and a new batch put in. The residual water is left in the still for the next operation. The stills are, in fact, cleaned only once a week; during the height of the season, they may be cleaned only once every three or four weeks. Consequently, the residual waters, containing all the accumulated products of fermentation cleavage (sugars, etc.) remain in the still, undergoing repeated heating and decomposition. It is not surprising that these waters assume a deep brown color and an empyreumatic odor—which may partly account for the peculiar smoky odor of genuine wintergreen oil.

Yield of oil is influenced by several factors—season of harvest, condition of leaf material, presence of foreign matter such as sand, twiglets, etc. Highest in summer, the yield declines toward autumn, and decreases sharply in winter. One hundred pounds of leaves and short stems yield from 8 to 9 oz. of oil; plants with longer stems give only 7 or 8 oz. The average yield is 0.66 per cent, or 1 lb. of oil per 150 lb. of leaf material. At the height of the season, when the supply of leaves is large, distillers sometimes speed up operations by shortening time of fermentation. This, of course, results in an inferior yield of oil.

Physicochemical Properties.—Genuine oil of wintergreen is an almost colorless, yellow, or reddish liquid, of strongly aromatic and very characteristic odor and flavor, quite different from those of the somewhat lower-priced oil of sweet birch (*Betula lenta*). The reddish color often noticed in the oil is usually due to the presence of metallic impurities (iron).

Gildemeister and Hoffmann [2] reported these properties for oil of wintergreen:

Specific Gravity at 15°......	1.180 to 1.193
Specific Gravity at 25°......	1.172 to 1.185
Optical Rotation..........	$-0° 25'$ to $-1° 30'$
Refractive Index at 20°.....	1.535 to 1.536
Ester Number.............	354 to 365
Ester Content, Calculated as Methyl Salicylate........	96 to 99%
Solubility at 20°...........	Clearly soluble in 6 to 8 vol. of 70% alcohol

[2] "Die Ätherischen Öle," 3d Ed., Vol. III, 580.

Numerous lots of genuine wintergreen oil examined by Fritzsche Brothers, Inc., had properties varying within the following limits:

Specific Gravity at 25°/25°......... 1.177 to 1.180
Optical Rotation.................. −0° 8′ to −0° 29′
Refractive Index at 20°............ 1.5350 to 1.5362
Ester Content, Calculated as Methyl
    Salicylate...................... 98.0 to 99.9%
Heavy Metals Test................ Usually positive in the crude
                            country oils
Solubility........................ Soluble in 5.5 to 7 vol. and more
                            of 70% alcohol

The traces of metals often present in the country oils can easily be removed by treatment with tartaric acid in the usual way (cf. Vol. 1 of the present work, p. 378).

For a rapid evaluation of oil of wintergreen by the so-called Alkali Solubility Test, also see Vol. I of this work, p. 331.

Adulteration.—Since natural wintergreen oil consists almost entirely of methyl salicylate (see below), the oil is frequently adulterated with synthetic methyl salicylate. Moderate additions of this ester are most difficult to detect. Large additions may result in a slight lowering of the optical rotation of the oil (which, however, is already very low in the genuine oils). Formerly synthetic methyl salicylate often contained small quantities of free phenol, and when identifying phenol in a wintergreen oil the conclusion could be drawn that the oil had been adulterated with synthetic methyl salicylate (for details of procedure, see Vol. I of this work, pp. 315 ff.). Today, however, synthetic methyl salicylate is manufactured in such a pure state that in most cases it no longer contains phenol.

Since chemical means are of little avail in proving adulteration, the oil should always be submitted to careful organoleptic tests. An expert recognizes genuine wintergreen oil by a characteristic heavy and smoky note, which is lacking in synthetic wintergreen oil (methyl salicylate).

Chemical Composition.—That oil of wintergreen contains methyl salicylate as chief constituent (96 to 99 per cent), was recognized more than a century ago by Procter,[3] and by Cahours.[4] As regards the trace substances, which occur in the oil and are responsible for the difference in the odor of synthetic methyl salicylate and that of genuine wintergreen oil, they have been investigated by Power and Kleber.[5] These authors isolated the methyl salicylate from the oil by shaking the latter repeatedly with a 7.5 per cent aqueous solution of potassium hydroxide. Under these conditions, methyl

[3] *Am. J. Pharm.* **14** (1842), 211. *Liebigs Ann.* **48** (1843), 66.
[4] *Ann. chim. phys.* [3], **10** (1844), 327. *Liebigs Ann.* **48** (1843), 60; **52** (1844), 327.
[5] *Pharm. Rund.* (New York) **13** (1895), 228.

salicylate forms an easily soluble salt, viz., potassium methyl salicylate. Power and Kleber found that only 1.05 per cent of the oil did not react with the potassium hydroxide solution and remained as a semisolid mass. The following compounds have been reported in oil of wintergreen:

Methyl Salicylate. The chief constituent, amounting from 96 to 99 per cent of the oil (Procter and Cahours).

Triacontane. The paraffin $C_{30}H_{62}$ observed in the oil was probably triacontane, as it melted at 65.5°.

An Aldehyde or Ketone(?). When purified through the bisulfite compound, the substance in question had an odor reminiscent of enanthaldehyde. On oxidation with potassium permanganate solution it gave an acid, whose silver salt had the empirical molecular formula $C_6H_9O_2Ag$.

An Alcohol(?). The oil also contains traces of an alcohol $C_8H_{16}O$, b. 160°–165°, which corresponds to the above-mentioned ketone or aldehyde.

An Ester(?). On saponification, this ester $C_{14}H_{24}O_2$, b. 230°–235°, b_{25} 135°, was hydrolyzed into the alcohol $C_8H_{16}O$ and into an acid, $C_6H_{10}O_2$, which originated also by oxidation of the above-mentioned ketone. The alcohol, as well as the ester, exhibited the pronounced characteristic odor by which genuine wintergreen oil can be distinguished from synthetic methyl salicylate.

(Cf. the monograph on "Oil of Sweet Birch," section "Chemical Composition," p. 15 of the present volume.)

Total Production.—The entire production takes place in a number of small stills scattered over a relatively large section and invariably located in rather inaccessible places. Perhaps no more than 1,500 to 2,000 lb. of oil are distilled in the northern producing section and several times this quantity in North Carolina and Tennessee.

Use.—Oil of wintergreen is used chiefly as a flavoring agent in candies, chewing gums, and certain soft drinks. In medicinal preparations (liniments, etc.) and in semipharmaceuticals (toothpastes and powders, mouth washes, etc.), the natural oil has been replaced largely by synthetic methyl salicylate. When applied externally, the oil is absorbed through the skin. Internally, it is best administered in emulsion form. An overdose may cause degenerative changes in the liver and kidneys.

CHAPTER II

ESSENTIAL OILS OF THE PLANT FAMILY *BETULACEAE*

OIL OF SWEET BIRCH

Essence d'Écorce de Bouleau   Aceite Esencial Betula Dulce
Birkenrindenöl   Oleum Betulae Lentae

Betula lenta L. (fam. *Betulaceae*), the so-called "Sweet Birch," "Black Birch," or "Cherry Birch," is a handsome tree, pyramidal while young. As it grows older, it often reaches a height of almost 80 feet. The heads are narrow and conical. The popular term "Cherry Birch" originated from the fact that the smooth, reddish-brown bark, and the leaves, closely resemble those of our garden cherry tree. The young bark has an aromatic and agreeable flavor, reminiscent of wintergreen.

Betula lenta L. grows wild in the eastern part of North America, from southeastern Canada to Alabama, and as far west as Ohio. It thrives in mountainous regions, particularly on steep, rocky slopes.

The bark and growing tissues of the tree contain an odorless glycoside $C_{19}H_{26}O_{12}$ (now named monotropitin or monotropitoside,[1] formerly called gaultherin, i.e., the primeveroside of methyl salicylate) which, under the influence of the enzyme primeverosidase, is decomposed into methyl salicylate and primeverose (6-xylosido-glucose). According to Bridel,[2] this is the same reaction that takes place in the production of wintergreen oil (which consists chiefly of methyl salicylate) from the leaves of *Gaultheria procumbens* L.:

$$\text{Monotropitin} \xrightarrow{\text{Enzyme}} \text{Methyl salicylate} + \text{Primeverose}$$

Prior to distillation of the oil, the bark of *Betula lenta* L., therefore, has to be macerated in lukewarm water for a certain length of time in order to free the essential oil (see below).

Oil of sweet birch is produced chiefly in the eastern part of Pennsylvania, and particularly in the section from Carbon County south to Berks County. This is roughly the same region that supplies oil of wintergreen. Another, but much less important, producing region lies in South Carolina; the quality of the so-called "Southern Oil," however, is usually inferior to that of the "Northern Oil." The production of sweet birch oil, like that of wintergreen oil, represents one of the few remaining "homespun" industries, dat-

[1] Monotropitin melts at 179.5°; it can be extracted from the plant material by extraction with hot alcohol.
[2] *Compt. rend.* **177** (1923), 642; **178** (1924), 1310. *J. pharm. chim.* [8], **3** (1926), 205. Bridel and Grillon, *Compt. rend.* **187** (1928), 609.

ing back to colonial days. It provides a meager income to a small number of families during slack seasons on the farm. Operators are usually farm hands who have a horse or mule and the necessary distillation equipment. Investment in the latter amounts to only about 250 dollars per post, most of the equipment being homemade.

The trees are cut during the cold months, from October to April, when they are without leaves. Second-growth timber is most frequently used for production of the oil, because the branches of the saplings fit best into the stills. Moreover, distillation of sweet birch provides convenient disposal of the sapling growth. In fact, landowners are usually glad to get rid of second-growth, the wood being of too poor a quality to be used for the making of furniture and agricultural implements. In most cases the second-growth occupies land which could support more valuable timber or crops. As Hardart [3] has pointed out, the sweet birch distillers act, in a way, as scavengers, clearing valuable land for more profitable growths of timber. According to Reinert,[4] areas that have been cropped may be cut over approximately every five years, since it requires this length of time for young growth to attain sufficient height for cutting. Young growth, however, is not the only material used for distillation; occasionally tall trees, from 50 to 60 ft. high, are felled. The bark and branches of older trees are said to give a better yield of oil than those of younger ones. Trees with a dark bark produce more oil than those with a reddish bark.

The distillation posts are usually located in the center of an area that has already been cut over, where sweet birch is the dominant second growth. The site should be accessible by road, and near a creek or some other plentiful supply of water. Often, members of a single household operate the stills. According to Ritter,[5] a crew of two members is required for the operation of one still; three men can run two stills located not too far apart. A horse or mule is needed to skid green material to the "set" and to draw away the waste. A three-man crew divides its time between cutting and skidding, chopping poles and brush into proper length, tending the fire, and charging and unloading the still.

The stills or vats resemble large chests, rectangular in shape ($6 \times 6 \times 6$ ft., or $4\frac{1}{2} \times 4\frac{1}{2} \times 9$ ft.), and constructed of planking, 2 to 3 in. thick. They hold about 2 tons of chipped birch. Some vats are completely lined with copper, but usually this high-priced material is used only on the bottom. The walls are made vapor-tight by tongue-and-groove construction, and held together by adjustable bolts. The cover, operated by block and

---

[3] *Nature Magazine* **34**, December (1941), 553.
[4] *American-German Rev.* **6** (1940), 30.
[5] *J. Forestry* **38** (1940), 518.

tackle, is sealed with clamps and wire; old automobile inner tubes are stretched along the edges as gaskets (Ritter). Because of their construction, location, and mode of operation, the stills are not considered good fire risks by those entrusted with the protection of forests. A sweet birch still is seldom provided with a spark arrester, and at least one man must be on duty at the set, watching day and night.

The glycoside, which yields the volatile oil on hydrolysis, occurs only in the bark and growing tissues of the tree. Therefore, it would seem advisable to use for distillation only the peeled bark of young trees. Peeling is a laborious task, however, and was abandoned about fifty years ago. Customary practice is to use stems, limbs, and twigs cut into 5½ ft. lengths. Branches and tops are bound with baling wire into bundles with the diameter of grain sheaves. The still is firmly packed half full with small material, after which the larger saplings and poles are placed on top to weigh down the lighter material. Some distillers reduce the wood to chips. For this purpose the young trees, branches, and split wood are placed in a trough, and fed into the cutting machine through a hole in the wall. The cutter consists of a heavy-spoked cast-iron wheel, usually 3 ft. in diameter, to which are bolted two heavy flat knives. It is driven by gasoline, steam, or water power. The chips are cut fine, like shavings; the finer the chips, the greater the yield of oil. One vat holds about 2 tons of chipped birch wood (Reinert).

After the wood has been charged into the still in the late afternoon, distillation water from the previous run is added until the water reaches to about 15 in. above the bottom. Then the lid is clamped down and the still is heated for about 1 hr. This serves the sole purpose of warming the still content to such a temperature that hydrolysis of the primeveroside monotropitin can take place, gradually freeing the methyl salicylate from its odorless, complex precursor. In the evening the fire is banked, the still contents being kept at a temperature of about 50° C. during the night. In the morning the fire is built up again, which marks the beginning of the next operation, requiring 5 to 10 hours of actual distillation, at a boiler pressure of 40 to 50 lb. The distillate (condensate) comes over as a milky liquid, from which the essential oil separates at the bottom of the receiver, as a layer heavier than water. The aqueous phase of the condensate remains milky, since it still contains small quantities of essential oil in fine dispersion. To recover this oil the aqueous phase of the distillate (locally called "low wine") is returned into the still for distillation of the next batch (see above). In other words, the distillation water is cohobated.

According to Ritter,[6] ¾ to 1 cord of birch poles, in addition to almost

[6] *Ibid.*

100 cu. ft. of branch wood, yield about 4 lb. of oil. Reinert [7] reported a yield of 1 to 1½ qt. of oil per ton of finely chipped wood. In a day's work, a distillery produces a little more than 1 gal. of oil.

A disagreeable feature of the operation is the unloading of the still. This must be done rapidly, and while the still contents are still hot; otherwise the waste material becomes very hard, making removal difficult. Men strip to the waist, enter the hot still and tear out the steaming material with heavy pitch forks. The man unloading the still must endure the heat and fumes of the still, and there is always the danger of a misstep into the hot water at the bottom of the still.

Prior to shipment to essential oil dealers, field producers often filter the oil through cotton cloth or other suitable material. Some distillers use filter paper for this purpose.

Physicochemical Properties.—Genuine oil of sweet birch is a pale yellow liquid with a characteristic and strong odor and flavor, resembling those of methyl salicylate and natural wintergreen oil (from *Gaultheria procumbens*). Despite the fact that both sweet birch and wintergreen oil consist almost entirely of methyl salicylate, experts are able to distinguish the two oils by odor tests. The difference in odor is a result of the presence of trace substances, which have not yet been identified. These substances are less pronounced in sweet birch than in wintergreen oil.

Gildemeister and Hoffmann [8] reported the following properties for sweet birch oil:

Specific Gravity at 15°...... 1.180 to 1.189
Optical Rotation........... Inactive (differing from natural wintergreen oil, which is slightly laevorotatory!)
Refractive Index at 20°..... 1.5360 to 1.5376
Ester Number............. 356 to 365
Ester Content, Calculated as
  Methyl Salicylate........ 97 to 99%
Solubility................. Clearly soluble in from 5 to 8 vol. of 70% alcohol, at room temperature
Boiling Range at 760 mm.... 218°–221°

Numerous lots of genuine sweet birch oils examined by Fritzsche Brothers, Inc., New York, had properties varying within these limits:

Specific Gravity at 25°/25°.. 1.177 to 1.182
Optical Rotation........... Inactive
Refractive Index........... 1.5350 to 1.5370

[7] *American-German Rev.* **6** (1940), 30.
[8] "Die Ätherischen Öle," 3d Ed., Vol. II, 486.

Ester Content, Calculated as
    Methyl Salicylate........ Not less than 98.5%
Solubility................. Soluble in 6.5 to 7.5 vol. of 70% alcohol
                            and more. Sometimes showing a slight
                            haziness

The red color occasionally encountered in sweet birch oils received directly from producing regions is usually caused by traces of iron. It can be removed by treatment of the oil with tartaric acid (cf. Vol. I of this work, p. 378).

For a rapid evaluation of sweet birch oil by the so-called Alkali Solubility Test, see Vol. I, p. 331.

Adulteration.—The remarks on adulteration in the monograph on "Oil of Wintergreen" (see present volume, p. 6) also apply to oil of sweet birch; adulteration in the case of the latter oil is more difficult to detect, however, since both the oil and the synthetic methyl salicylate are optically inactive.

Chemical Composition.—More than fifty years ago Power and Kleber [9] found that 99.8 per cent of the oil which they investigated consisted of *methyl salicylate*. Removing the methyl salicylate from an ethereal solution of the oil by means of a 7.5 per cent aqueous potassium hydroxide solution, and evaporating the ether, Power and Kleber obtained a semisolid mass, which they separated into two components by steam distillation. The nonvolatile part consisted of a paraffin $C_{30}H_{62}$, m. 65.5°, probably *triacontane*. The steam-volatile component b. 230°–235°, b_{25} ca. 135°, was *an ester* with the empirical molecular formula $C_{14}H_{24}O_2$. On saponification, this ester gave an alcohol $C_8H_{16}O$ and an acid $C_6H_{10}O_2$ (cf. the monograph on "Oil of Wintergreen," section "Chemical Composition," p. 7 of the present volume).

Using a complicated procedure, Albright [10] arrived at the conclusion that sweet birch oil, as well as wintergreen oil and methyl salicylate, contains a phenol C_6H_5OH. His conclusion, however, has never been corroborated and must be accepted as extremely doubtful.

Use.—Oil of sweet birch has the same uses as oil of wintergreen, and may be employed as a lower-priced substitute for it.

[9] *Pharm. Rundschau* (New York), **13** (1895), 228.
[10] *J. Am. Chem. Soc.* **39** (1917), 820.

OIL OF BIRCH BUDS

The resinous leaf buds of the white birch, *Betula alba* L., *B. pendula* Roth, *B. pubescens* Ehrh., *B. papyrifera* Marsh. (fam. *Betulaceae*), or varieties of them yield from 3.5 to as much as 8 per cent of an essential oil. It was first produced by Haensel [1] at the beginning of the century, and as a base of popular hair tonics ("Birkenwasser") attained some importance in the perfume industry of Germany. Today little if any oil of birch buds is produced on a commercial scale.

Physicochemical Properties.—Oil of birch buds is a yellow, viscous liquid with a very pleasant, soft, and balsamic odor. On cooling the oil separates crystals and finally congeals to a crystalline mass. Gildemeister and Hoffmann [2] reported these properties for the oil:

Specific Gravity at 15°...............	0.962 to 0.979
Optical Rotation...................	$-2°\,0'$ to $-15°\,0'$
Refractive Index at 20°.............	1.5015 to 1.5045
Acid Number......................	1 to 4
Ester Number.....................	35 to 77
Ester Number after Acetylation......	140 to 183
Solubility........................	Soluble in 1 to 2 vol. of 80% alcohol; soluble in 0.25 vol. of 90% alcohol, occasionally clearly, occasionally with separation of paraffins. On addition of more solvent, paraffins will always separate

Chemical Composition.—The following compounds have been identified in the volatile oil derived from the leaf buds of the white birch:

Naphthalene. Treibs [3] noted substantial quantities of naphthalene in the forerun of the oil.

Betulene. According to the same author,[4] the oil contains about 3 per cent of a sesquiterpene $C_{15}H_{24}$, which he named betulene (cf. Vol. II of the present work, p. 750).

Betulenene. Aside from betulene, Treibs isolated from the oil another sesquiterpene $C_{15}H_{22}$, which contains three double bonds, and which lends itself readily to autoxidation and polymerization. Treibs named this sesquiterpene betulenene (cf. Vol. II of this work, p. 750).

[1] *Chem. Zentr.* (1902), II, 1208.
[2] "Die Ätherischen Öle," 3d Ed., Vol. II, 491.
[3] *Ber.* **71B** (1938), 612.
[4] *Ibid.*, 620.

Betulenol (Betulol). A sesquiterpene alcohol $C_{15}H_{24}O$ (for details see Vol. II of this work, p. 264). Treibs found 16 per cent of free, and 34 per cent of esterified betulenols in the oil which he investigated.

A Compound(?) $C_{15}H_{22}O$. Observed in the oil by Treibs,[5] but not identified.

Paraffins. Present in the last runs of the oil. Treibs[6] reported that these paraffins melted at 49° and that they have the empirical molecular formula $C_{20}H_{24}$. Petrů and Hadáček[7] isolated from the oil a paraffin-hydrocarbon $C_{25}H_{52}$, m. 53°–54°.

Use.—As has been mentioned, oil of birch buds was formerly used in hair tonics and similar preparations but, to the author's knowledge, is no longer produced in appreciable quantities, collection of the leaf buds probably being too costly.

OIL OF BIRCH TAR

Essence de Goudron de Bouleau   Aceite Esencial Betula Brea
Birkenteeröl   Oleum Rusci Rectificatum

Origin and Production.—Although not an essential oil in the true sense, rectified oil of birch tar should be briefly described here because of its former importance in the perfume industry. At one time, substantial quantities of the oil were produced in the northeastern part of Germany, and particularly in the Baltic States and adjacent parts of Russia, with Reval (Tallinn) in Esthonia as center of production. The oil was used in medicinal preparations and in perfumery, serving as base for the popular "Russian leather" types of odor. Lately, however, true birch tar oil seems to have disappeared from the market. Preparations now offered under this label consist mostly of pyroligneous oils derived by rectification of the tar of all kinds of pinaceous trees ("Rectified tar oil," *Oleum picis rectificatum* —cf. p. 303 of the present volume). None of these substitutes, however, exhibit the characteristic "Russian leather" scent of rectified birch tar oil; all possess a more or less disagreeable, strongly phenolic odor.

The National Formulary describes rectified birch tar oil as the pyroligneous oil obtained by dry distillation of the bark and wood of *Betula pendula* Roth and related species of *Betula* (fam. *Betulaceae*), and rectified by steam

---

[5] *Ber.* **69** (1936), 41.
[6] *Ibid.*
[7] *Coll. Trav. Chim. Tschecoslovaquie* **7** (1935), 90. *Ber. Schimmel & Co.* (1936), 9.

distillation. In the actual process the bark of the European white birch is submitted to slow destructive distillation, the tar-like product thus obtained then being rectified with steam. The resultant volatile oil constitutes the official rectified birch tar oil. It seems quite possible that some of the medicinally valuable constituents of the tar are removed by the process of rectification. In 1931, von Winkler[1] in Reval processed birch bark completely freed from bast and scab, and repeatedly leached out by soaking in water; the bark contained from 12 to 20 per cent of moisture. Calculated upon the weight of the bark, the yield of rectified birch tar oil was 30.7 per cent. Aside from the volatile oil, von Winkler obtained water with varying amounts of acetic acid, methyl alcohol, and acetone, as well as combustible gases, carbon dioxide, and coke. The volatile oil (d_{20} 0.9443) contained 90 per cent of saponifiable constituents, and 0 per cent of compounds insoluble in ether. The ash content of the oil was 0.02 per cent. Tested on a blotter for odor, the oil first exhibited a cresol-like note but after 10 to 20 sec. this disappeared and the pure and characteristic odor of "Russian leather" came through. The disturbing off-odor was eliminated by treatment of the oil with calcined earth or silica gel.

Years ago Holmes[2] reported that prior to World War I birch tar oil was produced in the Government of Kostroma (Russia) from the external white bark of the birch, by the following method:

"An iron pot is filled with the (white) bark and covered with a close fitting lid, through which is inserted an iron pipe, and this pot is inverted over a similar one, and the rims are carefully fitted together and well luted with clay. The two are then turned upside down, so that the pot with the bark in it is uppermost. The apparatus is half sunken in the ground, well banked up with a mixture of sand and clay, and a wood fire is kindled round it. When the distillation has continued long enough the luting is removed and the pots separated, when the lower one is found to contain a thin oil floating on pyroligneous acid, or when the bark has been very impure on pitch. The yield of true birch bark oil is about one-third of the white bark used.

"To obtain 120 lb. of oil, ten to fourteen trees of thirty to fifty years old have to be stripped. The trees now are not, as formerly, felled, but are stripped standing and allowed to grow. In most cases the outer bark is only partially removed. The under layer blackens and dies, but new bark is formed beneath them. Recently the preparation has been carried on in Germany and Austria, where it is known as Birkentheer, Birkenöl, Juchtenöl, or Doggut."

Before World War I birch tar oil also came from the Government of Minsk (Russia); it was supplied in two forms, crude and rectified. The crude, dark colored oil was used in the manufacture of leather and in soaps; the rectified oil was weaker in odor.

[1] *Ber. Schimmel & Co.* (1944/47), 11.
[2] *Pharm. J.* [4], **31** (1910), 5.

Physicochemical Properties.—Rectified birch tar oil is a clear, dark brown liquid with a strong empyreumatic odor reminiscent of "Russian leather." Commercial lots of rectified birch tar oil imported from Europe by Fritzsche Brothers, Inc., New York, in the past had specific gravities which varied between 0.880 and 0.908. The apparent phenol content determined with dilute potassium hydroxide solution (see Vol. I, p. 291) varied between 5 per cent and 20 per cent; most of the shipments showing values above 10 per cent. Rectified birch tar oil should yield clear solutions with 3 vol. of anhydrous alcohol and with ether, benzene, chloroform, glacial acetic acid, amyl alcohol and turpentine oil. When mixed with 7 to 10 vol. of alcohol or with 3 vol. of petroleum benzin, the oil dissolves with no more than a slight turbidity. The oils imported previous to World War II yielded a turbid solution when mixed with 3 vol. of methanol. Recent lots of so-called rectified birch tar oil, however, have yielded clear solutions with 3 vol. of methanol.

When stored in metal containers, rectified birch tar oil rapidly darkens in color and becomes unsuitable for use. The oil should, therefore, be kept in dark, well-filled glass bottles, protected from light.

Chemical Composition.—Oil of birch tar contains a number of phenols and phenol ethers, among them:

Phenol (traces only)

Cresol (methylphenol)

Xylenol (dimethylphenol)

Guaiacol (*o*-methoxyphenol)

Creosol (2-methoxy-4-methylphenol)

Pyrocatechol (2-hydroxyphenol)

The chemical composition of the German rectified birch tar oil differs from that of the Russian oil. The latter contains *pyrobetulin,* an odorless and tasteless substance, which has antiseptic properties.[3] When heated to a temperature above 258° C., pyrobetulin emits a vapor with the characteristic odor of "Russian leather." In fact this odor develops only when the heat is sufficient to decompose the pyrobetulin.

More than twenty years ago Vesterberg and Nydahl[4] investigated the chemical composition of rectified birch tar oil and, from the neutral portion, obtained a number of sesquiterpene-like fractions with a low content of oxygenated compounds. Repeating the work of the two above-named

[3] *Chemist Druggist* **101** (1924), 945.
[4] *Svensk Kem. Tid.* **39** (1927), 117. *Chem. Zentr.* (1927), II, 1103.

authors, Ruzicka, Boer and Rey [5] noted the presence of many hydro-naphthalenes in birch tar oil. Analysis of the picrates provided evidence that dehydrogenation with sulfur produces a mixture of homologous alkyl-naphthalenes. It is also probable that these products are derived, not from a sesquiterpene fraction, but largely from *betulin,* a triterpenediol. Ruzicka and his collaborators arrived at the conclusion that the fractions declared to be sesquiterpenes by Vesterberg and Nydahl (see above), in reality consist of betulin pyrolysis products, and not of sesquiterpene-like compounds.

Use.—As long as it was available commercially, rectified birch tar oil was a valuable perfumer's raw material, forming the basis of numerous "Russian leather" scents. It served also as an antiseptic in local applications against chronic eczema and other skin diseases.

Suggested Additional Literature

C. T. Bennett, "Birch Tar Oil," *Pharm. J.* [4], **31** (1910), 4.

[5] *Helv. Chim. Acta* **27** (1944), 183.

CHAPTER III

ESSENTIAL OILS OF THE PLANT FAMILY *VALERIANACEAE*

OIL OF VALERIAN

Essence de Valériane   *Aceite Esencial Valeriana*   *Baldrianöl*
Oleum Valerianae

Introduction.—*Valeriana officinalis* L. (fam. *Valerianaceae*) is a hardy, herbaceous perennial growing from 2 to 4 ft. high. The flowers are white or rose-colored, and quite fragrant. In northern and central Europe and in Asia, its native habitat, the plant occurs wild in damp woods and meadows, as well as on dry, elevated grounds. In Europe and North America it is often grown as an ornamental plant ("garden heliotrope"). The dried rhizomes and roots form the well-known valerian root of the drug trade. They exhibit a characteristic, rather unpleasant odor, caused by the presence of an essential oil which can be isolated by steam distillation.

Valeriana officinalis is cultivated as a medicinal plant on a commercial scale in Belgium, northern France, central Germany, Hungary, in the southern part of the U.S.S.R., and in neighboring countries (Lithuania, Latvia, Estonia, etc.). Statistics of production are difficult to obtain, but in 1933, for example, the U.S.S.R. consumed 236 metric tons of dried valerian roots, which were cultivated on about 200 hectares.[1]

As regards western Europe, the principal producing regions are in Belgium. During World War II efforts were made to cultivate *Valeriana officinalis* on a large scale in Germany, but space does not permit reviewing articles on this subject, which appeared in the German literature.[2]

Cultivation.—*Valeriana officinalis* grows quite well in any ordinary soil, but best in a rich and rather heavy loam well supplied with moisture. According to Fauconnet,[3] the type of soil exerts no influence on the general chemical composition of the valerian root. However, meteorological conditions markedly influence the oil content of the root.

In Belgium,[4] where the plantings are spread over about fifteen communities in the province of Hainaut (around Lessines and Flobecq), valerian is planted in the beginning of spring, usually early in April, from young wild plants, which farmers collect in forests and damp meadows. After the

---

[1] Maizite, *Die Deutsche Heilpflanze* **10** (1944), 79.
[2] For details see Bauer, *Pharm. Zentralhalle* **83** (1942), 361. Bauer et al., *Landw. Jahrb.* **92** (1942), 1. Heeger and Bauer, *Pharmazie* **1** (1946), 27.
[3] *Ber. schweiz. botan. Ges.* **57** (1947), 122.
[4] Guenther, "Belgian Essential Oils," *Am. Perfumer* **34** (February, 1937), 75.

soil has been carefully tilled, harrowed, and fertilized, the plants are set out in straight rows, with a distance of 40 cm. between rows, and 30 cm. between plants. As the shrub grows, the ground must be tilled repeatedly, weeded, and fertilized. Valerian is a large herb, sometimes reaching a height of about 50 cm., and almost completely covering the ground around it.

The plant is cultivated exclusively for its fibrous root, which develops a great number of rootlets. These spread out under the surface of the ground in a circle roughly 30 or 40 cm. in diameter.

In September the leaves begin to turn yellow and wither, an indication that the plant is now ready for harvesting. First the leaf material is mowed, then raked up and piled along the edges of the fields. In a period of dry weather, the roots are pulled out, either by hand, or with a "trident." A light plow, ox- or horse-drawn, may also be employed. The roots are then gathered, roughly cleaned by shaking, and stacked up on a wooden picket stuck into the ground. They are cleaned again, this time more thoroughly, arranged into heaps, and covered with leaves. Thus protected against possible rain, the material can be left in the fields for a few days.

As the work advances, additional quantities of root material are wheeled from the fields to the farm. There, seated under a shed, women and girls cut the roots into four, six, or eight parts, according to size. The pieces are carefully cleaned, then carried to the bank of a nearby brook, where a large wicker bin with a dyke on one side has previously been constructed. Into this bin the roots are thrown and washed by stirring with long, tridented, wooden poles, then removed from the water and placed on the banks to drain off and dry. In this condition, the roots are generally sold to the exporters who, during the harvest period, daily truck the root material to large hot-air kilns. However, some of the farmers, possessing their own small kilns, dry a part of their root material, and often store it for speculation purposes.

Valerian root is exported from Belgium in several grades:

1. Entire root—fresh and washed. (Exported largely to France.)
2. Entire root—washed and dried.
3. Dried root pieces, varying in length from 2 to 5 cm., according to country of destination.
4. Powdered root.

Yearly production of Belgian root amounts to about 300 metric tons. Prices fluctuate widely. In normal times the root is sent to Germany, as well as France, the United States, England, and other countries.

For commercial cultivation in the United States, Stockberger [5] recommends propagating valerian by dividing the old roots, either in the fall or in the spring, and setting the divisions about 1 ft. apart in rows spaced at 2 to 3 ft. If the divisions are set very early in the fall in time to become well established before frost, a good crop may usually be harvested the following autumn. Plants may also be grown from seed, which are preferably sown as soon as they are ripe in well-protected seedbeds in the garden. Early in the spring the seedlings may be transplanted to the field and set at the same spacing as the divisions of the root. Growth will be favored by a liberal application of farmyard manure, which should be well worked into the soil before the plants are set out. Thorough cultivation is essential.

The roots of the plants propagated by division may be dug in the fall of the first year's growth, although the yield will probably be small. Those of seedling plants do not usually reach a size suitable for harvesting before the end of the second growing season. After digging, the roots are washed, preferably in running water, until all adhering soil is removed. Washing and drying will be facilitated if the thick portion of the roots is sliced lengthwise. The drying should be very thorough, and the use of artificial heat will be found advisable.

Under good conditions a yield of 2,000 lb. or more of dried roots per acre may reasonably be expected.

Distillation and Yield of Oil.—The characteristic valerian odor, which is caused chiefly by *l*-bornyl isovalerate, develops only on drying of the root material. Years ago Carles [6] expressed the opinion that the juice of the fresh valerian roots contains an oxidizing enzyme, which is perhaps responsible for the development of the typical valerian odor. It may also be assumed that the fresh roots contain glycosides, which on splitting yield *l*-bornyl isovalerate and other compounds of characteristic valerian odor. However, it has not been possible to isolate any such glycosides from the root. On prolonged aging of the root, the esters, particularly the bornyl isovalerate, are hydrolyzed, giving rise to free isovaleric acid, which imparts a most disagreeable odor to over-aged root material. According to Jaretzky, [7] the hydrolysis of esters cannot be caused exclusively by ferments, because it takes place also in the distilled valerian oil, which certainly is free of ferments.

The most appropriate material for distillation are well-dried roots, not too old. Over-aged material yields an oil with a high content of free fatty acids, particularly isovaleric acid, of disagreeable odor. Immediately prior

---

[5] "Drug Plants Under Cultivation," *U. S. Dept. Agr., Farmers' Bull.* No. 663 (1935), 35.
[6] *J. pharm. chim.* [6], **12** (1900), 148.
[7] *Arch. Pharm.* **280** (1942), 293.

to distillation, the roots should be triturated. Distillation of one batch with direct steam is completed in about 6 hr., whereas distillation with indirect steam (water distillation) may require up to 48 hr. The distillation waters contain substantial quantities of free acids, chiefly isovaleric acid, formed during distillation by hydrolysis of esters. To increase the yield of oil, some distillers cohobate the distillation waters and add the indirect oil to the direct (main) oil. If this is done the final (total) oil will exhibit a high acid number and most likely a rather disagreeable odor. (See also below—"Physicochemical Properties.")

The yield of oil depends upon several factors, among them the age of the root material, its geographical origin, meteorological conditions, the age of the plantation,[8] the method of distillation, etc. Yields of oil ranging from 0.1 to about 1.0 per cent have been reported,[9] especially in German literature. Distilling Belgian, French and German root material the author obtained yields ranging from 0.2 to 0.4 per cent. A yield of 0.4 to 0.6 per cent may be considered quite satisfactory, although Gildemeister and Hoffmann [10] claim yields of 0.5 to 0.9 per cent for roots from Thuringia.

In general, the yield of oil from *Valeriana officinalis* L. is very low. As a result, some essential oil producers no longer use the roots of true *Valeriana officinalis* L. for distillation of the oil, employing instead those of *Valeriana officinalis* L. var. *latifolia* Miq., the so-called "kesso root" from Japan, which yields from 4 to 5 per cent of oil (see the monograph on "Oil of Valerian Japanese," p. 28).

Physicochemical Properties.—Freshly distilled valerian root oil is a yellow-green to yellow-brown liquid, slightly acidic, and of characteristic, penetrating, but not disagreeable, odor. On aging or exposure to air, the oil assumes a dark color and a viscous consistency and becomes distinctly malodorous. The oil develops free isovaleric acid, and may deposit crystals of borneol. As was pointed out above, the properties of valerian oil are the result of several factors, primarily the age of the root material and the method of distillation. An oil possessing an abnormally high content of free isovaleric acid may be (a) a very old oil, or (b) have been distilled from over-aged root material, or (c) have been distilled with cohobation of the acidic distillation waters. In order to eliminate the obnoxious odor of isovaleric acid exhibited by such oils, their content of free acids has to be reduced by proper treatment (careful neutralization with cold solution of sodium carbonate, e.g.).

[8] Heeger and Bauer, *Pharmazie* **1** (1946), 27.
[9] Heeger, *Pharm. Ind.* **7** (1940), 371; **10** (1943), 136, 222. Maizite, *Die Deutsche Heilpflanze* **10** (1944), 79.
[10] "Die Ätherischen Öle," 3d Ed., Vol. III, 936.

Gildemeister and Hoffmann [11] reported these properties for valerian root oil from *Valeriana officinalis:*

Specific Gravity at 15°......	0.920 to 0.965
Optical Rotation...........	−8° 0' to −14° 0'
Refractive Index at 20°.....	1.486
Acid Number..............	5 to 50
Ester Number.............	50 to 130
Solubility.................	Turbid or sometimes insoluble in 80% alcohol; soluble in 0.5 to 1.5 vol. and more of 90% alcohol. Older oils are more easily soluble, in about 2 vol. and more of 80% alcohol

Oils distilled under the author's supervision in Seillans (Var), France from Belgian, French, and German root material, exhibited properties varying within the following limits:

Specific Gravity at 15°......	0.953 to 0.990
Optical Rotation...........	−2° 18' to −28° 40'
Refractive Index at 20°.....	1.4861 to 1.5021
Acid Number..............	7.0 to 45.3
Ester Number.............	31.7 to 106.9

Chemical Composition.—Little purpose would be served by discussing the early investigations of the chemistry of valerian root oil, which were carried out during the first half of the last century.[12] That valeric acid, which was named after the plant, is one of the constituents of the oil has been known for a long time. We owe our knowledge of the chemical composition of valerian root oil chiefly to Bruylants,[13] Oliviero,[14] and to a lesser extent to Gerock,[15] and Flückiger,[16] who reported the presence of the following compounds:

l-Pinene and *l*-Camphene. In the lowest boiling fractions.

l-Borneol Esterified with Formic, Acetic, Butyric, and Isovaleric Acids. By far the greater part of the bornyl esters present in the oil consists of *l*-bornyl isovalerate. According to Gerock, the oil contains about 9.5 per cent of bornyl isovalerate, and about 1 per cent each, of bornyl formate, acetate, and butyrate.

Terpineol. The fraction b_{50} 160°–165° yielded dipentene dihydrochloride, indicating the probable presence of terpineol.

An Alcohol(?). The fraction b_{50} 160°–165° also contains a substance $C_{15}H_{26}O$, which is probably an alcohol.

[11] *Ibid.*
[12] Cf. Gildemeister and Hoffmann, "Die Ätherischen Öle," 3d Ed., Vol. III, 937.
[13] *Ber.* **11** (1878), 452.
[14] *Compt. rend.* **117** (1893), 1096. *Bull. soc. chim.* [3], **11** (1894), 150; **13** (1895), 917
[15] *J. pharm. Elsass-Lothringen* **19** (1892), 82. *Jahresber. Pharm.* (1892), 445.
[16] *Arch. Pharm.* **209** (1876), 204.

A Sesquiterpene(?). In the same fraction a laevorotatory sesquiterpene $C_{15}H_{24}$ was observed.

An Alcohol(?). From the aqueous washings of a saponified oil, Oliviero isolated a strongly laevorotatory, crystalline alcohol $C_{10}H_{20}O_2$, m. 132°.

Borneol Ether(?) or Borneol Oxide(?). Basing his opinion solely upon a combustion analysis, Bruylants arrived at the conclusion that the fraction b. 285°–290° of the oil consists of borneol ether or borneol oxide, but according to Gildemeister and Hoffmann [17] this is quite improbable, and in any case further proof must be adduced.

A Blue Oil(?). According to Flückiger, the highest boiling fractions contain a blue oil b. ~300°.

Use.—Oil of valerian root is used as a tonic and stimulant in certain medicinal preparations. At one time the medicinal effectiveness of valerian root oil was thought to be due to the presence of isovaleric acid, but according to Bonnin,[18] this is not the case, the active principle being *l*-bornyl isovalerate.

Another use of valerian root oil is as an adjunct in the flavoring of certain blends of tobacco.

OIL OF VALERIAN JAPANESE *
(Oil of Kesso Root)

The plant from which the Japanese valerian or so-called "Kesso" root is derived ("Kesso Kanokoso") was formerly classified as *Patrinia scabiosae-folia* Link, later as *Valeriana officinalis* L. var. *angustifolia* Miq.; however, more recently it has been reclassified as *Valeriana officinalis* L. var. *latifolia* Miq. (fam. *Valerianaceae*). It gives a much higher yield of essential oil (from 4 to 5 per cent, and even more) than the European valerian root. For this reason European, and in particular, German, distillers prior to World War II used imported Japanese root material almost exclusively. As a matter of fact, the Japanese root became official in the German Pharmacopoeia. At that time Japan produced from 50 to 60 metric tons of kesso root per year. Since the war, production in Japan has declined to 12 to 18 tons annually. In 1948, total production in Japan amounted to only 10,870 kg., 10,800 kg. of which came from Hokkaido, and only 70 kg. from the Prefecture of Toyama. Years ago, most of the root was grown in the Prefectures of Toyama and Kanagawa on Japan's main island, but

---

[17] "Die Ätherischen Öle," 3d Ed., Vol. III, 938.
[18] *Pharma-Medico* **2** (1933), 60.

* The author is greatly obliged to Dr. Teikichi Hiraizumi, Tokyo, for much of the information contained in this monograph.

about 1930 plantations were started in the Kitami district of Hokkaido Island; this is now the principal producing region.

For planting, rootstocks weighing from 20 to 30 g. are set out in loose, well-fertilized soil, the spacing being 30 cm. between the plants, and 60 cm. between the rows. On the island of Hokkaido, planting is done in the early spring; on the main island (Hon-Shu), in the late fall. As in the case of other crops, the soil has to be fertilized and weeded. While the plants are developing, all young ears are plucked off, to force the roots to grow to larger size. In July or August the color of the leaves and stalks changes to yellow; the roots are then dug out of the ground, washed, and dried in the sun. Ten ares (1 are = 119.6 sq. yd., or 0.025 acre) yield from 220 to 250 kg. of dried roots.

Oil of valerian or kesso root has never been produced in Japan, except for experimental purposes. Small quantities of dried root are used in old-fashioned medicines of Chinese origin for the treatment of rheumatism in women. The bulk of the root has always been exported.

Physicochemical Properties.—The volatile oil derived from the Japanese valerian or kesso root is a yellowish to slightly brown liquid with an odor similar to, but slightly coarser and more camphoraceous than that of the oil distilled from the European root. The Japanese oil differs from the latter product chiefly in its higher specific gravity, and its higher laevorotation.

Gildemeister and Hoffmann [1] reported the following properties for Japanese valerian root oil (distilled in Germany):

Specific Gravity at 15°.............. 0.960 to 1.004
Optical Rotation................... −23° 0′ to −34° 30′
Refractive Index at 20°............. 1.477 to 1.487
Acid Number...................... 1 to 20
Ester Number..................... 92 to 138
Ester Number after Acetylation...... 139 to 166
Solubility........................ Soluble in 1 to 2.5 vol. and more of 90% alcohol. The diluted solution occasionally exhibits faint opalescence

Kariyone and Wakabayashi [2] investigated the influence of various fertilizers upon the yield of root per acre, and upon the oil content of the root. They found that a total exclusion of fertilizers, like a complete absence of nitrogen, results in a poor harvest and a low oil content in the root. The properties of ten oils distilled experimentally by these workers varied within the following limits:

[1] "Die Ätherischen Öle," 3d Ed., Vol. III, 940.
[2] *J. Pharm. Soc. Japan* **49**, No. 7 (No. 569), (1929), 108 (Abstracts in German).

Specific Gravity at 15°...... 0.947 to 0.988
Optical Rotation at 15°..... −30° 42′ to −45° 30′
Acid Number.............. 1.1 to 5.9
Ester Number............ 136.6 to 159.6

These values differ from those indicated by Gildemeister and Hoffmann (see above), probably for the simple reason that Kariyone and Wakabayashi distilled the root material in Japan, whereas the properties of the oils reported by Gildemeister and Hoffmann apply to oils distilled in Germany from imported Japanese roots. During the long transport the volatile oil contained in the roots undoubtedly underwent certain changes (hydrolysis of esters, evaporation of low boiling constituents, etc.).

An oil distilled under the author's supervision in Seillans (Var), France, from imported Japanese roots exhibited these properties:

Specific Gravity at 15°...... 0.989
Optical Rotation.......... −27° 28′
Refractive Index at 20°..... 1.4850
Acid Number.............. 3.8
Ester Number............ 111.1
Solubility................ Soluble in 0.5 vol. and more
                of 80% alcohol

Distilling dried valerian (kesso) root experimentally in Japan, Hiraizumi [3] obtained 1.2 per cent of a volatile oil which had the following properties:

Specific Gravity at 15°/15°...... 0.996
Optical Rotation.............. −31° 45′
Refractive Index at 20°........ 1.4850
Acid Number................. 6.0
Ester Number................ 142.5
Solubility at 20°.............. Soluble in 1 vol. and
                more of 80% alcohol

The oil had a very good odor and flavor; because of its low acid number the odor of the Japanese oil differed greatly from the oils distilled from Indian root material (see p. 33, below).

Chemical Composition.—The chemical composition of the volatile oil derived from Japanese valerian root was first investigated by Bertram and Gildemeister, [4] and Bertram and Walbaum. [5] They found that it resembles that of the oil from the European type of root, except for the fact that the former contains kessyl alcohol and kessyl acetate, which are not present in the European oil (from *Valeriana officinalis* L.).

[3] Private communication of Dr. Teikichi Hiraizumi, Tokyo, February (1950).
[4] *Arch. Pharm.* **228** (1890), 483.
[5] *J. prakt. Chem.* [2], **49** (1894), 18.

The kessyl alcohol has been the subject of numerous investigations by Japanese researchers; details will be found in Vol. II of the present work, p. 288. Unfortunately, it was not possible in that volume to incorporate results of work carried on in Japan from 1944 to 1948, including studies of the configuration of kesso glycol, its anhydride, and of kessyl alcohol— results which have only recently become known in the United States. This latest research will be summarized below.

The presence of the following compounds in Japanese valerian root oil has been reported:

Acetic Acid, Isovaleric Acid and Valeraldehyde(?). The first runs obtained on fractionation of the oil contain highly acidic substances of obnoxious odor, viz., acetic and isovaleric acids, and probably valeraldehyde.

l-α-Pinene. In the fraction b. 155°–160°. Identified by means of the nitroso compound m. 101° (Bertram and Gildemeister).

l-Camphene. In the same fraction. Identified by hydration to isoborneol m. 212° (Bertram and Walbaum).

Dipentene. In the fraction b. 170°–180°. Identified by means of the tetrabromide m. 123° (Bertram and Gildemeister). It is doubtful whether dipentene is a natural constituent of the oil or an artifact, formed from pinene or terpineol by the action of acids.

l-Bornyl Acetate and Isovalerate. Identified by Bertram and Gildemeister. Unlike the oil derived from the European root, the Japanese oil does not contain any bornyl formate.

Terpineol. In the fraction b. 200°–220°. Identified by means of dipentene dihydroiodide m. 76° (Bertram and Gildemeister).

Kessyl Alcohol and Kessyl Acetate. According to Bertram and Gildemeister, the high boiling fractions of the oil contain chiefly kessyl acetate (cf. Vol. II of the present work, p. 288, and below). This ester is responsible for the high specific gravity of the Japanese oil.

A Blue Oil(?). Also observed by Bertram and Gildemeister in the high boiling fractions.

As regards the structure of kessyl alcohol and related compounds, Kaneoka and Tutida [6] studied the problem in 1941, but did not arrive at any definite conclusions. They assigned the empirical molecular formula $C_{15}H_{26}O_3$ to kesso glycol. The compound, which is also called kesso glycol anhydride, melts at 128°.

[6] *J. Pharm. Soc. Japan* **61** (1941), 6, 8, 9, 123. *Chem. Abstracts* **35** (1941), 4773.

More recently Ukita [7] suggested the following structural formula for kesso glycol m. 128°:

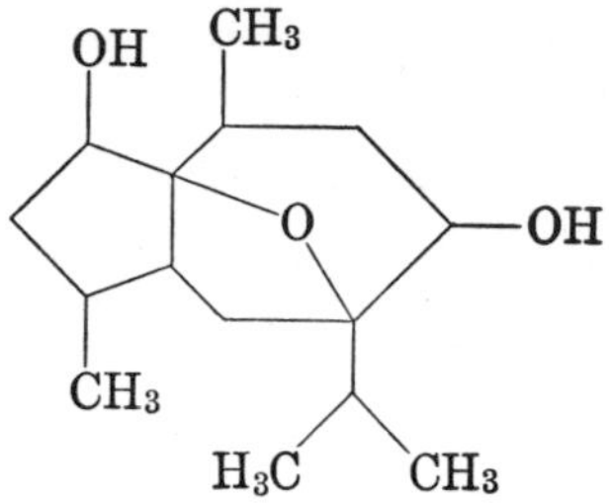

Kesso glycol hydrate, on the other hand, has the empirical molecular formula $C_{15}H_{26}O_3 \cdot H_2O$, and melts at 58°–59°.

Judging from the structural formula of kesso glycol, Ukita [8] finally arrived at the conclusion that kessyl alcohol has this configuration:

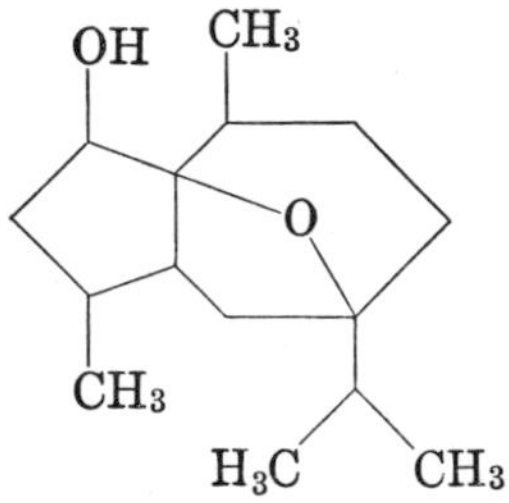

Kessyl alcohol has the empirical molecular formula $C_{15}H_{26}O_2$,[9] and melts at 85°.

The latest work on α-kessyl alcohol, a natural azulene-forming hydroxy-sesquiterpene oxide, is that of Treibs [10] who emphasizes the possible existence of *cis* and *trans* isomers, because of the linkage between the two rings. Moreover, there probably exist also *cis* and *trans* isomers through side chains and other substituents, hydroxy groups among them. According to observations made by Treibs, natural oxidized derivatives of sesquiterpenes occur in essential oils much more frequently than was formerly assumed. On the basis of his own investigations and those of Asahina,[11] Treibs suggested the following structural formula for α-kessyl alcohol:

[7] *J. Pharm. Soc. Japan* **64** (1944), 285.

[8] *Ibid.* **65** (1945), 458.

[9] The molecular formula of this compound, given on p. 288 of Vol. II of this work, should be corrected to read $C_{15}H_{26}O_2$.

[10] *Liebigs Ann.* **570** (1950), 165.

[11] *J. Pharm. Soc. Japan* **506** (1924), 13; **536** (1926), **75**; **544** (1927), 65.

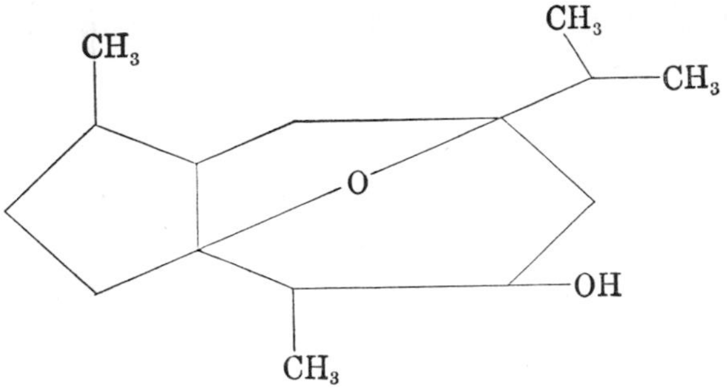

In this configuration the two rings are in the *trans* position.

Use.—The Japanese valerian oil is used for the same purposes as the European type of oil (see above).

OIL OF VALERIAN INDIAN

Introduction.—*Valeriana wallichii* DC. (fam. *Valerianaceae*), the so-called Indian valerian, is a perennial herb growing in the temperate parts of the Himalaya and Khasia Mountains. In India the dried rhizomes are used in perfumes and hair preparations, and as incense, rather than in medicines. Indian valerian is shipped in curved pieces from 4 to 8 cm. long, and from 5 to 10 mm. thick, dull brown in color. The odor is strong, resembling that of isovaleric acid; the taste, bitter and camphoraceous.

Owing to the unavailability of supplies of European valerian (*Valeriana officinalis* L.) during World War II, the dried rhizomes and roots of *Valeriana wallichii* were recognized by the National Formulary, Seventh Edition, Supplement 1, as a war emergency product, but were deleted from the Eighth Edition.

The dried rhizomes and roots contain a volatile oil of typical valerian odor, which can be isolated by steam distillation. In the experience of Fritzsche Brothers, Inc., New York, the yield of oil averages 0.7 per cent. The odor of the oil is somewhat inferior to that of the oil derived from *Valeriana officinalis*.

Physicochemical Properties.—Genuine oils distilled by the same firm had properties varying within these limits:

Specific Gravity at 15°/15°...... 0.931 to 0.960
Optical Rotation................ −15° 8′ to −25° 10′
Refractive Index at 20°......... 1.4733 to 1.4975
Acid Number.................... 50.4 to 114.8
Ester Number.................. 9.1 to 34.5
Solubility..................... Soluble in 0.5 vol. of 90%
                                       alcohol and more

An Indian valerian oil derived from *Valeriana wallichii* DC., and analyzed by Schimmel & Co.,[1] had the following properties:

Specific Gravity at 15°.............. 0.9361
Optical Rotation.................. −34° 6′
Refractive Index at 20°............ 1.48712
Acid Number...................... 37.3
Ester Number..................... 39.8
Ester Number after Acetylation...... 69.1
Solubility........................ Soluble in 0.3 and more vol. of 90%
                                   alcohol. Not soluble in 80% alco-
                                   hol up to 10 vol.

The color of the oil was yellowish-green, the odor strong and persistent. Distilling Indian valerian root, Bullock[2] obtained two oils (yield 0.35 per cent) with these properties:

	I	II
Specific Gravity at 19°.................	0.9819	0.9776
Refractive Index......................	1.5025	1.5042
Acid Number.........................	51.76	36.6
Acid Content, Calculated as Isovaleric Acid	9.4%	6.66%
Ester Content, Calculated as Isovalerate of a Sesquiterpene Alcohol..............	7.56%	7.07%
Alcohol Content, Calculated as $C_{15}H_{26}O$...	4.58%	14.87%

Chemical Composition.—The same author reported the presence of the following compounds in his oils:

A Sesquiterpene(?). B. 250°–258°; the chief component of the oil.

A Sesquiterpene Alcohol(?). Present in small quantities.

Isovaleric Acid. Present in ester form.

Acetic Acid(?) or Formic Acid(?). Also present in ester form.

Free Saturated Acids. The oil contained free saturated acids, probably a mixture of stearic and palmitic acids (m. of the mixture, 60°–61°).

Free Unsaturated Acids. Small quantities only.

A Blue Oil(?). On distillation over metallic sodium the deep blue color of this oil disappeared completely.

Use.—The oil distilled from Indian valerian root has the same uses as the oil derived from true *Valeriana officinalis* L., although the odor and flavor of the former do not quite equal those of the latter.

[1] *Ber. Schimmel & Co.* (1922), 8.
[2] *Pharm. J.* **117** (1926), 152.

CHAPTER IV

ESSENTIAL OILS OF THE PLANT FAMILY *VERBENACEAE*

OIL OF VERBENA

Essence de Verveine   *Aceite Esencial Verbena*   *Verbenaöl*

Botany and Producing Regions.—There is much confusion in literature about oil of verbena. A good many oils described [1] as verbena oils appear to have been distilled from plants other than true verbena. The so-called "Spanish Verbena Oil," or "Thyme Lemon Oil," e.g., is derived from *Thymus hiemalis* Lange, and perhaps also from *Thymus hirtus* Willd. (see Vol. III of this work, pp. 758 and 759, respectively).[2]

True verbena oil comes from *Lippia citriodora* Kunth., syn. *Verbena triphylla* L'Herit., *Aloysia citriodora* Ort. (fam. *Verbenaceae*), the so-called "Lemon Verbena," a shrub 1.2 to 1.5 m. high, which is occasionally grown as an ornamental plant in the gardens of southern Europe and Central America. Commercially the plant is cultivated on a small scale in the Grasse region of Southern France (near Pégomas and Valbonne), in Algeria (near Boufarik), and in Tunis. The leaves are sold to the herb and drug trade; very small quantities serve for distillation of the essential oil. The yield of oil, however, is so poor that the price of the oil by far exceeds its value (cf. "Adulteration," below).

Lippia citriodora is very sensitive to cold, and requires frequent irrigation. According to Naves and Mazuyer,[3] the first cutting takes place in July, as soon as the first inflorescence appears, the second cutting in October, before the plants are hilled up to protect them from the cold of the winter. Some growers harvest three times, viz., the end of June, the middle of August, and the end of October. The plants are cut 10 cm. above the ground. One hectare produces from 4 to 6 metric tons of plant material. The stalks with adhering leaves are tied into bundles and delivered to the distilleries where they must be processed immediately after arrival.

Distillation gives only a very small yield of oil; the distillation waters have to be cohobated. The yield of oil from fresh leaves varies between 0.072 and 0.195 per cent.[4] For leaves and twigs a yield of 0.0118 per cent

---

[1] Cf. Gildemeister and Hoffmann, "Die Ätherischen Öle," 3d Ed., Vol. III, 613.

[2] True verbena must not be confused with *Verbena officinalis* L., nor with the "verveine des tisanes," which in southern France is used in verbena teas and infusions. [Naves and Mazuyer, "Les Parfums Naturels," Paris (1939), 284]. *Verbena officinalis* L. (fam. *Verbenaceae*) is a common weed occurring widely all over Europe.

[3] "Les Parfums Naturels," Paris (1939), 285.

[4] Theulier, *Bull. soc. chim.* [3], **27** (1902), 1113. *Repts. Roure-Bertrand Fils,* April (1906), 38.

has been reported;[5] from leaves, twigs, and blossoms 0.65 per cent of oil was obtained.[6]

Physicochemical Properties.—Oil of verbena is a mobile, greenish-yellow liquid with a very agreeable lemon odor. Characteristic of the genuine oil is its laevorotation. Most of the true laevorotatory verbena oils described by Gildemeister and Hoffman [7] were of French origin; only one laevorotatory oil came from Spain (this oil was used by Schimmel & Co. for identification of its constituents—see below). *Dextrorotatory* "verbena" oils are derived not from *Lippia citriodora,* the true verbena, but from *Thymus hiemalis* (see above, "Botany").

According to Igolen and Igolen,[8] the properties of true verbena oil vary within these limits:

Specific Gravity at 15°................	0.890 to 0.912, rarely up to 0.920
Optical Rotation.....................	−10° 0′ to −18° 0′
Refractive Index at 20°..............	1.482 to 1.488, exceptionally 1.4793
Citral Content (Bisulfite Method)......	26 to 39%, usually 32 to 38%
Solubility...........................	Soluble in 1 to 6 vol. of 80% alcohol. Soluble in 1 to 2 vol. of 90% alcohol, sometimes with turbidity on dilution

Chemical Composition.—The chemical composition of verbena oil was investigated by Barbier,[9] Tiemann,[10] Theulier,[11] and particularly by Schimmel & Co.[12] (who examined a laevorotatory oil of Spanish origin). The findings of these investigators, however, do not need to be discussed here, because practically all of the compounds reported by them as constituents of verbena oil were identified also by Igolen and Igolen [13] who in 1938 investigated a true verbena oil from Algeria. According to these two workers, verbena oil contains:

Pyrrole and Furfural. Characterized by color reactions.

Methyl Heptenone. Identified by means of its semicarbazone m. 135°.

l-Carvone. Preparation of the 2,4-dinitrophenylhydrazone m. 194°.

α- and β-Citral. Identified by means of the citrylnaphthocinchoninic acid m. 198°, and of two 2,4-dinitrophenylhydrazones m. 107°–108°, and m. 95°–96° (α-citral, and β-citral, respectively).

[5] La Face, *Rivista ital. essenze profumi* **6** (1924), 109.
[6] Rutovski and Vinogradova, *Riechstoff Ind.* **3** (1928), 191.
[7] "Die Ätherischen Öle," 3d Ed., Vol. III, 615.
[8] *Rev. marques parfums France* **16** (1938), 113.
[9] *Bull. soc. chim.* [3], **21** (1899), 635.
[10] *Ber.* **33** (1900), 884.
[11] *Bull. soc. chim.* [3], **27** (1902), 1113.
[12] *Ber. Schimmel & Co.,* October (1913), 103.
[13] *Rev. marques parfums France* **16** (1938), 113.

Cineole. Characterized through its iodol compound.

l-Limonene. Identified by means of its tetrabromide m. 104°.

Dipentene. Tetrabromide m. 123°.

β-Caryophyllene. Nitrosochloride m. 162°, nitrosate m. 148°.

A Tricyclic Sesquiterpene(?). With these properties: b_3 115°, d_{15} 0.937, α_D −15°20′, n_D^{20} 1.5025.

Borneol. Diphenylurethane m. 53°. Oxidation to camphor; latter identified by means of its semicarbazone m. 236°.

Linaloöl. Diphenylurethane m. 49°. Oxidation to citral, the latter characterized by preparation of its naphthocinchoninic acid compound m. 198°.

d-α-Terpineol. 3,5-Dinitrobenzoate m. 78°–79°; nitrosochloride m. 106°–108°.

Nerol. Diphenylurethane m. 52°–53°; allophanate m. 101°.

Geraniol. 3,5-Dinitrobenzoate m. 58°–60°; diphenylurethane m. 81°–82°; allophanate m. 111°–112°.

Nerolidol. Diphenylurethane m. 52°.

Cedrol. 3,5-Dinitrobenzoate m. 92°–93°.

Acetic Acid. Identified by means of the silver salt in the saponification lye of the oil.

Igolen and Igolen were unable to identify myrcene, the presence of which in a French oil had been reported years ago by Barbier.[14] Nor could they identify verbenone, which Kerschbaum[15] had isolated from a dextrorotatory Spanish verbena oil. Most likely the oil investigated by Kerschbaum was derived not from true verbena, *Lippia citriodora*, but from *Thymus hiemalis* (see above—"Botany").

Examining a laevorotatory verbena oil from Spain, Schimmel & Co.[16] reported the presence of 0.5 per cent of verbenone. However, the melting point of the semicarbazone could not be raised above 200°–202°, which permits the conclusion that the ketone isolated by Schimmel & Co. was perhaps not verbenone. In the same oil Schimmel & Co. identified *d-citronellol* by preparation of the silver salt of the acid phthalic ester, m. 122°–124°.

In a laevorotatory verbena oil from the Caucasus, Rutovski and Vinogradova[17] reported the presence not only of some of the compounds listed above, but also of *isovaleric acid*.

The findings of Igolen and Igolen, as well as those of Schimmel & Co., and of Rutovski and Vinogradova, indicate that oil of verbena has the following approximate quantitative composition:

[14] *Bull. soc. chim.* [3], **21** (1899), 635.
[15] *Ber.* **33** (1900), 889. Cf. Vol. II of the present work, p. 444.
[16] *Ber. Schimmel & Co.,* October (1913), 103.
[17] *Riechstoff Ind.* **3** (1928), 194.

Acids (traces)	Acetic acid
	Isovaleric acid
Terpenes (22%)	*l*-Limonene
	Dipentene
Oxides (4%)	Cineole
Aldehydes and Ketones (33%)	α-Citral
	β-Citral
	Methyl heptenone
	Carvone
	Furfural (traces)
Alcohols (20%)	Linaloöl
	α-Terpineol
	Borneol
	Nerol
	Geraniol
	Citronellol
	Nerolidol
	Cedrol
Sesquiterpenes (15%)	*d*-β-Caryophyllene
	A tricyclic sesqui-terpene(?)
Nitrogenous Compounds (traces)	Pyrrole

Use.—Because of its high price, only very small quantities of true verbena oil are produced. As a matter of fact, most commercial "verbena" oils offered on the market are mixtures, and more or less skillful blends, chiefly of citral, or fractions of lemongrass oil, and natural isolates from other essential oils, all of them compounded in about the same proportions in which they occur in the natural verbena oil.

Provided it could be produced at economical prices, oil of verbena would be a valuable adjunct in toilet waters and eaux de Cologne, to which it imparts refreshing tonalities. The oil could also be used to great advantage in certain types of flavors (liqueurs, nonalcoholic beverages, etc.).

CONCRETE AND ABSOLUTE OF VERBENA

According to Naves and Mazuyer,[18] extraction of true verbena with petroleum ether yields from 0.25 to 0.30 per cent of a waxy, light to dark green concrete (m. 40°–52°, acid number about 30, ester number 24.1 to 38.4) which, on treatment with alcohol in the usual way, gives from 50 to 60 per cent of an alcohol-soluble absolute, a viscous, syrupy, dark green

[18] "Les Parfums Naturels," Paris (1939), 285.

liquid. Both the concrete and the absolute are produced only rarely, and in small quantities. The absolute contains from 30 to 36 per cent of a steam-volatile oil with properties resembling those of the oil obtained by steam distillation of the plants themselves. Naves, Sabetay and Palfray [19] reported these values for four steam-volatile oils derived from concretes of Algerian origin:

> Specific Gravity at 15°......... 0.894 to 0.907
> Optical Rotation.............. −4° 40' to −6° 16'
> Refractive Index at 20°........ 1.4741 to 1.4794
> Acid Number................. 3.8 to 7.2
> Aldehyde Content, Calculated as
>   Citral (Hydroxylamine Hydro-
>   chloride Method)........... 39.5 to 42.1%

The chemical composition of this type of volatile verbena oil has not yet been investigated, but can be assumed to resemble that of the oils obtained by distillation of the plants directly.

SUGGESTED ADDITIONAL LITERATURE

C. J. Zufall and W. O. Richtmann, "A Pharmacognostical Study of Certain American Species of Verbena," *Pharm. Arch.* **14** (1943), 65, 81. *Chem. Abstracts* **38** (1944), 2387.

[19] *Perfumery Essential Oil Record* **28** (1937), 337.

CHAPTER V

ESSENTIAL OILS OF THE PLANT FAMILY *CISTACEAE*

OIL OF LABDANUM

Essence de Ladanum   Aceite Esencial Labdano   Ladanumöl

Introduction.—The essential oil expert and perfumer who has traveled extensively is inclined to associate some places he has visited with certain odors. The scent of otto of rose will always remind him of the "Valley of Roses" in Bulgaria, the fragrance of jasmine may recall nights in Seville or Granada, the heavy perfume of ylang ylang will bring back memories of tropical Nossi-Bé, a little island off Madagascar. One of the most unforgettable scents is that of labdanum, whose sweet, warm, balsamic odor permeates sunny patches in the pine forests that cover some of the islands in the Mediterranean or stretch along the rocky coasts of that beautiful, blue sea. In the natural habitat of the plant its perfume blends with that of pine, and perhaps sage, lavender, or thyme, producing an aroma that may be truly called Mediterranean. The classical Greeks and Romans must have been familiar with labdanum, for *Ladanos* is described by Dioscorides, Herodotus and Pliny. The modern Spanish term *Jara* for gum of labdanum clearly shows its Moorish origin, and indicates that the Moors of Spain made use of the drug.

Cistus ladaniferus L. (fam. *Cistaceae*) is a perennial shrub, up to 2 m. high, which grows wild, and in large stands, in sunny, warm, and well-sheltered places on some Mediterranean islands (Crete, Cyprus, Corsica, Dalmatian Islands, Isles de Lérin near Cannes) and in Mediterranean countries (Spain, Morocco, Greece, Estérel Mountains on the French Riviera, etc.). In hot and sunny localities, protected against wind and cold, the plant grows much taller than in unsheltered places. Small, white flowers appear in June, but they are very short-lived. The leaves possess glandular hairs consisting of two or three cells, which contain a very viscous gum-balsam; this exudes during the hot months and covers the leaves as well as the upper parts of twigs and branches with a sticky mass, agreeable, balsamic, and ambergris-like in odor. This resin is used in perfumes and soaps.

The older literature on perfumery frequently refers to gum labdanum from Crete, said to be obtained by combing the hair of sheep that had browsed through stands of labdanum, the sticky gum having adhered to the hair of the animals. Labdanum gum from Crete, however, has long since disappeared from the market. Today the odoriferous principles of the labdanum plant are isolated by several methods; the following products are obtained:

A. The crude, dark, gum of labdanum, prepared in Spain by boiling the dried twigs and leaves in water, skimming the liquefied mass from the surface of the water, and drying it.

B. The resinoid of labdanum, prepared by treating the dark, crude gum with alcohol, then filtering and concentrating the solution. The resulting resinoid is an alcohol-soluble, viscous mass, of dark color.

C. The essential oil of labdanum, prepared by steam distillation of the crude gum. The resulting volatile oil is of golden-yellow color and powerful odor, representing the odoriferous principles of the gum in most concentrated form.

D. The concrete and absolute of labdanum, prepared by extracting the dried twigs and leaves with volatile solvents, usually benzene. Large quantities of these concretes and alcohol-soluble absolutes are produced in the Grasse region of Southern France. They are employed in the perfume, cosmetic and soap industries.

E. The essential oil obtained by steam distillation of the dried or fresh twigs and leaves themselves. This oil possesses a terpene-like odor, quite different from that of the plant exudation; it is, therefore, of little use in perfumery. Only small quantities are produced.

A. Gum of Labdanum

Producing regions lie in the northeastern part of Spain, near the Portuguese frontier, in the provinces of Zamora and León, particularly in the triangle formed by the roads connecting Zamora, Benavente, and Mombuey. Today most of the gum labdanum is produced in this comparatively small section. Another potentially very rich, but so far relatively little exploited, producing region lies in Andalusia, south of Seville. This agriculturally rich land, however, offers opportunities for other and more remunerative activities.

The best time for collection of the plant material is the period of most intense heat, i.e., in July and August, because the plant then exudes a maximum of resin. At this season, however, the peasants are busy with their regular crops; as a consequence, they cut the labdanum, which grows wild on hillsides, during the winter months, when they have ample time. The cut twigs with adhering leaves are tied into bundles, dried for several weeks, and then boiled with water in large kettles for a number of hours. The gum resin softens under the influence of the boiling water, and rises to the surface as a dark scum, which is continually skimmed off with large spoons, and poured into wooden molds. The soft gum thus collected is freed of water by repeated decantation and slight pressure. As time goes on, the gum hardens and blocks of about 10 kg. are cut out, wrapped in sack cloth, and stored in cellars. On aging, the gum loses more water and turns into a plastic, very dark mass. This represents the crude gum of labdanum offered by the trade (*Droga de Jara*). Spain produces from 15 to 20 metric tons of labdanum per year. Frequently the gum is adulterated by the rural producers with all sorts of inert material—earth and even dried cow dung, for example.

Crude gum of labdanum possesses a "heavy," balsamic odor, somewhat reminiscent of ambergris. The ambergris note appears to become stronger as the gum ages; it is much less pronounced in freshly prepared gum. Being only partly soluble in alcohol, the crude gum cannot be used in its natural state in perfumery. It may be utilized in the form of alcoholic tinctures; these, however, are quite dark in color.

B. Resinoid of Labdanum

The other way of employing the gum in a convenient form is by preparing alcohol-soluble resinoids. This can be done most easily by treating the crude gum with hot alcohol of high proof, cooling and filtering the solution, and concentrating the clear filtrate in a vacuum still. The very viscous resinoid possesses a balsamic, lasting, and ambergris-like odor. However, because of the very dark color, its application in perfumes, cosmetics and soaps is limited.

A good grade of crude gum labdanum yields from 70 to 85 per cent of alcohol-soluble resinoid. According to Naves and Mazuyer,[1] resinoid of labdanum has these properties:

Acid Number........ 76 to 112
Ester Number....... 136 to 188

C. Oil of Labdanum

To isolate the odoriferous principles of gum labdanum in most concentrated form, soluble in alcohol and light in color, the crude gum is submitted to steam distillation, whereby the volatile or essential oil of labdanum is obtained. The yield of oil depends upon the origin, quality and age of the gum; it is small and ranges from about 1 to 2 per cent.

The oil, a somewhat viscous liquid of golden-yellow color, possesses a powerful, balsamic, very lasting odor, in dilution reminiscent of ambergris.

[1] "Les Parfums Naturels," Paris (1939), 312.

Oils distilled under the author's supervision in Seillans (Var), France, from imported Spanish gum, and by Fritzsche Brothers, Inc., New York, also from Spanish gum, had properties varying within these limits:

Specific Gravity at 15°/15°.......... 0.947 to 0.980
Optical Rotation.................... +2° 20' to +6° 32', sometimes too dark to determine optical rotation
Refractive Index at 20°............. 1.4919 to 1.5048
Acid Number...................... 18.8 to 59.7
Saponification Number.............. 42.0 to 93.3
Ketone Content, Calculated as Aceto-
  phenone (Hydroxylamine Hydro-
  chloride Method)................. 9.9 to 19.4%
Solubility......................... Soluble in 0.5 vol. of 90% alcohol, usually opalescent to turbid with more

Oil of labdanum (distilled from the gum) is a most valuable perfumer's raw material. Because of its great strength it has to be dosed carefully. The oil is used in high-grade perfumes, to which it imparts characteristic and lasting notes, difficult to identify, if skillfully blended. Many modern perfumes, particularly those of the French type, contain oil of labdanum. as one of the basic notes. The oil is used also in many specialties offered by European and American essential oil houses, and marketed as synthetic ambergris compounds. Moreover, it forms the base of the various "Clair de Labdanum" compositions, which reproduce the odor of the labdanum gum, but are of light color, soluble in alcohol, and less concentrated than the oil itself.

D. Concrete and Absolute of Labdanum

By far the most popular and widely used labdanum products are the so-called concretes and absolutes, large quantities of which are produced in the Grasse region of Southern France. Bundled dried twigs and leaves, which originate from Spain, Corsica, Morocco, or from the Estérel Mountains near Grasse, are extracted with volatile solvents, usually benzene (cf. Vol. I of this work, pp. 200 ff.). According to Naves and Mazuyer,[2] extraction with petroleum ether yields from 3 to 6 per cent of concrete, which on treatment with alcohol gives from 45 to 65 per cent of alcohol-soluble absolute. The concrete contains from 3.2 to 5 per cent of a steam-volatile oil which, however, is not a regular commercial article. Extraction with benzene, the usual procedure, yields from 4 to 7 per cent of concrete, which gives from 85 to 88 per cent of absolute.

[2] *Ibid.,* 206.

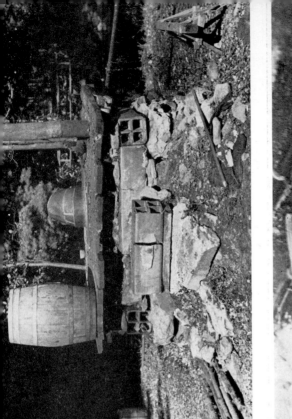

(*Top Left*) Production of wintergreen oil (*Gaultheria procumbens*) in northern Pennsylvania. Collection of the plant material, which grows wild in the woods. (*Top Right*) Wintergreen oil, northern Pennsylvania. A very primitive field still. (*Bottom Left*) Wintergreen oil, northern Pennsylvania. A more advanced field distillery. (*Bottom Right*) Wintergreen oil, northern Pennsylvania. An oil separator. The oil separates as a heavy layer beneath the milky distillation water. *Photos Fritzsche Brothers, Inc., New York.*

(*Top Left*) Production of oil of sweet birch (*Betula lenta*) in Pennsylvania. Arrival of the distillation material in front of a distillery. (*Top Right*) Oil of sweet birch, Pennsylvania. A typical field distillery. (*Bottom Left*) Oil of sweet birch, Pennsylvania. A box still half filled with chopped branches. *Photos Fritzsche Brothers, Inc., New York.*

For the production of concrete up to 250 metric tons of labdanum plants have been known to be processed, per year, in the Grasse region.

The concretes obtained by extraction with benzene are dark green, solid masses. Two concretes produced under the author's supervision in Seillans (Var), France, had the properties given below. Concrete (I) was extracted with benzene from dried plant material of Spanish (Zamora) origin, concrete (II) from plants of French (Estérel Mountains) provenience:

	I	II
Acid Number	71.4	72.8
Ester Number	95.7	94.3

Absolute of labdanum is a brown-greenish, very viscous liquid, soluble in high-proof alcohol, with a most agreeable, balsamic, warm, and very lasting odor. Naves and Mazuyer [3] reported for an absolute of labdanum prepared in Provence (France):

Acid Number	61.6
Ester Number	84.9

Absolute of labdanum is widely used in perfumes, cosmetics and soaps. It imparts warm, balsamic tonalities to perfume compositions, and at the same time acts as an excellent natural fixative. Its odor blends particularly well with chypre, fougère, clary sage, lavender, and pine compositions.

Although steam-volatile oils from concrete or absolute of labdanum are not produced commercially, two oils of this type were obtained experimentally by Naves, Sabetay and Palfray,[4] who steam-distilled two (petroleum ether) concretes of labdanum from Provence. The oils had these properties:

Specific Gravity at 15°	0.987	1.003
Optical Rotation	−4° 42′	−5° 50′
Refractive Index at 20°	1.4971	1.4936
Acid Number	31.0	46.2
Ester Number	56.6	59.2
Solubility	Soluble in 1 vol. of 90% alcohol	

E. Oil of Labdanum Leaves

The volatile oil contained in the glandular hairs of the leaves and in the exudation on the leaves and twigs of the labdanum plant can also be isolated directly by steam distillation of the twigs and adhering leaves themselves. However, samples of such oils examined by the author had a harsh odor of terpenes, the balsamic odor of the gum being quite concealed. For

[3] *Ibid.*, 207.
[4] *Perfumery Essential Oil Record* **28** (1937), 336.

this reason, oils of this type are not produced on a large scale. They offer little interest to the perfume industry, but will be discussed here for scientific interest. Gildemeister and Hoffmann,[5] and Igolen[6] described the properties of two oils distilled from fresh leaves (I and II), and those of oils distilled from dried plants (III and IV):

	I	*II*	*III*	*IV*
Specific Gravity at 15°.........	0.9223	0.917	0.9450	0.9443
Optical Rotation..............	−11° 12′	−9° 52′	−2° 36′	−3° 8′
Refractive Index at 20°........	...	1.4878	1.4900	...
Acid Number................	5.31	3.73	16.8	14.56
Ester Number................	23.10	30.8	22.4	32.9
Solubility in 90% Alcohol......	Soluble in 0.5 vol.	Soluble in 0.2 vol.	Soluble in 0.5 vol., with turbidity up to 5 vol.	

Sabetay and Trabaud[7] reported the properties of two volatile oils obtained in the Estérel Mountains (A.M., France) by steam distillation of freshly cut plant material:

	With Stems	*Without Stems*
Yield of Oil........................	0.059%	0.118%
Specific Gravity at 15°..............	0.9473	0.9270
Optical Rotation...................	−0° 50′	−4° 20′
Refractive Index at 20°.............	1.4901	1.4838
Acid Number......................	9.3	6.5
Ester Number.....................	24.3	18.6
Ester Number after Acetylation......	104.5	97.07
Solubility in 90% Alcohol..........	Soluble with separation of paraffins	

CHEMICAL COMPOSITION OF LABDANUM PRODUCTS

Little is known about the chemical composition of the volatile oil derived from *gum labdanum,* except that it contains two ketones and other still unidentified compounds.

Acetophenone. Identified in the fraction b_{15} 85°–90° by Masson,[8] who prepared the semicarbazone m. 207°.

1,5,5-Trimethyl-6-cyclohexanone. From the fraction b_{15} 70°–78° the same author obtained an oxime m. 106° which, on regeneration, yielded a ketone $C_9H_{16}O$, b. 178°–179°, b_{10} 66°–67°, d_0 0.922, α_D ±0°, n_D^{23} 1.4494. The ketone reacted with sodium bisulfite; it gave a monobromide m. 41°, and a semicarbazone m. 220°–221°. On treatment with metallic sodium and moist ether, the ketone could be reduced to the corresponding secondary alcohol m. 51°, b_{28} 87°. Oxidation of the ketone with a 3 per cent solution of potassium permanganate yielded geronic

[5] "Die Ätherischen Öle," 3d Ed., Vol. III, 247.
[6] *Parfums France* **15** (1937), 170. [8] *Compt. rend.* **154** (1912), 517.
[7] *Ind. parfum.* **5** (1950), 548.

acid b_{31} 190°–191°; semicarbazone m. 164°. The structural formula of geronic acid is: $CH_3 \cdot CO \cdot CH_2 \cdot CH_2 \cdot CH_2 \cdot C(CH_3)_2 \cdot COOH$.

Ladaniol(?). Examining a gum labdanum from Crete, Emmanuel [9] isolated an alcohol $C_{17}H_{30}O$, m. 89°, viz., ladaniol, which he thought to be related to guaiol (cf. Vol. II of this work, p. 278), without, however, giving any details.

Other Compounds(?). According to Masson, the oil contains still other compounds, among them esters, phenols and sesquiterpenes, none of them, however, further characterized.

As regards the chemical composition of the *concrete and absolute of labdanum,* no investigations have been undertaken.

On the other hand, the volatile oil obtained in the Estérel Mountains by steam distillation of the leaves and twigs directly (labdanum leaf oil) has been examined by Sabetay and Trabaud,[10] and Sabetay and Gilly,[11] who reported the presence of the following compounds:

Terpenes(?). B. 154°–159°, d_{15} 0.8594, α −30° 30′, n_D^{20} 1.4725. No individual terpene could be identified.

l-α-Pinene. According to Fesneau,[12] 45 per cent of the oil boils below 160°. This fraction consists largely of *l-α*-pinene which Fesneau identified by preparation of the nitrosochloride m. 103.5°–104.5°, and by oxidation to pinonic acid m. 64°–67° (semicarbazone m. 204°).

Benzaldehyde. Characterized by means of its semicarbazone m. 238°.

Other Aldehydes(?). Aside from benzaldehyde, the oil contained other aldehydes which reacted with bisulfite.

Acetophenone. Identified through its semicarbazone m. 207°.

Other Ketones(?). Aside from acetophenone, the oil contained other ketones, which combined with the reagent of Girard and Sandulesco. Among them was a ketone with a minty odor. It gave a semicarbazone m. 232°, and perhaps was identified with the ketone isolated by Masson from the oil of *gum* labdanum (see above).

Eugenol. Characterized by means of its benzoate m. 68°.

Other Phenols(?). Aside from eugenol, the oil contained other phenols which were not identified. Judging from its methoxy number, the phenol content of the oil was about 3.3 per cent.

Ledol. On standing, the alcoholic fraction b_7 127°–132°, α +7° 40′ of the oil deposited crystals m. 105°–106°, which were shown to be ledol (cf. Vol. II of this work, p. 280), a tricyclic tertiary sesquiterpene alcohol, which occurs in nature quite rarely.

[9] *Arch. Pharm.* **250** (1912), 111.
[10] *Bull. soc. chim.* [5], **10** (1943), 398. *Ind. parfum.* **5** (1950), 548.
[11] *Bull. soc. chim.* [5], **10** (1943), 398. Cf. *Perfumery Essential Oil Record* **41** (1950), 65. *Ind. parfum.* **5** (1950), 548. *Rec. trav. chim.* **69** (1950), 545.
[12] *Ind. parfum.* **5** (1950), 315.

Acids. The acids occur in the oil as esters. Among the acids Sabetay and Trabaud identified *acetic acid*. The presence of formic acid is possible. The oil also contains an acid of rancid odor, but this has not yet been identified.

Fesneau [13] investigated a volatile oil obtained in Spain by direct steam distillation of freshly harvested labdanum leaves (yield 0.1 per cent to 0.2 per cent), and reported the presence of these compounds:

Diacetyl

Furfural

Cineole

Borneol

l-Pinene

The oil contained 1 per cent of aldehydes (bisulfite method), and 1 per cent of phenols.

USE

Of the various labdanum products described above, the most important ones are the concretes and absolutes. The alcohol-insoluble concretes lend themselves particularly well to soap work, acting as excellent natural fixatives, and at the same time imparting agreeable balsamic notes. The alcohol-soluble absolutes are widely used in perfumes and cosmetics. They, too, are good fixatives and odor adjuncts, forming the base of many a composition. The volatile oil derived from the gum has the most concentrated and powerful odor among all the labdanum products. Its light color permits use in high-grade perfumes, to which the oil imparts exotic and alluring tonalities, if carefully blended and dosed. The resinoids, because of their very dark color, are limited in application.

SUGGESTED ADDITIONAL LITERATURE

A. M. Burger, "Dalmatian Labdanum," *Riechstoff Ind.* 8 (1933), 211.

F. W. Freise, "Brazilian Labdanum," *Perfumery Essential Oil Record* 25 (1934), 135.

S. Sabetay, "Constantes Analytiques des Essences Concrètes et Absolues de Ciste-Labdanum de L'Estérel," *Ind. parfum.* 5, No. 1 (1950), 33.

L. Trabaud, "The Ciste-Labdanum of Provence," *Soap, Perfumery Cosmetics* 23, No. 4 (1950), 372; 24 (1951), 449.

[13] *Ibid.,* 551.

CHAPTER VI

ESSENTIAL OILS OF THE PLANT FAMILY *CRUCIFERAE*

OIL OF BLACK MUSTARD SEED
(Oil of Mustard)

Essence de Moutarde   *Aceite Esencial Mostaza*   *Senföl*
Oleum Sinapis

The seeds of *Brassica nigra* (L.) Koch and of *Brassica juncea* (L.) Czerniaew (fam. *Cruciferae*) contain fixed oils of mild taste, which can be isolated by expression of the seeds in hydraulic presses. The chemical composition of these fatty oils resembles that of oil of rapeseed (*Brassica napus* L.).

Much more important than the fixed oils from the point of view of flavor are the volatile oils derived from the seeds of *Brassica nigra* and *Brassica juncea*. Both of these varieties are classified as "Black Mustard" in the United States Pharmacopoeia and the United States Dispensatory. The volatile oils are not contained in the seeds, in the free state, but in the form of glucosides. To isolate them from the seed, it is necessary to remove the fixed oil by expression, to submit the pressed cake to fermentation, and to distill the fermented mass (see below).

The volatile oil derived from black mustard seed (*Brassica nigra* or *B. juncea*) consists almost entirely of allyl isothiocyanate. This compound can also be prepared synthetically. In fact, most of the mustard oil or "Allyl Mustard Oil" offered on the market today consists of the synthetic product. The natural oil has lost much of its former importance. Official standard works in the United States recognize both the natural and the synthetic oils as "Volatile Oil of Mustard" or "Allyl Isothiocyanate." It is required, however, to specify on the label whether the product is natural or synthetic. In both cases the actual content of C_3H_5NCS in the oil should not be below 93 per cent.

For full information regarding natural and synthetic allyl isothiocyanate the reader is referred to Vol. II of the present work, p. 734. Suffice it here to discuss the production of the natural oil.

Brassica nigra (L.) Koch, the "Black Mustard," is a native of central and southern Europe and western temperate Asia. The plant, an annual, attains a height of 2 ft. or more. It is cultivated extensively in countries of temperate climate, particularly Holland and Italy, the seed from Holland being considered of best quality.

Brassica juncea (L.) Czerniaew, also called "Brown Mustard," "Indian Mustard" or "Rai," is cultivated in northern India, in Astrakhan, Sarepta, and other parts of southern Russia. The seed of this species closely resembles that of *Brassica nigra*, hence both are accepted as "Black Mustard" in the United States. The volatile oils derived from the seeds of the two species are practically identical.

Production of the Volatile Oil.—As was pointed out above, allyl isothiocyanate does not occur in the seed as such, but in the form of a glucoside, viz., sinigrin (potassium myronate), which, in the presence of water and a ferment (viz., myrosinase), is hydrolyzed to allyl isothiocyanate, d-glucose, and potassium bisulfate:

$$CH_2{=}CH \cdot CH_2 \cdot N{=}C \underset{S \cdot C_6H_{11}O_5}{\overset{OSO_3K}{\big\langle}} \quad \xrightarrow{H_2O}$$

Potassium Myronate

$$CH_2{=}CH \cdot CH_2 \cdot N{=}C{=}S + C_6H_{12}O_6 + KHSO_4$$
Allyl Isothiocyanate

According to Wrede, Banik and Brauss,[1] the empirical molecular formula $C_{10}H_{18}NS_2KO_{10}$ of the glucoside sinigrin (m. 128°) applies to the crystalline compound, which contains water. The formula should be resolved into $C_{10}H_{16}NS_2KO_9 + H_2O$. On boiling of the methyl alcoholic solution, after addition of absolute alcohol, sinigrin (m. 179°), free of water, will be obtained. This latter form of the glucoside is readily soluble in water. Hérissey and Boivin [2] succeeded in preparing pure sinigrin $[\alpha]_D -17° 25'$ (in 82–83% alcohol).

The structural formula for sinigrin, pictured above, was established by Gadamer.[3]

As regards the ferment myrosinase, Heiduschka and Pyriki [4] carried out experiments in an attempt to prepare a ferment of high potency.

The hydrolysis of the glucoside sinigrin does not always proceed smoothly according to the scheme pictured above, and side reactions may take place. Thus, allyl cyanide and carbon disulfide may be formed. Many years ago Schmidt [5] observed that the allyl isothiocyanate may be accompanied by small quantities of the isomer, allyl thiocyanate, if fermentation is conducted at low temperature. Perhaps allyl thiocyanate is always formed

---

[1] *Z. physiol. Chem.* **126** (1923), 210.
[2] *J. pharm. chim.* [8], **6** (1927), 337.
[3] *Arch. Pharm.* **235** (1897), 47. *Ber.* **30** (1897), 2322, 2328.
[4] *Arch. Pharm.* **264** (1926), 694.
[5] *Ber.* **10** (1877), 187.

first in the course of the hydrolysis of sinigrin; but at higher temperatures the allyl thiocyanate is converted to allyl isothiocyanate. Billeter [6] expressed the opinion that the reaction proceeds in these steps:

$$
\begin{array}{ccccc}
\text{S}\!-\!\!-\text{C}\!\equiv\!\text{N} & & \text{S}\!-\!\!-\text{C}\!=\!\text{N} & & \text{S}\!=\!\text{C}\!=\!\text{N} \\
| & \rightarrow & |\quad|\quad| & \rightarrow & | \\
\text{CH}_2\cdot\text{CH}\!=\!\text{CH}_2 & & \text{CH}_2\cdot\text{CH}\cdot\text{CH}_2 & & \text{CH}_2\!=\!\text{CH}\cdot\text{CH}_2
\end{array}
$$

Several factors influence the fermentation process. These should be carefully considered in order to obtain a high yield and quality of volatile mustard oil:

1. Duration of maceration. According to experiments carried out by Viehoever,[7] maceration of the pressed cake for a period exceeding 2 hr. results in an abnormally low yield of volatile oil. Rosenthaler [8] explained this on the following theoretical grounds:

(*a*) Hydrolytic decomposition of the formed allyl isothiocyanate, possibly as a result of influence of a ferment; (b) decomposition of allyl isothiocyanate into allyl cyanide and sulfur; (c) addition reaction between the allyl isothiocyanate and other compounds; (d) decomposition of the allyl isothiocyanate by means of bacteria.

2. Condition of the pressed cake. Lasausse [9] found that the yield of oil depends greatly upon the particle size of the ground pressed cake. The smaller the particles, the higher will be the yield of oil.

3. The temperature at which the fermentation is conducted. Experimenting with different temperatures, Astruc and Mousseron [10] arrived at the conclusion that at 70° C. the yield of oil increases to more than twice that obtained at 20°. However, at a temperature higher than 70°, hydrolysis stops, because at 75° the ferment myrosinase becomes ineffective.

4. Potency of the ferment. It has been claimed in literature that black mustard does not contain sufficient ferment (myrosinase) to split all of the glucoside (sinigrin) present; the addition of some white mustard (*Brassica alba* Coles) has been recommended to obtain a higher yield of volatile oil. According to the findings of Greenish and Bartlett,[11] this is not necessary; black mustard seed contains more than sufficient myrosinase to split all the sinigrin contained in the seed. The same authors found that even six-year-old black mustard seed still had a normal myrosinase content.

[6] *Helv. Chim. Acta* **8** (1925), 337.
[7] *J. Assocn. Official Agr. Chem.* **3** (1920), 381.
[8] *Schweiz. Apoth. Ztg.* **62** (1924), 508, 519.
[9] *Ann. fals.* **20** (1927), 328. *Brit. Chem. Abstracts* **46** (1927), B. 667.
[10] *J. pharm. chim.* [8], **5** (1927), 313.
[11] *Pharm. J.* **88** (1912), 203.

Greenish and Bartlett [12] also confirmed the earlier contention of Brioux [13] that addition of a small quantity of sodium fluoride to the fermentation mass influences the hydrolysis favorably. As little as 0.4 per cent of sodium fluoride is sufficient to destroy all microorganisms that may have a harmful influence upon the allyl isothiocyanate formed in the course of fermentation.

5. The type of apparatus. Fermentation should be carried out in well-enameled tanks. Copper must be avoided, because on prolonged contact with metallic copper, allyl isothiocyanate is converted into allyl cyanide and copper sulfide:

$$C_3H_5NCS + Cu \rightarrow C_3H_5CN + CuS$$

Under these circumstances so much allyl cyanide ($d_{17.5}$ 0.835) may be formed that the final volatile oil will have a specific gravity below 1.0 (Will and Körner [14]).

According to Marta and Halley,[15] the enzymes responsible for the splitting of the thioglucosides have a specific action on the thioglucoside complex. These enzymes consist of two components: one of them is sulfatase, the enzyme responsible for the potassium bisulfate; the other is thioglucosidase, the enzyme causing the splitting of the thioglucoside linkage. In the seeds, the myrosinase and the thioglucosides occur in different cells; hence the seeds usually must be crushed to bring about hydrolysis. If well preserved, seeds will retain their active principles for a long time.

The yield of volatile oil ranges from 0.5 to more than 1.0 per cent. Huber and van der Wielen [16] obtained 1.23 per cent of oil from Dutch seed, 0.87 per cent from Italian, 0.63 per cent from Russian, and 1.07 per cent from Bombay seed. Koblic [17] found that Czechoslovakian seed had a mustard oil content of 0.775 per cent, Roumanian seed 0.524 per cent.

Assay of Volatile Oil Content in the Seed.—For the quantitative determination of the volatile oil contained in mustard seed, the Association of Official Agricultural Chemists [18] specifies the following method:

"Place 5 g. of ground seed (No. 20 powder) in 200 ml. flask, add 100 ml. of H_2O, stopper tightly, and macerate for 2 hours at ca. 37°. Add 20 ml. of alcohol and distill ca. 60 ml. into 100 ml. volumetric flask containing 10 ml. of NH_4OH (1 + 2), taking care that end of condenser dips below surface of soln.

[12] *Ibid.*
[13] *Ann. chim. anal. chim. appli.* **17** (1912), 6.
[14] *Liebigs Ann.* **125** (1863), 278.
[15] *J. Biol. Chem.* **96** (1932), 443. Cf. Kosker, Fellers, and Esselen, Jr., *Glass Packer* **28** (1949), 818.
[16] *Pharm. Weekblad* **52** (1915), 1410.
[17] *Sbornik Českoslov. Akad. Zemědělske* **15** (1940), 94. *Chem. Abstracts* **37** (1943), 502.
[18] "Official and Tentative Methods of Analysis," 6th Ed. (1945), 542.

Add 20 ml. of 0.1 N AgNO$_3$ to distillate, set aside overnight, heat to boiling on water bath in order to agglomerate (Ag)$_2$S, cool, make to 100 ml. with H$_2$O, and filter. Acidify 50 ml. of filtrate with ca. 5 ml. of HNO$_3$ and titrate with 0.1 N NH$_4$CNS, using 5 ml. of 10% FeNH$_4$(SO$_4$)$_2 \cdot$12H$_2$O as indicator. 1 ml. of 0.1 N AgNO$_3$ consumed = 0.004956 g. of allyl isothiocyanate."

Other methods for the assay of the volatile oil content of mustard seed have been described by Terry and Curran,[19] André and Kogane-Charles,[20] and by Böhme.[21]

Physicochemical Properties.—The volatile oil derived from the seed of black mustard is a mobile, colorless to yellowish, optically inactive liquid, highly refractive to light. It possesses an acrid taste and a most pungent, irritating, lachrymatory odor. On the skin the oil forms blisters. Great care must be exercised when tasting or smelling the oil; neither should be done unless the oil is diluted.

Gildemeister and Hoffmann [22] reported these properties for oil of mustard:

Specific Gravity at 15°............ 1.014 to 1.022, occasionally as high as 1.030. The specific gravity is influenced by the factors discussed above (see section "Production of the Volatile Oil")

Optical Rotation................. ±0°

Refractive Index at 20°........... 1.52681 to 1.52908

Allyl Isothiocyanate Content...... 94% [23]

Boiling Range at 760 mm......... Mostly between 148° and 154°

Solubility...................... Soluble in 160 to 300 parts of water. Soluble in 7 to 10 vol. of 70% alcohol; in 2.5 to 3 vol. of 80% alcohol; in 0.5 vol. of 90% alcohol. Clearly miscible with ether, amyl alcohol, benzene and petroleum ether in all proportions

Regarding the changes which take place on aging of the oil, exposure to air and light, contact with metals, etc., see Vol. II of the present work, p. 736.

Quantitative Determination of Allyl Isothiocyanate.—See Vol. I of this work, p. 303.

Chemical Composition.—If prepared under normal conditions, the volatile oil derived from black mustard seed contains about 94 per cent of *allyl isothiocyanate;* the balance consists of *allyl cyanide* and *carbon disulfide.* (For the quantitative assay of carbon disulfide in mustard oil, see the methods of Hofmann,[24] and Macagno.[25])

[19] *Analyst* **64** (1939), 164.

[20] *Compt. rend.* **222** (1946), 103.

[21] *Pharm. Zentralhalle* **87** (1948), 299. Cf. *Ber. Variochem. Schimmel* (1950), 104.

[22] "Die Ätherischen Öle," 3d Ed., Vol. II, 761.

[23] *Ber. Schimmel & Co.* (1948), 101.

[24] *Ber.* **13** (1880), 1732.

[25] *Z. anal. Chem.* **21** (1882), 133. Cf. Gildemeister and Hoffmann, "Die Ätherischen Öle," 3d Ed., Vol. II, 764.

Years ago, Pomeranz [26] expressed the opinion that natural mustard oil contains not only allyl isothiocyanate $CH_2{=}CH{\cdot}CH_2{\cdot}N{=}C{=}S$, but also the isomeric propenyl isothiocyanate $CH_3{\cdot}CH{=}CH{\cdot}N{=}C{=}S$. According to Gildemeister and Hoffmann,[27] this is true of the synthetic oil, but for the natural oil no definite proof has yet been adduced.

In 1910, Schimmel & Co.[28] examined a mustard oil which they had prepared from the seed of *Brassica juncea* and found that it possessed quite abnormal properties (d_{15} 0.9950, α_D $+0°$ 12', n_D^{20} 1.51849) and an unusual boiling range (b. 40°–150°, 7%; b. 150°–160°, 30%; b. 160°–174°, 20%; b. 174°–178°, 40%). Unlike normal mustard oil, only insignificant quantities of which distill below 155°, the oil derived from *Brassica juncea* was not a uniform substance. It contained about 50 per cent of crotonyl mustard oil (γ-butenyl isothiocyanate, cf. Vol. II of the present work, p. 738), and only 40 per cent of allyl mustard oil (allyl isothiocyanate), instead of more than 90 per cent of the latter, as do normal oils. The abnormal oil also contained a compound probably identical with allyl cyanide, and traces of dimethyl sulfide. Schimmel & Co. offered no explanation for the abnormal composition of this oil.

A few years ago, Schmalfuss and Müller [29] reported that the volatile oil distilled from the seed of Sarepta mustard (*Brassica juncea*) contains only allyl mustard oil, but no crotonyl mustard oil.

Use.—Oil of mustard is used widely in the flavoring of all kinds of food products—table sauces, salad dressings, etc.

Being a powerful rubefacient, it forms the active ingredient in mustard plasters and other medicinal preparations. (Cf. United States Dispensatory.)

Recently Kosker, Fellers, and Esselen, Jr.[30] found that the addition of 1.1 to 2.2 per cent of mustard oil, or its equivalent in ground mustard, to fresh apple cider exerts a favorable preservative effect in retarding fermentation.

SUGGESTED ADDITIONAL LITERATURE

O. von Schoerebeck, "Chemical and Physiological Investigations of Mustard Plants, Mustard Seeds and Mustard Oils," *Biedermanns Zentr. B. Tierernähr.* **8** (1936), 373. *Chem. Abstracts* **31** (1937), 174.

[26] *Liebigs Ann.* **351** (1907), 354.
[27] "Die Ätherischen Öle," 3d Ed., Vol. II, 763.
[28] *Ber. Schimmel & Co.*, October (1910), 112.
[29] *Forschungsdienst* **17** (1944), 205. *Chem. Zentr.* (1944), II, 776.
[30] *Glass Packer* **28** (1949), 818.

OIL OF WHITE MUSTARD SEED

Brassica alba Boiss. (fam. *Cruciferae*), the so-called "White" or "Yellow" Mustard," is a native of southern Europe and western temperate Asia. It seldom exceeds 2 ft. in height. The plant is an annual, cultivated now in many countries with a temperate climate. It requires well manured soil. In Great Britain the seedlings are often used in salads of the "Mustard and Cress" type.[1]

Unlike that derived from black mustard (*Brassica nigra* and *B. juncea*), the fixed or fatty oil expressed from the seed of the white mustard has a mildly burning taste; hence the use of white mustard seed in our common table mustards. The seed of the white mustard adds pungency to this preparation; that of the black mustard is required for aroma.

As in the case of black mustard, the *essential* oil of white mustard is not contained in the seed in the free state, but in the form of a glucoside. To free the essential oil, the fixed oil must first be removed from the seed by expression. The residual pressed cake is then powdered and submitted to fermentation, whereby the glucoside sinalbin is split into sinalbin mustard oil (*p*-hydroxybenzyl mustard oil), *d*-glucose and sinapin bisulfate:

$$C_{30}H_{42}O_{15}N_2S_2 + H_2O \rightarrow C_7H_7ONCS + C_6H_{12}O_6 + C_{16}H_{24}NO_5HSO_4$$

| Sinalbin | Sinalbin Mustard Oil | *d*-Glucose | Sinapin Bisulfate |

Sinalbin mustard oil, or *p*-hydroxybenzyl mustard oil, is only sparingly volatile with steam. Therefore the essential oil cannot be isolated from the fermentation mass by distillation; extraction with volatile solvents has to be resorted to. (Because of the very low volatility of the sinalbin mustard oil, white mustard seed crushed and triturated with water has a strong pungency, but almost no odor.)

For further details regarding sinalbin mustard oil, the reader should consult Vol. II of the present work, p. 742.

SUGGESTED ADDITIONAL LITERATURE

É. André, "Mustard Oil from the Seed of the White Mustard, *p*-Hydroxybenzyl Isothiocyanate," *Ann. agron.* **19** (1949), 764. *Chem. Abstracts* **44** (1950), 1230.

[1] H. S. Redgrove, "Spices and Condiments," Sir Isaac Pitman and Sons, Ltd., London (1933), 300.

A. L. Winton and K. B. Winton, "The Analysis of Foods," John Wiley and Sons, Inc., New York (1945).

O. Kosker, C. R. Fellers, and W. B. Esselen, Jr., "Mustard as a Preservative for Fruit Juices," *Glass Packer* **28** (1949), 818.

OIL OF RADISH

Distilling the root of the white radish *Raphanus sativus* L. var. *albus* DC. (fam. *Cruciferae*), Heiduschka and Pyriki[1] obtained from 0.032 to 0.035 per cent of volatile oil; the root of the black radish *Raphanus sativus* L. var. *niger* DC. yielded from 0.038 to 0.40 per cent of oil. In a later investigation, Heiduschka and Zwergal[2] obtained 0.01 to 0.02 per cent of essential oil, respectively, from the roots of the white and the black radish.

According to the last-named authors, the oil consists chiefly of *butyl-crotonyl isothiocyanate sulfide* $C_9H_{17}NS_2$ or $C_9H_{15}NS_2$, i.e., $(CH_3 \cdot CH_2 \cdot CH_2 \cdot CH_2 \cdot S \cdot CH{=}CH \cdot CH_2 \cdot CH_2 \cdot N{=}C{=}S)$ (?), b_{20} 140°–142° (a compound with a pungent odor and a flavor characteristic of fresh radishes), and of a *thiocyanate* b_{20} 150°, a substance with a salve-like consistency. This thiocyanate probably belongs to the aromatic series of hydrocarbons. Despite intensive research, Heiduschka and Zwergal did not succeed in confirming the presence of the so-called "Raphanol" m. 62°, which years ago had been reported as a component of the oil by Moreigne.[3]

According to Nakamura,[4] the disagreeable odor of radish oil is caused by the presence of *methyl mercaptan.*

In the volatile oil derived from the green leaves of the radish plant, Takei, Sakato and Ono[5] identified *2-hexen-1-al* ("leaf aldehyde"), *3-hexen-1-ol* ("leaf alcohol"), and small quantities of *n-* and *isobutyraldehyde,* and *iso-valeraldehyde.*

From the seed of *Raphanus sativus* L. var. *albus,* Schmid and Karrer[6] isolated *sulforaphene,* a mustard oil containing a sulfoxide group and possessing this formula:

[1] *Arch. Pharm.* **264** (1926), 693.
[2] *J. prakt. Chem.* [2], **132** (1931), 201.
[3] *Bull. soc. chim.* [3], **15** (1896), 797.
[4] *Biochem. Z.* **164** (1925), 31.
[5] *Sci. Papers Inst. Phys. Chem. Research Tokyo* **23**, Nos. 482–497 (1934). *Chem. Abstracts* **28** (1935), 3178.
[6] *Helv. Chim. Acta* **31** (1948), 1017, 1087.

$$CH_3 \cdot S \cdot CH = CH \cdot CH_2 \cdot CH_2 \cdot N = C = S$$
$$\downarrow$$
$$O$$

Sulforaphene occurs in the seeds as a glucoside.

Schmid and Karrer also isolated *4-methylsulfoxide-3-butenyl cyanide* ($CH_3 \cdot S \cdot CH = CH \cdot CH_2 \cdot CH_2 \cdot C \equiv N$) from the seed. This compound
$$\downarrow$$
$$O$$
is a cleavage product of the mustard oil glucoside occurring in the seed.

According to the author's knowledge, oil of radish is not produced at present on a commercial scale.

OIL OF HORSERADISH

According to Gadamer,[1] the pungent odor and flavor of the root of *Cochlearia armoracia* L., now classified as *Armoracia lapathifolia* Gilib. (fam. *Cruciferae*), the common horseradish, is probably caused by the presence of sinigrin, a sulfur-containing glucoside (see Vol. II of the present work, p. 734), which in the presence of water and under the influence of a peroxidase[2] yields allyl mustard oil. Distillation of the triturated root gives about 0.05 per cent of volatile oil.

That sinigrin is actually the parent substance of the volatile horseradish oil was recently proved by Stoll and Seebeck,[3] who obtained 10.6 g. of sinigrin by extracting 3 kg. of fresh horseradishes with methanol at a temperature of 10° C. The purified sinigrin melted at 127°–128° (with decomp.). Sinigrin is split enzymatically by myrosinase, which occurs in the seed of white mustard.

Extracting comminuted fresh horseradish root with benzene, Chiris[4] obtained 2 per cent of a semisolid concrete which, on steam distillation, yielded a volatile oil with these properties:

Refractive Index at 20° 1.505
Acid Number 33.6
Ester Number 91

[1] *Arch. Pharm.* **235** (1897), 577. Cf. Krüger, "Der Meerrettich und seine Geschichte," *Mitt. Geschichte Med. Naturw.* **21** (1922), 183.
[2] Cf. Willstätter and Stoll, *Liebigs Ann.* **416** (1918), 21.
[3] *Helv. Chim. Acta* **31** (1948), 1432.
[4] *Parfums France* **15** (1937), 228.

Sulfur Content (Determined by
Oxidation)................ 17.8%

Steam-distilling the comminuted roots of *Cochlearia armoracia* L., and extracting the distillation waters with ether, Heiduschka and Zwergal[5] obtained from 0.146 to 0.216 per cent of an essential oil which contained the following compounds:

Allyl Isothiocyanate.   The principal constituent, b. 150° (cf. Vol. II of the present work, p. 734).

Phenylethyl Isothiocyanate.   From one-fifth to one-quarter of the oil consisted of this compound, b_{14} 140°–142° (cf. Vol. II of this work, p. 741).

Phenylpropyl Isothiocyanate $C_{10}H_{11}NS$.   A mass of salve-like consistency, b_{15} 163°–166°.   Only traces of this compound were present in the oil.

According to the author's knowledge, oil of horseradish is not produced commercially.

[5] *J. prakt. Chem.* [2] **132** (1931), 201.

CHAPTER VII

ESSENTIAL OILS OF THE PLANT FAMILY *LILIACEAE*

OIL OF GARLIC

The bulbs or cloves of the common garlic *Allium sativum* L. (fam. *Liliaceae*) have been used since antiquity, particularly in Mediterranean countries, as a popular prophylactic and curative against all kinds of intestinal ailments (chronic infections of the stomach and the intestines, dysentery, typhoid fever, cholera, etc.), and even against arteriosclerosis and hyperpnea. Phoenician sailors carried good stocks of garlic on their long sea voyages, and the Romans complained about the bad breath of Phoenician emissaries. Because of the considerable curative power of garlic, many attempts have been made to isolate its antibacterial principle. It is only recently, however, that this has been achieved with the identification of *allicin*.

It is a well-known fact that whole (undamaged) bulbs of garlic possess a relatively weak odor. However, when cut up or crushed, the bulbs emit their well-known, powerful and obnoxious odor, due to an essential oil consisting chiefly of disulfides.

The essential oil of garlic was first prepared more than a century ago by Wertheim,[1] who reported that it consists largely of allyl sulfide $(C_3H_5)S$. However, about fifty years later, Semmler [2] found that the oil contains no allyl sulfide at all, but a number of disulfides and trisulfides, among them chiefly diallyl disulfide (see below). Steam-distilling fresh garlic bulbs, Wertheim, and Semmler, obtained from 0.1 to 0.2 per cent of volatile oil. Distillation of the whole plant gave from 0.05 to 0.09 per cent of oil (Schimmel & Co.).[3]

In 1909 Rundqvist [4] advanced the theory (later disproved) that the parent substance from which the disulfides originate after crushing of the garlic bulbs, is a glucoside. This substance he named *alliin;* he did not, however, succeed in isolating it in pure form.

The actual mechanism of the reaction, by which the antibacterial principle of garlic, and the disulfides in the volatile oil, originate, was finally elucidated only a few years ago through the brilliant work of Cavallito and his collaborators,[5] and Stoll and Seebeck.[6] Their findings can be summarized as follows:

[1] *Liebigs Ann.* **51** (1844), 289; **55** (1845), 297.
[2] *Arch. Pharm.* **230** (1892), 434.
[3] *Ber. Schimmel & Co.,* October (1889), 52; October (1890), 25.
[4] *Pharm. Notisblad* **18** (1909), 323. *Apoth. Ztg.* **25** (1910), 105.
[5] *J. Am. Chem. Soc.* **66** (1944), 1950, 1952; **67** (1945), 1032.
[6] *Experientia* **3** (1947), 114. *Helv. Chim. Acta* **31** (1948), 189; **32** (1949), 197, 866.

The antibacterial principle of *Allium sativum* L. is *allicin:*

$$CH_2{=}CH \cdot CH_2 \cdot S \cdot S \cdot CH_2 \cdot CH{=}CH_2$$
$$\overset{\|}{O}$$

Allylsulfinyl-allyl Sulfide

(For details re Allicin see Vol. II of this work, p. 733.)

Allicin does not occur as such in *whole* garlic bulbs, but in the form of a thermostable precursor, viz., *alliin* $C_6H_{11}O_3NS$, $\frac{1}{2}H_2O$, m. 163°–165°, $[\alpha]_D^{21}$ $+62°\,48'$ (c $=2$), easily soluble in water. Alliin in crystalline form has this structural formula:

$$CH_2{=}CH \cdot CH_2 \cdot S \cdot CH_2 \cdot CH \cdot COOH \cdot \tfrac{1}{2}H_2O$$
$$\quad\quad\quad\overset{\|}{O}\quad\;\overset{|}{NH_2}$$

Alliin itself does not possess any bactericidal properties. However, when garlic cells are crushed, alliin, under the influence of the lyoenzyme *alliinase,* is rapidly broken down to the antibacterial allicin. The typical odor of garlic appears when the lyoenzyme converts the alliin to allicin.

Allicin is rather unstable; it can be isolated by steam distillation only at reduced pressure. Allicin possesses an odor characteristic of garlic but is not obnoxious. On steam distillation at atmospheric pressure allicin is decomposed to diallyl disulfide and other disulfides, which explains why the volatile garlic oil obtained by steam distillation of the bulbs or of the whole plant consists chiefly of disulfides. In the fermentation cleavage of alliin, the parent substance present in the uncrushed material, allicin is therefore only an intermediary product, being finally converted into the obnoxious disulfides so characteristic of the volatile oil:

$$\text{Alliin} \xrightarrow[\text{Alliinase}]{\text{H}_2\text{O}} \text{Allicin} \xrightarrow{\text{distillation}} \text{Diallyl disulfide and other sulfides}$$

According to Stoll and Seebeck, allyl sulfenic acid and α-aminoacrylic acid are intermediates in the enzymic splitting of alliin (2 mols.), while pyruvic acid and ammonia, together with diallyl disulfide, are among the end-products.

(For details of the reaction, the reader is referred to the original literature, particularly to the work by Stoll and Seebeck.[7])

Physicochemical Properties of Garlic Oil.—Because of its offensive odor, only a few samples of garlic oil appear to have been examined. Gildemeister and Hoffmann [8] reported these meager data:

[7] *Helv. Chim. Acta* **32** (1949), 197. *Chem. Abstracts* **43** (1949), 3482.
[8] "Die Ätherischen Öle," 3d Ed., Vol. II, 407.

Specific Gravity at 15°......... 1.046 to 1.057
Optical Rotation............... ±0°

Shipments of genuine oil of garlic examined by Fritzsche Brothers, Inc., New York, had the following properties:

Specific Gravity at 15°/15°...... 1.055 to 1.098
Refractive Index at 20°......... 1.5578 to 1.5745

Chemical Composition.—Semmler [9] and other workers reported the presence of these compounds in volatile garlic oil:

Diethyl Disulfide. Very small quantities.

Allylpropyl Disulfide(?). The oil investigated by Semmler contained about 6 per cent of a disulfide $C_6H_{12}S_2$, b_{16} 66°–69°, which was probably allylpropyl disulfide (cf. Vol. II of this work, p. 731).

Diallyl Disulfide(?). The chief constituent (about 60 per cent) of the oil was a disulfide $C_6H_{10}S_2$, b_{16} 79°–81°, $d_{14.8}$ 1.0237, probably diallyl disulfide (cf. Vol. II, p. 731).

Diallyl Trisulfide(?). A compound $C_6H_{10}S_3$, b_{16} 112°–122°, d_{15} 1.0845, amounted to about 20 per cent of the oil and was probably diallyl trisulfide (cf. Vol. II, p. 731).

Diallyl Polysulfide(?). The distillation residue contained polysulfides, probably diallyl polysulfide $C_6H_{10}S_4$(?).

According to U. S. Patent 2,554,088 (C. J. Cavallito, 1951), the residue of garlic, obtained by alcoholic extraction, and distillation, contains a bacteriostatic and bactericidal substance identified as *allyl disulfide oxide*.

Use.—Oil of garlic has lately come to be appreciated as a valuable flavoring agent, for use in all kinds of meat preparations, soups, canned goods, and table sauces.

SUGGESTED ADDITIONAL LITERATURE

A. Stoll and E. Seebeck, "Specific Constituents of Garlic," *Scientia pharm.* **18** (1950), 61.
M. B. Jacobs, "A Study of the Garlic Flavor," *Am. Perfumer* **57** (1951), 301.

[9] *Arch. Pharm.* **230** (1892), 434. Cf. Stoll and Seebeck, *Helv. Chim. Acta* **31** (1948), 189. Cf. Fenerolli, *Rivista ital. essenze profumi* **5** (1923), 28; Laland and Havrehold, *Z. phys. Chem.* **221** (1933), 180.

OIL OF ONION

On steam distillation, the bulbs of *Allium cepa* L. (fam. *Liliaceae*), the common onion, yield a volatile oil of pungent and very lasting odor. The content of oil differs greatly and depends upon the variety of the onion. Arasimovich and Ivanova [1] noted yields of oil ranging from 0.018 to 0.04 per cent in different Russian onion varieties. Distilling common kitchen onions, Haensel [2] obtained 0.015 per cent of a brown oil which remained turbid even after warming. It had these properties:

Specific Gravity at 35°...... 0.9960
Optical Rotation........... −3° 40′
Solubility................. Difficultly soluble in the usual sol-
vents

Distilling dried onion plants, Chiris [3] obtained 0.05 per cent of a brownish semisolid oil which, on standing, separated a crystalline deposit. The oil had the following properties:

Specific Gravity at 15°...... 1.0118
Optical Rotation at 18°..... +1° 30′
Refractive Index at 20°..... 1.5236
Solubility................. Soluble in 0.1 vol. of 95% alcohol,
with pronounced turbidity

Shipments of genuine onion oils distilled from bulbs in the United States, and analyzed by Fritzsche Brothers, Inc., New York, exhibited properties varying within the following limits:

Specific Gravity at 15°/15°....... 1.047 to 1.098
Optical Rotation............... +1° 3′ to +3° 53′
Refractive Index at 20°.......... 1.5373 to 1.5588
Acid Number.................. 12.0 to 19.8
Carbonyl Number (Hydroxylamine
Hydrochloride Method—1 hour). 9.8 to 15.1
Iodine Number (½ hour)......... 59.9 to 66.2
Solubility...................... Most oils not completely soluble in
10 vol. of 95% alcohol. Occa-
sionally soluble in 1 to 2 vol. and
more of 95% alcohol

[1] *Doklady Vsesoyuz. Akad. Sel'sko-Khoz. Nauk im Lenina* (1939), No. 5–6, 17–22.
Khim. Referat. Zhur. (1940), No. 3, 66. *Chem. Abstracts* **36** (1942), 2373.
[2] *Apoth. Ztg.* **18** (1903), 268.
[3] *Parfums France* **15** (1937), 228.

Chemical Composition.—Little is known about the chemical composition of the volatile onion oil. Semmler [4] isolated, as chief constituent, a *disulfide* $C_6H_{12}S_2$, b_{10} 75°–83°, d_{12} 1.0234, which, on reduction with zinc dust, gave a substance $C_6H_{12}S$, b. 130°. Reduction of the disulfide $C_6H_{12}S_2$ with nascent hydrogen yielded a disulfide $C_6H_{14}S_2$, b_{10} 68°–69°.

The oil furthermore contains *a higher sulfide* which, on reduction with zinc dust, also yields $C_6H_{12}S$. Semmler [5] observed in the oil still *another sulfur-containing compound*, identical perhaps with one of the high boiling constituents present in oil of asafoetida (cf. Vol. II of the present work, p. 730–1). According to Semmler, the oil does not contain any terpenes or allyl sulfide.

Examining freshly pressed *juice* of common onions, Kooper [6] identified thiocyanic acid and allyl thiocyanate.

Use.—Although known for a long time, oil of onion has only recently been produced on a commercial scale. The oil is now used as an important ingredient in the flavoring of meats, sausages, soups, tablesauces, and all kinds of culinary preparations.

CONCRETE AND ABSOLUTE OF HYACINTH

Years ago *Hyacinthus orientalis* L. (fam. *Liliaceae*) was cultivated on a commercial scale in the Grasse region of Southern France for the extraction of its flower oil. Hyacinth plantings were located near Grasse, Vence, Le Bar, Tourette, Callian, Mouans-Sartoux, Valbonne, etc. In addition to the cultivated *Hyacinthus orientalis,* extraction plants in Grasse also treated the blue hyacinth (*Hyacinthus non scriptus* L., *Scilla nutans* Sm.), which grows wild in olive groves and meadows. According to Naves and Mazuyer,[1] the perfume of the latter is fresher, more flowery, but less pronounced than that of the cultivated variety. From 1920 to 1928, up to 80 metric tons of hyacinth flowers were processed in Grasse per year. Since then the quantity has declined almost to nil.

Another producing region for the cultivated hyacinth lies in Holland,

[4] *Arch. Pharm.* **230** (1892), 443.
[5] *Ibid.*
[6] *Z. Untersuch. Nahr. Genussm.* **19** (1910), 569.
[1] "Les Parfums Naturels," Paris (1939), 221.

between Haarlem and The Hague, from where large quantities of bulbs and cut flowers are exported to florists in various parts of Europe. In 1926, an essential oil house in Holland treated 85 metric tons of flowers for the extraction of their perfume. As in Southern France, production of hyacinth flower oil in Holland has been greatly curtailed.

In the Grasse region extraction of cultivated hyacinth flowers with petroleum ether yields from 0.13 to 0.22 per cent, in most cases from 0.17 to 0.20 per cent of concrete, which on treatment with alcohol in the usual way gives from 10 to 14 per cent of alcohol-soluble absolute (cf. Vol. I of this work, pp. 200 ff.). The concrete contains from 1.8 to 3.0 per cent of steam-volatile oil, which, however, has never been a commercial article. The wild growing hyacinth gives a higher yield of concrete (0.19 to 0.23 per cent) than the cultivated. It is claimed that light-colored flowers contain more perfume than the darker colored (Naves and Mazuyer [2]).

Concrete of hyacinth is a solid waxy mass with a color ranging from greenish-brown to dark brown.

Naves, Sabetay and Palfray [3] (I and II) steam-distilled two concretes from the Grasse region; Hoejenbos and Coppens [4] (III) a concrete of Netherlands origin, and obtained volatile oils with these properties:

	I	II	III
Specific Gravity at 15°............	1.037	1.029	1.0423
Optical Rotation at 20°...........	−0° 44′	−1° 12′	−0° 12′
Refractive Index.................	1.4998	1.5021	1.4981
Acid Number....................	3.6	2.8	3.0
Ester Number...................	152.1	136.1	143.0
Ester Number after Acetylation..... ...		...	272.0

Chemical Composition.—Examining an absolute of hyacinth prepared by Spalteholz in Haarlem (Holland), Enklaar [5] reported the presence of the following compounds:

Benzyl Benzoate.

Benzyl Alcohol(?). In free form.

Cinnamyl Alcohol(?). In ester form.

Vanillin(?).

A Basic Substance(?). Did not contain nitrogen. It exhibited fluorescence.

[2] *Ibid.*
[3] *Perfumery Essential Oil Record* **28** (1937), 336. Cf. Vol. I of the present work, p. 215.
[4] *Rev. marques* **9** (1931), 583, 624.
[5] *Chem. Weekblad* **7** (1910), 1.

More recently, Hoejenbos and Coppens [6] identified a number of components in the steam-volatile oil which they had obtained from a concrete of Netherlands origin (see above):

Alcohols. Phenylethyl alcohol, benzyl alcohol, cinnamyl alcohol, and *n*-heptanol(?).

Aldehydes. Benzaldehyde, cinnamaldehyde, and *n*-heptaldehyde(?).

Acids. Benzoic acid.

Esters. Benzyl acetate, benzyl benzoate, cinnamyl acetate, methyl-(or ethyl?)-*o*-methoxy-benzoate.

Phenols and Phenol Ethers. Eugenol, methyleugenol, hydroquinone, hydroquinone dimethyl ether.

Basic Substances. Dimethyl anthranilate.

Lactones. Absent.

Use.—In the past, when it was still produced, absolute of hyacinth formed a valuable adjunct in high-grade perfumes of floral as well as oriental type. Of late the natural product has been replaced by synthetic compositions, based chiefly upon phenylacetaldehyde (see Vol. II of this work, p. 353).

CONCRETE AND ABSOLUTE OF LILY

Lilium candidum L. (fam. *Liliaceae*), the common Easter lily, is a native of the Orient, but has been grown for many years in various parts of Europe. The beautiful white flowers emit a strong and heavy perfume.

In the Grasse region of Southern France lilies are cultivated by many farmers on small plots, primarily for the export of the bulbs. Flowers not sold to florists are therefore a relatively low priced by-product, which in years past was used in the extraction plants of Grasse and Seillans for the recovery of their natural perfume. Prior to World War I up to 3 metric tons of lily flowers were processed annually in the Grasse region; from 1919 to 1939 the quantity of flowers extracted decreased gradually almost to the vanishing point.

In the author's experience, 480 to 500 kg. of lily flowers, on extraction with petroleum ether, yield 1 kg. of concrete which, in turn, gives 0.28 to 0.30 kg. of alcohol soluble absolute. Extracting lilies with petroleum ether,

[6] *Rev. marques* **9** (1931), 583, 624. Cf. *Am. Perfumer* **57** (1951), 365, 453.

Igolen [1] obtained 0.22 per cent of a green-brown, waxy concrete which yielded 35 per cent of a viscous green-brown absolute. Two absolutes examined by Igolen had these properties:

	I	II
Specific Gravity at 15°	0.9592	0.9423
Refractive Index at 20°	1.4787	1.4861
Acid Number	27.16	19.6
Ester Number	122.04	115.03
Carbonyl Number	18.9	22.4

Co-distillation of the two absolutes with diethylene glycol at reduced pressure yielded 8.2 and 10.9 per cent, respectively, of two volatile oils which had the following properties:

	I	II
Specific Gravity at 15°	0.9013	0.915
Optical Rotation at 20°	+1° 28'	+0° 55'
Refractive Index at 20°	1.4681	1.4764
Acid Number	12.62	. . .
Ester Number	96.80	. . .

Chemical Composition.—In the volatile oil (I) Igolen identified these compounds:

p-Cresol.

Linaloöl.

α-Terpineol.   ⎫
Phenylethyl Alcohol.   ⎬ Esterified with acetic, palmitic and cinnamic acids.

Remarkably enough, perfumers were able, a long time ago, to reproduce the odor of lily flowers by various mixtures of synthetics, containing chiefly linalyl cinnamate and terpinyl cinnamate, although unaware that these substances are actual constituents of the natural flower oil.

Use.—In the author's opinion, absolute of lily is a most interesting natural flower oil which could be used to great advantage in many high-grade perfume compositions of floral as well as oriental type. It is an excellent fixative and imparts to new creations alluring notes which are hard to trace. The absolute has the property of "rounding out" synthetic mixtures and merits much wider application than it has found so far.

[1] *Compt. rend.* **214** (1942), 772.

CONCRETE AND ABSOLUTE OF LILY OF THE VALLEY

Convallaria majalis L. (fam. *Liliaceae*), the common lily of the valley, is a small plant which grows wild in many parts of Europe, particularly in moist forests.   The white flowers exhale a delightful fragrance which, however, cannot be captured by steam distillation.   According to Naves and Mazuyer,[1] extraction of the flowers and stalks with petroleum ether yields from 0.42 to 0.55 per cent of a concrete, while extraction of the flowers alone gives 0.9 to 1.05 per cent of concrete.

The chemical composition of the natural flower oil derived from lilies of the valley was first studied more than one hundred years ago by Herberger[2] who isolated a crystalline substance with a very strong odor.   Many years later Kerschbaum[3] reported the presence of *farnesol* in the flower oil without, however, giving any definite proof.

The natural flower oil is not an article of commerce[4] because the perfume of lilies of the valley can be reproduced by blends of synthetic aromatics and natural isolates (hydroxycitronellal, linaloöl, etc.) and certain essential oils.

[1] "Les Parfums Naturels," Paris (1939), 250.
[2] *Rept. pharm.* **2** (1836), 397.
[3] *Ber.* **46** (1913), 1732.
[4] Recently Sabetay [*Ind. parfum.* **5** (1950), 86] reported that a house in Grasse succeeded in developing a satisfactory concrete. According to Meunier (*ibid.*, 28) the solvent used for this purpose is butane.

CHAPTER VIII

ESSENTIAL OILS OF THE PLANT FAMILY *IRIDACEAE*

OIL OF ORRIS ROOT

Essence d'Iris   *Aceite Esencial Lirio de Florencia de la Raiz*
Iris- or Veilchenwurzelöl   *Oleum Iridis*

Introduction.—There are several species within the genus *Iris* (fam. *Iridaceae*), the rhizomes of which, on drying and aging, develop an essential oil that can be isolated by various methods. By far the most important of these species is *Iris pallida* Lam., commercially known as "Florentine Orris," because it is cultivated near Florence, in the province of Tuscany. The rhizomes of this species yield an oil of pleasant violet-like odor, highly esteemed in perfumes and for the scenting of cosmetics.

Other species are *Iris florentina* L., the rhizomes of which contain very little oil, and *Iris germanica* L., the rhizomes of which yield an oil of a somewhat harsh odor. *Iris florentina* L. develops white flowers and can readily be distinguished from *Iris pallida* Lam. (the "Florentine Orris") with its light blue-violet flowers. Limited quantities of *Iris germanica* L. are grown near Verona (Italy); hence the commercial term "Verona Orris." Its rhizomes, washed and peeled, are occasionally utilized for the flavoring of wines and in powdered sachets, but not for distillation or extraction purposes. *Iris germanica* is also cultivated in the high valleys of the Grand Atlas in Morocco, and in certain parts of India. It is not customary in these areas to prepare the rhizomes properly for market—as has always been the practice with those of *Iris pallida*—by washing, removal of the foliaceous collet and by careful paring. The Moroccan and Indian product usually exhibits a dark color and a poor odor; frequently the rhizomes are infected with insect larvae. No wonder then that distillers employ *Iris pallida* Lam. almost exclusively. The following will describe only the oils derived from the rhizomes of this latter species.

History, Botany, Producing Regions and Total Production.—*Iris pallida* Lam. was introduced to the environs of Florence in 1842 by Adriano Piazzesi who planted it near the village of San Polo in the community of Greve (Chianti), which region has remained the center of orris production in Tuscany. About fifty years ago orris cultivation spread to the districts of Siena, Arezzo, and Lucca, and to the regions of Grosseto, Perugia, and Faenza, but more recently the demand for orris root has declined substantially. Today production is restricted to the upper Valdarno and to the Chianti section, with San Polo as center. At one time the orris plantations

in Tuscany covered about 400 hectares; now less than 100 hectares are
devoted to its cultivation. Production reached its peak between 1902 and
1905 with about 1,600 metric tons per year; today it amounts to about 200
or 350 tons at the most. According to Chauvet,[1] Tuscany produced the
following quantities of dried orris root in the years from 1946 to 1949:

Year	Metric Tons
1946..........	300
1947..........	270
1948..........	250
1949..........	200

There is also a small production of *Iris pallida* Lam. in Southern France
(Var and Alpes Maritimes), but this amounts to only about one-tenth of
the Tuscan total.

Iris pallida Lam. develops an aerial stem about 60 cm. high and surrounded at the base by a rosette of long, lance-shaped leaves. The flowers,
which in Tuscany and Southern France are usually sold to florists, are of
delicate light blue-violet color. The freshly unearthed rhizomes exhibit
quite a disagreeable, herb-like, earthy odor reminiscent of fresh potatoes,
and a somewhat sharp, slightly bitter taste. The unpleasant odor and
flavor of the fresh rhizomes disappear on drying and aging. The pleasant,
violet-like odor, for which the dried rhizomes are so highly esteemed, develops only very slowly and gradually. The rhizomes should, therefore, be
stored for at least three years before being used for distillation or extraction; otherwise they will give a low yield of oil of inferior odor. The peeled
and dried rhizomes are of whitish color, hard texture, and irregular shape.
Their length varies between 4 and 11 cm. The best quality originates from
Tuscany, the so-called "Florentine Orris"—a somewhat plump type, very
light in color and delightfully fragrant. The odor is particularly noticeable
in freshly broken pieces of dried rhizomes. The lower grades are less
fragrant and darker in color.

Cultivation and Harvest.—Yield, quality, and odor of the rhizomes are
greatly influenced by the type of soil—calcareous and loamy soils, stony
and dry, giving the best results. Plantings are never laid out in valleys,
but on the slopes of hills, at altitudes of 300 and 500 m., and with southeastern exposure if possible. Near Florence, orris is usually cultivated by
small farmers, often on a crop-sharing basis. There are no large fields—
only small patches in clearings of woods or between vineyards. Arrange-
ments between landowner and tenant farmer require that the latter plant
and cultivate the whole field. Prior to the harvest, the field is divided into
two equal parts. The owner then collects half of the crop, paying his own

[1] Private communication from Mr. Pierre Chauvet, Seillans (Var), France.

(*Left*) Production of gum labdanum in Spain. Transport of the freshly cut plant material to a nearby village in Andalusia. (*Bottom Left*) Gum labdanum, Spain. The dried twigs are boiled in water and the separated gum is skimmed from the surface. (*Bottom Right*) Gum labdanum, Spain. Cases containing the crude gum. Dried plant material on the left. *Photos Fritzsche Brothers, Inc., New York.*

(*Top*) Plantings of *Iris pallida* on the hillsides of Tuscany, near Florence, Italy. *Photo A. Piazzesi, Florence, Italy.* (Bottom) Orris root, Italy. Air drying of the roots. The roots on the left side have been peeled. The dark roots in the background are unpeeled. *Photo Fritzsche Brothers, Inc., New York.*

expenses for labor, etc., while the tenant farmer harvests the other half, which he may sell for his own benefit.

The growing of orris is comparatively easy, little cultural care being required. Ample rainfall in spring and in early summer favors growth of healthy rhizomes and helps to develop new fibrous rootlets when the old ones disappear. Prior to planting the soil should be thoroughly cleaned of weeds and old roots. The plantings are usually started in September. For this purpose, small, horizontal and parallel furrows are drawn with a hoe, 20 to 25 cm. apart, on the slope of a hill. For planting, freshly harvested,

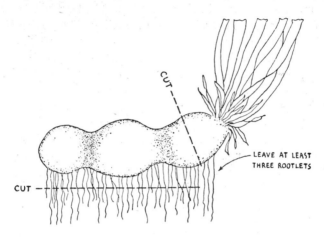

three-year-old rhizomes containing three swellings (*strumae*) are used. The first *struma* (beneath the collet) is cut carefully with a sharp knife, three fibrous rootlets being left adhering to the shoot to be used for replanting (see drawing). According to Borghesani,[2] and to information gathered by the author during a visit to Tuscany, the shoots are then set carefully, at least 20 cm. apart, along the ridges between the furrows, which should not be more than 10 cm. and not less than 7 or 8 cm. deep. The cut surface of the piece of rhizome (*struma*) which was left on the shoot must face upward, so that the rootlets can form the very first growth straight down into the soil of the ridge, and develop into perfect rhizomes, easy to harvest. The plants are covered with soil. Cultivation is usually limited to two thorough hoeings and weedings every year, in April or May, and in September. Experience so far has not shown any need for fertilization.

The rhizomes are usually harvested in the second or, still better, in the third year after planting, preferably in the latter part of July or in August and, if possible, after a good rain. The whole plant, including the rhizome, is lifted from the soil with a simple garden hoe, and the aerial stem is cut

[2] *Heil- und Gewürzpfl.* **13** (1930), 49. Through *Ber. Schimmel & Co.* (1931), 79.

off the root system. The latter must then be divided into the rhizome to be dried and sold on the market as orris root, and the part to be used for replanting. As was explained above, the division is made by a cut through the first swelling (*struma*) beneath the collet. The remaining *strumae* on each rhizome are freed of earth and fibrous rootlets, placed into water, and thoroughly cleansed and peeled. Peeling is done with short, curved knives, and requires considerable skill, the rhizomes being tough and hard, yet elastic. The peeled rhizomes are then thrown into running water, rinsed, spread on cane mats and dried in the sun, which requires five to six days. In the final operation the dried rhizomes are polished (cleaned) and assorted into two grades, viz., a first, and a second quality. The older classification into four grades is no longer practiced.

Yield varies considerably with the soil, ranging from 4,000 to 12,000 kg. of fresh rhizomes per hectare. One hundred kilograms of fresh rhizomes give 25 to 35 kg. of dried and prepared rhizomes.

In years of low prices, farmers sometimes prefer not to harvest the rhizomes, but to leave them in the ground, where they may remain for four or five years (instead of the usual three years). When finally dug up, such rhizomes will be too tough and hard for peeling. To utilize them the farmers wash such rhizomes carefully, and then simply cut them into three longitudinal slices, without removing the peel from the outer surface. Drying on mats in the sun for six or seven days yields the so-called "dark, un-peeled orris," a quality lower than the two described above ("peeled, 1st and 2nd quality"). This is not well suited to distillation, because it yields an oil of somewhat harsh odor. Extraction with volatile solvents gives resinoids of dark color.

Orris should be cultivated in rotation with other crops; the interval of time between one orris planting and the next, on the same field, should be not less than three years. After orris, the field must be thoroughly plowed, fertilized, and planted with oats or cockshead. In the next year wheat is grown, and orris again in the third or fourth year. In general, orris has proved very resistant to parasitic diseases, but suffers from extreme drought or continued wet weather. It requires a well-drained soil and exposure to the sun.

Storage of the Dried Rhizomes.—As has been pointed out, the characteristic, violet-like scent of dried orris develops only gradually, two or three years of storage being required to bring out the full odor. Distillation or extraction of freshly dried rhizomes gives a poor yield and a low-grade oil. Storage of the rhizomes in high piles, with consequent exertion of some pressure, appears to favor development of the aromatic principles in orris. During the maturing period the rhizomes must be protected from insects and microorganisms. They are liable to attack by the larvae of a *Coleoptera* which Naves [3] identified as *Sitodrepa panicea* (fam. *Anobiidae*). Other frequently encountered microorganisms are *Trichoderma lignorum* and *Penicillium crustaceum*.

The development of the odorous constituents (particularly the irones—see below) in the rhizomes is thought to result from the action of diastases on the heterosidic components; but this has not been conclusively proved. It seems quite probable, however, that diastatic action plays an important role in the liberation of the aromatic principles, in the light of several experiments carried out years ago by Flückiger: [4] immersing fresh rhizomes for a few minutes in water of 90° C., he noted that they retained their herbaceous odor and did not develop any violet odor after drying. In another experiment, rapid drying of thin slices at about 40° C. did not produce a violet odor, but digestion in warm water, particularly after addition of small quantities of hydrochloric acid, brought out the desired aroma. Any treatment of the rhizomes which inactivates diastatic processes would thus appear to inhibit the liberation of irone, whereas the action of highly diluted mineral acids re-establishes the diastatic process. Naves,[5] who has studied the odorous components of orris thoroughly, admits the possibility that the irones are present in the rhizomes as heterosides, although no direct proof has been published in support of this theory. All that can be said is that the heterosides seem to undergo decomposition during the three-year storage of the rhizomes.

EXTRACTION WITH VOLATILE SOLVENTS
(Resinoids of Orris)

The natural perfume can be isolated from the dried and aged rhizomes either by extraction with volatile solvents—which yields the so-called "Resinoids of Orris"—or by distillation, which produces the so-called "Concrete of Orris" or "Orris Butter" (see below).

Prior to any treatment, the rhizomes must be triturated to small pieces, a rather difficult operation, best accomplished in strong hammer mills. For extraction with solvents or for distillation, peeled rhizomes are usually employed, because unpeeled orris yields dark colored products with a somewhat harsh odor, suitable only for the perfuming of soaps or in preparations where price is of prime consideration.

Extraction can be carried out by percolation with volatile solvents such as high-proof alcohol, acetone, benzene, or petroleum ether. Despite their high yields of resinoids, alcohol and acetone are seldom used because they

[3] *Drug Cosmetic Ind.* **59** (1946), 479.
[4] Tschirch, "Handbuch der Pharmacognosie," Vol. II, Part II, pp. 1148 and 1153.
[5] *Drug Cosmetic Ind.* **59** (1946), 587.

give hard products, quite insoluble in alcohol, and difficult to handle. Much better results are obtained with benzene or petroleum ether, the latter yielding light brown to red-brown resinoids of honey-like consistency and a warm, very lasting odor. Benzene gives a higher yield than petroleum ether, but the petroleum ether resinoid has a more characteristic odor. Naves and Mazuyer,[6] and Naves [7] reported the following yields of (crude) resinoids:

Solvent	Alcohol (95%)	Benzene	Petroleum Ether
Yields..............	14 to 22.8%	2.1 to 3.5%	1.15 to 2.0%
Average Yields.....	...	2.4 to 3.3%	1.6 to 1.9%

The resinoids thus obtained are not completely soluble in high-proof alcohol. To prepare alcohol-soluble products, the crude resinoids are treated with 95 per cent alcohol in the usual way, the insoluble portions removed, the solutions filtered clear and concentrated *in vacuo*. The resulting resinoids may be called "Soluble Resinoids." According to Naves,[8] benzene resinoid (crude) yields from 70 to 88 per cent of soluble resinoid, petroleum resinoid (crude) from 50 to 60 per cent of soluble resinoid. These soluble resinoids are of viscous consistency and possess a soft, mellow, very lasting odor. Their relatively low price permits use not only in high-grade perfumes, but also in cosmetics and soaps.

Physicochemical Properties.—Naves [9] reported these properties for (crude) benzene and petroleum ether resinoids:

	Benzene Resinoid (*Crude*)	Petroleum Ether Resinoid (*Crude*)
Acid Number.......	30 to 50	31 to 60
Ester Number......	75 to 95	70 to 90

Naves [10] prepared "Absolute Resinoids" from the crude resinoids by using the method of Glichitch and Naves,[11] in which the fatty acids are precipitated and removed as insoluble lithium salts. (For details of this method see below.) The absolute resinoids thus obtained had the following properties:

	Benzene Resinoid Absolute	Petroleum Ether Resinoid Absolute
Specific Gravity at 20°.............	0.929 to 0.943	0.930 to 0.946
Optical Rotation.................	$+18° 21'$ to $+34° 9'$	$+19° 24'$ to $+32° 45'$
Refractive Index at 20°...........	1.4938 to 1.4986	1.4953 to 1.4989
Ester Number....................	26 to 47	39 to 72
Irone Content (By Oximation)......	62.2 to 77.8%	70.8 to 79.4%

[6] "Les Parfums Naturels," Paris (1939), 310.
[7] *Drug Cosmetic Ind.* **59** (1946), 479.   [10] *Ibid.*
[8] *Ibid.*   [11] *Parfums France* **9** (1931), 371.
[9] *Ibid.*

Naves [12] also submitted the (crude) benzene and petroleum ether resinoids of orris root to distillation with superheated steam at reduced pressure [13] and obtained 8 to 13 per cent, and 3 to 7 per cent, respectively, of distillates which exhibited these values:

	Distillate from Benzene Resinoid	*Distillate from Petroleum Ether Resinoid*
Acid Number	102 to 146	33 to 68
Ester Number	16 to 80	60 to 72
Content of Neutral Fraction	18.1 to 23.2%	40.6 to 57.4%

These distillates are not commercial products, but are prepared in the laboratory for the analytical examination of resinoids of orris.

DISTILLATION
(Concrete of Orris or "Orris Butter")

It should be kept in mind, throughout the following discussion, that the term "concrete" is usually applied only to natural flower oils obtained by solvent extraction (cf. Vol. I of this work, pp. 200 and 210). In the case of orris, however, the term "concrete" means simply that the product obtained by steam distillation is of solid consistency.

The most common method of isolating the odorous substances from dried and aged orris rhizomes is not extraction with volatile solvents (see above), but distillation. Of course, it would be possible to extract the rhizomes first with volatile solvents and then to submit the resinoids thus obtained to distillation with superheated steam at reduced pressure. Some manufacturers, in fact, employ this technique. But in most cases the peeled and triturated rhizomes are submitted directly to the action of steam of normal pressure, yielding the so-called "Concrete of Orris" or "Orris Butter." At room temperature this is a solid mass of light yellow to yellow color, with a very strong odor, characteristic of orris root. At 40° to 45° C. the concrete melts to a yellow or yellow-brown liquid. Compared with that of the resinoids, the aroma of the concrete is stronger, sharper, much more pronounced. Depending upon the method of distillation, and particularly its length, the concrete contains from about 83 to 96 per cent of myristic acid; hence its hard, tallow-like consistency. Since the myristic acid is odorless and only a "ballast" in the concrete, the myristic acid is sometimes removed from the concrete by various means (see below), thus yielding the so-called "Absolute of Orris," "Orris Tenfold," or "Irone Absolute." Com-

[12] *Givaudanian* (February 1947), 4.
[13] Cf. Naves and Mazuyer, "Les Parfums Naturels," Paris (1939), 173.

pared with the concrete, the absolute has the advantage of much greater odor concentration and better solubility in ethyl alcohol. On the other hand, the concrete possesses a higher odor-fixation value.

Distillation of the rhizomes involves considerable difficulty and requires much experience. Only peeled root, stored for at least three years, should be used. Prior to distillation the rhizomes must be triturated to a coarse powder. They contain from 55 to 60 per cent of starch which, under the influence of steam and hot water, may be partly converted into a viscous solution of dextrin. This can result in much foaming and frothing over into the condenser, giving a lot of trouble. For this reason stills of large capacity should be used, leaving ample space above the relatively small charge. Sufficiently high and wide columns are advisable. The condenser tubes should be wide and long, heavily tinned on the inside, or constructed of specially prepared aluminum or, still better, of stainless steel. Myristic acid has a tendency to form salts with some metals, and these salts may precipitate in alcoholic solutions of the concrete, causing much inconvenience. The temperature of the condensate should never fall below 60° C., as otherwise the myristic acid will congeal and obstruct the tubes—i.e., the condensate must flow quite warm.

The steam-volatility of the irones, the most important odorous constituents of orris concrete, differs considerably from that of the fatty acids (chiefly myristic acid). The first fractions distilling over are richest in irones, and the content of fatty acids increases as distillation progresses.[14] The distillation of powdered orris is a lengthy process. The irones, the most valuable odorous constituents, distill over in the course of 20 to 30 hr.; they are accompanied in the successive fractions by increasing proportions of fatty acid mixtures, principally myristic acid. Due to economic considerations (excessive consumption of steam and fuel) distillation is often stopped before complete recovery of the irones. The more prolonged the distillation, the higher will be the content of myristic acid in the concrete, and the lower the irone content, and vice versa. According to Naves,[15] the unusual length of time required to distill the irones can probably be attributed to two factors, acting simultaneously: the difficulty encountered in the extraction of the irones from the powdered rhizomes, and the protracted period required for their formation from complex compounds.

As has already been mentioned, the odoriferous components occur in the

[14] Guenther, *Am. Perfumer* **30** (1935), 17, 56. Naves, *Drug Cosmetic Ind.* **59** (1946), 479, 586; **60** (1947), 364. *Givaudanian* (February 1947), 4. *Rivista ital. essenze profumi* **29** (1947), 242.
[15] *Helv. Chim. Acta* **32** (1949), 1059.

rhizomes perhaps as heterosides, but the only heteroside actually isolated from orris is iridine,[16] the glucoside of irigenine (5,7,3'-trihydroxy-6,4,5'-trimethoxy isoflavone). Nevertheless, it was formerly thought that the action of highly diluted aqueous mineral acids would speed up the hydrolysis of the heterosides and that a quicker release of the odorous compounds might thereby be achieved. Most manufacturers, therefore, submitted the powdered rhizomes to a pretreatment before actual distillation: the material was dispersed in warm water and, after the addition of 1 to 8 per mill of sulfuric acid, macerated overnight, care being taken that the temperature never rose above 65° C. The following day the acid was carefully neutralized with magnesium carbonate or calcium carbonate, and then the mass was transferred to the still for distillation. This pretreatment has now largely been abandoned. It offers, however, one advantage: maceration with acids brings about hydrolysis of the starch to *water-soluble* substances which, during distillation, cause much less trouble than the viscous dextrins. Moreover, pretreatment with dilute acids produces a certain granulation of the powdered orris, favorable to the conduct of the distillation (Robert [17]).

In this connection it should be mentioned that, according to experiments undertaken by Naves,[18] the small quantities of acids used in the pretreatment of the powdered rhizomes exert no noticeable influence upon the irones. Practically no isomerization of α- or γ-irone into β-irone, or of γ-irone into α-irone takes place; nor is irene formed from the irones.

Yield of Concrete.—The yield of concrete depends upon the age of the rhizomes and the length of distillation. According to the author's experience in Seillans (Var) and Grasse (A.M.), Southern France (whence the bulk of the orris concretes originates), the yield from three-year-old rhizomes should be at least 0.2 per cent. The quantitative yield can be increased by prolonged distillation, but in this case the increase will consist chiefly of myristic acid. Naves [19] reported average yields ranging from 0.20 to 0.24 per cent on distillation for 20 to 36 hr., and 0.32 to 0.40 per cent on distillation to completion. The same author [20] also showed how the neutral and the acidic fractions come over in the course of distillation:

Hours of Distillation	1 to 8	9 to 16	17 to 24	25 to 32
Percentage of Concrete Distilled......	0.073	0.058	0.044	0.031
Percentage of Concrete Obtained.....	0.073	0.131	0.175	0.206
Acidity, Expressed in Per Cent of Myristic Acid......................	61.0	83.8	91.9	94.3

[16] De Laire and Tiemann, *Ber.* **26** (1893), 2010. Bargellini, *Gazz. chim. ital.* **55** (1925), 945. Baker, *J. Chem. Soc.* (1928), 1022.
[17] *J. parfum. savon.* **23** (1910), 65. *Ber. Schimmel & Co.,* October (1910), 56.
[18] *Helv. Chim. Acta* **32** (1949), 1060.   [20] *Ibid.,* 6.
[19] *Givaudanian* (February 1947), 4.

Hours of Distillation	1 to 8	9 to 16	17 to 24	25 to 32
Mean Molecular Weight of the Acids..	241	238	229	225
Percentage of Absolute Oil...........	41.0	20.0	8.0	5.4
Percentage of Irone in the Absolute Oil	82.0	77.4	53.0	16.1

As Naves [21] pointed out, it may be granted that the irones occur in the rhizomes as heterosides, although no direct proof in support of this assumption has been given. In fact, it does not appear that the action of diastases or of reagents favorable to hydrolysis increases the yield of irone during the pretreatment of rhizomes dried and stored for a minimum of three years. All that can be said is that the heterosides are destroyed in the course of this process. The idea that a higher yield of irone could be obtained after such pretreatment probably arose from the fact that the irones distill more easily after the starch has been hydrolyzed. When this hydrolysis is accompanied by formation of alcohol, a fraction of the fatty acids is esterified, resulting in a higher yield of absolute oil, often incorrectly calculated as irone.

Physicochemical Properties of Orris Concrete.—Like the yield, the physicochemical properties of an orris concrete depend largely upon the quality of the rhizomes and the length of distillation.

As was mentioned above, concrete of orris at room temperature is a solid mass of light yellow or yellow color. The odor is very strong and lasting, characteristic of aged rhizomes, but somewhat sharp.

Gildemeister and Hoffmann [22] reported these properties for orris concrete:

Melting Point.............	40° to 50°
Optical Rotation..........	Slightly dextrorotatory
Acid Number.............	About 204 to 236
Acid Content, Calculated as Myristic Acid...........	83 to 96%
Ester Number............	2 to 10

Four lots of orris concrete produced under the author's supervision in Southern France (Seillans, Var) exhibited the following values:

	I	II	III	IV
Melting Point.................	41.5° to 44.5°	43° to 45°	42° to 45°	42° to 45°
Acid Number.................	198.8	205.8	198.8	199.8
Acid Content, Calculated as Myristic Acid..................	81.0%	83.9%	81.0%	81.5%
Ester Number.................	6.5	3.5	7.5	8.3
Ketone Content, Calculated as Irone (Hydroxylamine Hydrochloride Method)............	14.8%	14.4%	15.4%	13.4%

[21] *Ibid.,* 5.
[22] "Die Ätherischen Öle," 3d Ed., Vol. II, 420.

Genuine lots of orris concrete produced in Seillans (Var) and examined by Fritzsche Brothers, Inc., New York, had properties ranging within these limits:

Acid Number...................... 176.2 to 211.5
Saponification Number............. 192.2 to 221.1
Ketone Content, Calculated as Irone 9.1 to 19.7%, usually
    (Hydroxylamine Hydrochloride   about 15.0%
    Method)

Chiris [23] reported the following values for pure orris concretes:

Acid Number....... 165 to 200, seldom up to 205
Ester Number...... 10 to 27, seldom up to 30

According to Naves,[24] the properties of orris concrete vary within these limits:

Melting Point..................... About 40° to 45°
Acid Number...................... 162 to 216
Ester Number..................... 4 to 36
Content of Neutral Fractions....... 13 to 25.5%

Analysis.—By far the greater part of orris concrete consists of higher fatty acids, chiefly myristic acid, which contribute nothing to the odor of the product, except fixation value. The higher the content of myristic acid, the higher will be the melting point of the concrete. The content of acids, calculated as myristic acid, can be assayed in the usual way (cf. Vol. I of the present work, p. 263).

The most important part of the examination of an orris concrete is the determination of the neutral (nonacidic) portions. This can be carried out by the lithium salt method of Glichitch and Naves,[25] details of which are given in the following section on "Absolute of Orris." The liquid or absolute oil thus isolated contains all the odorous compounds, including the important irones.

The laboratories of Fritzsche Brothers, Inc., New York, employ the hydroxylamine hydrochloride method in the evaluation of orris concretes. It gives very good results. However, one should keep in mind that in this method not only the ketones (chiefly irones), but also the small quantities of aldehydes present in the concrete are quantitatively determined. (For details see Vol. I of the present work, p. 285.) The presence of certain ketones other than the irones (e.g., ionones as adulterants!) can often be detected by this method (cf. Vol. I, p. 290, second footnote).

A very efficient method of isolating the ketones quantitatively from con-

[23] *Parfums France* **6** (1928), 133.   [25] *Parfums France* **9** (1931), 371.
[24] *Givaudanian* (February 1947), 4.

cretes (or absolutes) of orris, employing reagent P of Girard and Sandulesco,[26] is detailed in Vol. II of the present work, p. 814. A modification of the general procedure, more suitable for the isolation of the irones, has been suggested by Naves.[27]

ABSOLUTE OF ORRIS
("Orris Tenfold" or "Irone Absolute")

It has been mentioned on several occasions that the concretes obtained by distillation of the rhizomes consist to the greater part of odorless higher fatty acids, chiefly myristic acid. Removal of these acids results in the so-called "Absolute of Orris,"[28] also called "Orris Tenfold" (the odor concentration is *approximately* tenfold), or "Irone Absolute" (the absolute consists chiefly of isomeric irones). The absolutes thus isolated from the concretes represent the odorous compounds of the dried and aged rhizomes in highest concentration. They are viscous, yellow to brownish liquids, usually soluble in 80 per cent alcohol, and possess a strong but delightful odor characteristic of orris root. Because of their concentration, the absolutes belong among the most valuable and expensive of perfumers' raw materials.

Elimination of the fatty acids from the concrete has to be carried out with the greatest of care, as otherwise a part of the liquid portions (absolute) may be lost, or the odor of the absolute be impaired. To remove the fatty acids from the concrete, some manufacturers precipitate them as potassium salts,[29] or as insoluble calcium salts in ethereal solution and, after filtration, concentrate the ethereal solution *in vacuo*, working throughout the entire process at low temperatures. Or the fatty acids are neutralized with a measured quantity of earth alkali, and then the odorous substances, which have not reacted with the alkali, are driven off by steam distillation, and collected. Obviously, this is a harsher technique than the former, and yields an absolute of somewhat inferior odor.

Far better than these two methods, which give a lot of trouble by the formation of emulsions, is that developed by Glichitch and Naves;[30] it can be used not only for the quantitative determination of the nonacidic portions (absolute) of a concrete, but in a modified form also for the prepara-

---

[26] *Helv. Chim. Acta* **19** (1936), 1098.

[27] *Ibid.* **31** (1948), 907.

[28] The term "absolute" is generally applied to natural flower oils freed of their alcohol-insoluble waxes. In connection with orris, the term indicates that the higher fatty acids have been removed from the concrete.

[29] Cf. Naves, *Helv. Chim. Acta* **31** (1948), 907.

[30] *Parfums France* **9** (1931), 371. Cf. Naves, *Helv. Chim. Acta* **31** (1948), 907.

tion of the absolutes on a technical scale. In this method an ethereal solution of orris concrete is treated with a hot solution of lithium acetate in absolute alcohol. Lithium salts of the fatty acids present in the concrete are thus formed; being quite insoluble in ether, they can easily be separated from the liquid portions of the oil. These latter are then determined gravimetrically, after removal of the solvent.

"Dissolve 5 g. of concrete in a 50 cc. glass-stoppered Erlenmeyer flask containing 25 cc. of anhydrous alcohol-free ether, add gradually, with continual stirring, a hot solution of 2.5 g. of lithium acetate (or preferably its equivalent of anhydrous lithium acetate) dissolved in 4 g. of absolute alcohol, let stand at room temperature for 1 hr., and filter on a 50 mm. Büchner funnel, using moderate suction. Transfer the solution to a 150 cc. glass-stoppered separation funnel, rinse the flask twice with 15 cc. of anhydrous ether pouring through the Büchner funnel and then transfer to the separation funnel, and wash the solution twice with 15 cc. of a 20% sodium carbonate solution. Wash the combined sodium carbonate washings with 10 g. of ether, add to the main ether solution, wash twice with 20 cc. of distilled water, dry the ether solution by adding 4 to 5 g. of anhydrous sodium sulfate, and filter into a tared 125 cc. Wurtz flask. Wash the separation funnel and filter with 10 cc. of ether, evaporate all but 2 or 3 cc. of the solvent on a water bath and remove the last traces on the water bath at 25° under a vacuum of 12 mm. for 30 min., wipe dry and weigh."

According to Naves,[31] the absolute oil contains, in addition to the irones, some esters of fatty acids, particularly methyl myristate, and some aldehydes—oleic aldehyde among others. The presence of *ethyl* esters is exceptional, and results from the deliberate addition of esters prepared from the fatty acids [32] present in concrete of orris, or from the use of unpeeled rhizomes. The determination of the ketones, calculated as irone, permits conclusions regarding such additions or preparations.

Physicochemical Properties of Orris Absolute.—Gildemeister and Hoffmann [33] reported these properties for absolute of orris:

Specific Gravity at 15°...... 0.93 to 0.94
Optical Rotation........... +14° 0' to +35° 0'
Refractive Index at 20°..... 1.492 to 1.500
Acid Number............. 1 to 8
Ester Number............ 15 to 40
Solubility................. Soluble in 1 to 1.5 vol. and
more of 80% alcohol

Three lots prepared under the author's supervision in Southern France (Seillans, Var) exhibited the following values:

[31] *Givaudanian* (February 1947), 4.
[32] *Rev. marques parfum. savon.* **9** (1931), 40. French Patent No. 673,341.
[33] "Die Ätherischen Öle," 3d Ed., Vol. II, 420.

	I	II	III
Specific Gravity at 15°....................	0.939	0.941	0.938
Optical Rotation.........................	+37° 56'	+34° 20'	+35° 8'
Refractive Index at 20°..................	1.4975	1.4970	1.4950
Acid Number............................	1.4	1.4	8.4
Acid Content, Calculated as Myristic Acid..	0.6%	0.6%	3.4%
Ester Number...........................	17.3	22.9	21.5
Ketone (and Aldehyde) Content, Calculated as Irone (Hydroxylamine Hydrochloride Method)...............................	79.7%	72.0%	73.9%
Solubility in 80% Alcohol...............	Soluble in 1 and more vol.		

Glichitch and Naves [34] reported these properties for absolute of orris prepared by their lithium salt method (see above):

Specific Gravity at 15°........ 0.920 to 0.945
Specific Optical Rotation...... +14° 0' to +30° 0'
Refractive Index at 20°........ 1.4905 to 1.501
Acid Number................ Less than 2.0
Ester Number............... 14 to 67
Irone Content................ 50 to 70%
Solubility.................... Soluble in 0.5 to 2.5 and
more vol. of 80% alcohol

Naves [35] recently indicated the following limits for the neutral fractions isolated from concrete of orris:

Specific Gravity at 20°......... 0.932 to 0.941, occasionally as low as 0.923
Optical Rotation.............. +17° 36' to +36° 43', occasionally as low as +14°
Refractive Index at 20°........ 1.4940 to 1.4980, occasionally as low as 1.4880
Ester Number................ 29 to 38, rarely as high as 49.8 in oils derived from
young rhizomes
Irone Content (By Oximation).. 60 to 79.5%

Genuine lots of orris absolute prepared by Fritzsche Brothers, Inc., New York, had properties varying within these limits:

Specific Gravity at 15°/15°.............. 0.922 to 0.942
Optical Rotation....................... +20° 6' to +36° 28'
Refractive Index at 20°................. 1.4862 to 1.4985
Acid Number........................... Up to 7.4
Saponification Number................... 22.0 to 64.4
Ketone (and Aldehyde) Content, Calculated
as Irone (Hydroxylamine Hydrochloride
Method)............................ 52.8 to 73.5%
Solubility............................. Soluble in 0.5 vol. of 90% alcohol,
usually opalescent to slightly turbid with more

[34] *Parfums France* **9** (1931), 371.
[35] Private communication of Dr. Y. R. Naves, Geneva, Switzerland.

A genuine absolute of orris prepared in Seillans (Var), France and examined in the laboratories of Fritzsche Brothers, Inc., New York, exhibited the following properties:

Specific Gravity at 15°/15°.............. 0.931
Optical Rotation....................... +21° 53′
Refractive Index at 20°................. 1.4900
Acid Number.......................... 1.8
Ester Number......................... 28.4
Ketone (and Aldehyde) Content, Calculated
  as Irone (Hydroxylamine Hydrochloride
  Method)............................ 67.7%
Solubility............................. Soluble in 0.5 vol. of 90% alcohol;
                                hazy in 4 vol. and more of 90%
                                alcohol

ADULTERATION OF CONCRETE AND ABSOLUTE OF ORRIS

Since they command very high prices, concrete and absolute of orris are frequently adulterated. In fact, sophistication of these products by a skilled essential oil chemist is so easy that they have become strictly articles of confidence, which should be purchased only from reliable suppliers.

Since concrete of orris contains a high percentage of myristic acid, it can be "cut" most readily by the addition of this acid, derived from low-priced sources, or obtained as by-product in the preparation of absolute of orris. (In fact, some manufacturers standardize their concretes of orris at a certain irone content—15 per cent, e.g.—by the addition of *natural* myristic acid obtained in the making of absolute of orris.) Unscrupulous dealers cut the concretes with myristic acid and reconstitute the lowered irone content by the addition of other, low-priced ketones, chiefly ionones. This form of adulteration cannot be detected readily and requires a good deal of experience to discover (cf. Vol. I of the present work, pp. 285 and 290, second footnote). Absolute of orris can be adulterated quite easily by the addition of ionones and esters of myristic acid. Careful odor tests and comparison with an authentic standard sample are, therefore, most important.

CHEMICAL COMPOSITION OF ORRIS OIL

The chemical composition of the oil derived from dried and aged orris rhizomes is complex and has been the object of numerous and lengthy investigations by some of the most brilliant minds in organic chemistry. The following can, therefore, give only a brief résumé of the subject.

As far back as 1876, Flückiger [36] recognized that concrete of orris consists chiefly of odorless higher fatty acids, the most important being *myristic acid*. Later, Tiemann and Krüger [37] reported the presence of *palmitic acid*. More recently, Langlais and Goby [38] fractionated a concrete of orris at 40 mm., and identified the following fatty acids:

Caprylic Acid. Anilide m. 51°. Silver salt.

Pelargonic Acid. Anilide m. 57°.

Capric Acid. M. 31°; anilide m. 65.5°. Silver salt.

Undecylic Acid. Anilide m. 71°. Silver salt.

Lauric Acid. M. 43.5°; anilide m. 75.5°.

Tridecylic Acid. M. 39°; anilide m. 81.5°.

Benzoic Acid. Observed in the mother liquor after crystallization of the pelargonic acid.

Some of these acids occur in the concrete not only free, but also as methyl esters. Years ago, Tiemann and Krüger [39] observed *methyl myristate* and *methyl oleate* in an oil extracted from orris root. Naves [40] expressed the opinion that the presence of high-boiling fatty esters in the concrete can be explained only by the long distillation (20 to 30 hr.) to which the rhizomes are subjected. A good percentage of the esters probably undergoes hydrolysis during distillation, and the corresponding acids remain perhaps in the still. It also seems possible that the distillates obtained from orris resinoids (distillation of benzene resinoids with superheated steam at reduced pressure) contain proportionally more esters than the concretes derived by direct distillation of the rhizomes.

Naves [41] submitted the neutral (nonketonic) fraction of an orris concrete to distillation with superheated steam (125°–130°) at reduced pressure (30 to 35 mm. Hg.) and identified the following esters:

Methyl Myristate and Methyl Oleate. Already reported by Tiemann and Krüger (see above).

Methyl Caprylate.

Methyl Pelargonate.

Methyl Caprate.

Methyl Laurate.

[36] *Arch. Pharm.* **208** (1876), 481.
[37] *Ber.* **26** (1893), 2675.
[38] *Compt. rend.* **179** (1924), 173.   *Bull. soc. chim.* [4], **35** (1924), 1307.
[39] *Ber.* **26** (1893), 2675.   [41] *Ibid.,* 2307.
[40] *Helv. Chim. Acta* **32** (1949), 2306.

Methyl Palmitate.

Methyl Stearate.

Methyl Linoleate.

A Methylate(?). Methyl ester of an unsaturated, optically active acid, which was not identified.

A Salicylate(?). Tavel [42] observed an ester of salicylic acid.

Oil of orris also contains a number of miscellaneous compounds, of which the following have been reported:

Furfural. In the first runs (Schimmel & Co.[43]).

A Terpene(?). Noted by the same authors [44] in the fraction b. 171°–173°. The terpene in question (d_{15} 0.8611, α_D +10° 40′) was not identified.

Naphthalene. On cooling to low temperature, the fraction b_4 73°–75° precipitated a substantial quantity of leafy crystals m. 80°–80.5°, which Schimmel & Co.[45] identified as naphthalene.

A Base(?). First observed by Schimmel & Co.; presence later confirmed by Tavel.[46] Only traces are present in the oil. Odor reminiscent of skatole. Constitution not elucidated.

A Phenol(?). Also first reported by Schimmel & Co., and later confirmed by Tavel,[47] who prepared a 2,5-dinitrobenzoate m. 127.5°, and established the empirical molecular formula $C_8H_{10}O$.

As regards the alcohols, Tavel [48] noted the presence of the following:

Benzyl Alcohol. In the foreruns; identified by preparation of the anthraquinone-β-carboxylic ester m. 151°–152°, and of the allophanate m. 178°–179°.

Linaloöl. Identified as phenylurethane m. 66.5°.

Geraniol. Allophanate m. 112°–113° (not entirely pure).

Alcohols $C_{10}H_{16}O$(?) and $C_9H_{14}O$(?). Constitution unknown; separated by means of the allophanates. The alcohols in question were perhaps not homogeneous compounds.

More important than the alcohols, so far as odor is concerned, are the aldehydes, of which the following have been observed:

[42] Dissertation Eidgenössische Technische Hochschule, Zurich (1946).
[43] *Ber. Schimmel & Co.*, April (1907), 53.
[44] *Ibid.*
[45] *Ibid.*
[46] Dissertation Eidgenössische Technische Hochschule, Zurich (1946).
[47] *Ibid.*   [48] *Ibid.*

Benzaldehyde. In the fraction b_{10} 45°–46°; isolated through the bisulfite compound. Oxidation yielded benzoic acid m. 122°–123° (Schimmel & Co.[49]).

n-Decylaldehyde. Small quantities in the fraction b_5 ~60°; semicarbazone m. 100°–101° (Schimmel & Co.).

A Nonylaldehyde(?). From the fraction b_4 65°–90° Schimmel & Co.[50] isolated, with sodium bisulfite, an aldehyde b_5 80°, which yielded a semicarbazone m. 167°–168°. Oxidation gave a nonylic acid b_4 128°; zinc salt m. 127°–128°, copper salt m. above 200°. The aldehyde in question was a nonylaldehyde which, on oxidation, yielded a nonylic acid similar to pelargonic acid.

Oleic Aldehyde. Years ago, Tiemann and Krüger [51] reported oleic aldehyde as a constituent of *extracted* orris oil. Later, Schimmel & Co.[52] proved that this aldehyde does *not* occur in distilled orris oil.

The most important odorous constituents of orris oil are the ketones, principally the irones (see below). Aside from the irones, the oil contains several ketones of minor importance, most of which have been identified by Naves: [53]

Acetovanillone. Concrete of orris contains about 0.5 per cent of acetovanillone (also called apocynine). It is hydroxy-4-methoxy-3-acetophenone.

Acetophenone. Isolated from the oil after removal of the acidic substances, by means of reagent P of Girard and Sandulesco. Semicarbazone m. 199°–199.5°; dinitro-2,4-phenylhydrazone m. 248°–249°.

Acetoveratrone. This dimethoxy-3,4-acetophenone was also isolated with the reagent P of Girard and Sandulesco. Semicarbazone m. 217°–218°; dinitro-2,4-phenylhydrazone m. 206°–207°.

A Hydroxy Ketone(?). In the fraction b_3 153°; α_D +13° 0'. This α,β-unsaturated hydroxy ketone $C_{14}H_{24}O_2$ is perhaps a hydroxydihydroirone. Semicarbazone m. 243°–244°; dinitro-2,4-phenylhydrazone m. 168°–168.5°.

A Ketone $C_{10}H_{16}O$. In the fraction b_3 65°–85°. This α,β-unsaturated ketone $C_{10}H_{16}O$ gave a semicarbazone m. 167°–168°, and a dinitro-2,4-phenylhydrazone m. 148°–149°. On regeneration from its semicarbazone the ketone exhibited a minty odor.

A Ketone $C_{10}H_{18}O$. Previously Schimmel & Co.[54] had noted that the fraction b_4 65°–71° of orris concrete contains a ketone $C_{10}H_{18}O$ of mint-like odor. The semicarbazone melted at 217°–218°.

Irones. By far the most important constituents of orris oil are the irones, a mixture of hydroaromatic, unsaturated ketones $C_{14}H_{22}O$, first discovered in the oil by Tiemann and Krüger, and since then the object of a great many investigations. Details will be found in Vol. II of the present work, pp. 466 ff. Since the printing of that volume at the end of 1948, however, the lively polemic between Ruzicka and his co-workers on the one side, and Naves and his collaborators, on the other,

[49] Gildemeister and Hoffmann, "Die Ätherischen Öle," 3d Ed., Vol. II, 421.
[50] *Ber. Schimmel & Co.,* April (1907), 53.   [52] *Ber. Schimmel & Co.,* April (1907), 53.
[51] *Ber.* **26** (1893), 2675.   [53] *Helv. Chim. Acta* **32** (1949), 1351, 2171.
[54] *Ber. Schimmel & Co.,* April (1907), 65. Cf. *ibid.,* October (1908), 62.

has continued and new data have been brought to light. In general, the two groups of researchers have not deviated much from their original contentions, but details, particularly new derivatives of the various isomeric forms, have been added. These will be briefly reported in a special section below.

The irones can be isolated in absolutely pure form from oil of orris by fractional distillation of the neutral (nonacidic) constituents in a high vacuum, and by subsequent treatment with reagent P of Girard and Sandulesco.

Acetaldehyde.

Methyl Alcohol.

Diacetyl.

Furfural.

} Found by the Schimmel chemists, in the cohobation waters.

In 1950 Treibs [55] published the results of his investigation on the first and last fractions of orris oil—work which he had completed a few years earlier (in 1944). For the isolation of the ketonic constituents from mixtures Treibs used the acid phthalic esters of their oximes, and thus succeeded in separating a number of alcohols, aldehydes and ketones, some of which had already been identified by Naves (see above):

Furfural. In the first fraction.

A Terpene(?). Also in the first fraction. Not identified.

An Aldehyde(?). In the second fraction. Not identified.

A Monoketone $C_{10}H_{16}O_2$. B_9 66°–72°, d_4^{20} 0.9180, α_D^{20} +5° 15′, n_D^{20} 1.46988; semicarbazone m. 151°–152°. In the third fraction.

Another Monoketone $C_{10}H_{16}O_2$. B_9 65°–70°, d_4^{20} 0.9596, α_D^{20} +16° 40′, n_D^{20} 1.48348; semicarbazone liquid. Also isolated from the third fraction.

2-Nonen-1-al. In the fourth fraction. Characterized by means of the semicarbazone m. 165.5°–166.5°.

Two α,β-Unsaturated Monocyclic Ketones $C_{10}H_{16}O$. Both possessed an agreeable, slightly minty and carvone-like odor. The properties of the two ketones were similar: b_8 82°–86° and 85°–92°, d_4^{20} 0.9242 and 0.9345, α_D^{20} +10° 10′ and +5° 0′, n_D^{20} 1.46802 and 1.47292, respectively. The semicarbazone of the first ketone did not crystallize; that of the second ketone melted at 165°–166°. Naves had reported a melting point of 167°–168° for the semicarbazone of his ketone $C_{10}H_{16}O$ (see above). Hence the ketone noted by Naves is probably identical with the second of the two ketones reported by Treibs.

A Ketone $C_{10}H_{16}O$. B_8 80°–85°, d_4^{20} 0.9410, α_D^{20} +25° 50′, n_D^{20} 1.48071. This ketone exhibited a sweet carvone-like odor. It yielded a semicarbazone m. 218°; hence it may be identical with the ketone $C_{10}H_{18}O$ observed years ago in orris oil by Schimmel & Co. (see above), which gave a semicarbazone m. 217°–218°.

[55] *Chem. Ber.* **83** (1950), 431. Cf. Treibs and Röhnert, *ibid.*, 186.

As regards the last fraction of orris oil, Treibs isolated these substances:

Ethyl Myristate. In the neutral portion.

Irone $C_{14}H_{22}O$. In the first and second fractions of the last run.

Sesquiterpene Alcohols $C_{15}H_{26}O$. Probably bicyclic, d_4^{20} 0.9762, α_D^{20} +2° 45', n_D^{20} 1.51600; odor agreeable, reminiscent of cedarwood and Russian leather. Dehydration of these sesquiterpene alcohols yielded no azulene, nor any clearly characterized aromatic hydrocarbon. Oxidation with chromic acid gave partly acids, partly a ketone $C_{15}H_{24}O$, with a vetivone-like odor.

The total alcohols of the orris oil (which had been isolated from the fore- and last runs by the boric acid method) were separated into seven fractions. Fraction I had a geraniol-like odor; Fractions II and III an odor reminiscent of camphor; from Fraction III to Fraction V the odor became increasingly agreeable, mild and tea-like. The following compounds were isolated from these fractions:

A Secondary Alcohol $C_{10}H_{16}O$. Oxidation with chromic acid gave a ketone $C_{10}H_{14}O$ (similar to thujone), the semicarbazone of which melted at 226°.

Another Secondary Alcohol $C_{10}H_{16}O$. Oxidation with chromic acid yielded a ketone $C_{10}H_{14}O$ (similar to carvone), the semicarbazone of which was viscous.

Irol(?). Oxidation of Fraction VI with chromic acid resulted in a ketone $C_{14}H_{22}O$ (similar to γ-irone), the odor of which resembled that of ionone and irone. The semicarbazone melted at 153°–154°. The parent alcohol, therefore, was probably irol $C_{14}H_{24}O$.

A Hydroxy Ketone $C_{14}H_{24}O_2$. Separated from Fraction VII. It had a pleasant and mild, tobacco-like odor, and yielded a semicarbazone m. 239°–241°. The ketone undoubtedly is identical with the hydroxy ketone of Naves (see above).

Eugenol. Identified in the combined phenolic portions of the fore- and last runs.

Acetophenone. Characterized by means of its semicarbazone m. 198°–199°. Presence previously reported by Naves (see above).

Acetoveratrone. Identified by preparation of its semicarbazone m. 215°–216°. Presence also previously noted by Naves (see above).

Composition of the Natural Irones

It is primarily on the question of the relative proportions of the irone isomers composing the irone mixture in orris oil that the two research groups—Ruzicka and his collaborators, and Naves and his co-workers—are in disagreement.

Ruzicka et al., reported a ratio of about 75 per cent of γ-irone to about 25 per cent of α-irone in all the irone samples which they isolated from orris concretes. The γ-irone was determined by the quantity of formaldehyde formed on ozonization (correction factor 100/35).[56] Results were

---

[56] Ruzicka, Seidel, Schinz and Tavel, *Helv. Chim. Acta* **31** (1948), 257. Seidel, Schinz and Ruzicka, *ibid.* **32** (1949), 1739, 2560.

confirmed by means of quantitative spectroscopic determination in the infrared spectrum. γ-Irone exhibited the δ(CH)—vibration frequency at 890 cm.$^{-1}$, and ν(CC)—vibration frequency at 1642 cm.$^{-1}$; α-irone exhibited the same vibrations at 812 and 1675 cm.$^{-1}$, respectively.[57]

Naves and his co-workers, on the other hand, at first reported that the irones which they isolated from orris concretes (distilled from Tuscany rhizones) were practically homogeneous and, in regard to physical properties, analogous to α-ionone. They, therefore, concluded that pure α-irone was the principal constituent.[58] This interpretation appeared to be supported by the similarity between the ultraviolet and the Raman spectra of natural irone and those of synthetic 6-methyl-α-ionone.[59] However, in oils of various origin investigated more recently, Naves et al. have noted a content of γ-irone ranging from 10 to 53 per cent.[60]

Isomerization of Natural Irone

When a natural irone consisting of 75 per cent of γ-irone is heated with formic acid to 100°, or permitted to stand with a 10% alcoholic solution of potassium hydroxide or sodium hydroxide, the γ-irone disappears completely, and a mixture of α- and β-irone is formed.[61] On boiling of the natural irone with a concentrated aqueous solution of oxalic acid, the content of γ-irone decreases to about 50 per cent. On shaking with a cold 40% aqueous solution of potassium hydroxide, or with 2-normal hydrochloric acid, no appreciable isomerization takes place. Isolation of the natural irones from orris concrete by means of Girard and Sandulesco's reagent P hardly influences the content of γ-irone.[62] No isomerization takes place with aqueous sulfuric acid below 60°.[63] On treatment with concentrated sulfuric acid isomerization to β-irone occurs.[64]

Stereoisomerism of the Irones

For a discussion of the theoretically possible stereoisomeric forms of α-, β-, and γ-irone the reader is referred to Vol. II of the present work, p. 468.

[57] Günthard and Ruzicka, *ibid.* **31** (1948), 642; **32** (1949), 2125. Günthard, Ruzicka, Schinz and Seidel, *ibid.* **32** (1949), 2198.
[58] Naves and Bachmann, *ibid.* **30** (1947), 2222.
[59] Naves et al., *ibid.* **30** (1947), 1599, 2221, 2233, 2241; **31** (1948), 893, 1427.
[60] Naves, *ibid.* **31** (1948), 893, 912, 2047; **32** (1949), 2186.
[61] Ruzicka, Seidel, Schinz and Tavel, *ibid.* **31** (1948), 257. Cf. Vol. II of the present work, p. 468.
[62] Seidel, Schinz and Ruzicka, *Helv. Chim. Acta* **32** (1949), 1739.
[63] Naves, *ibid.* **32** (1949), 1058.
[64] Köster, *Ber.* **77** (1944), 559. Bächli, Seidel, Schinz and Ruzicka, *Helv. Chim. Acta* **32** (1949), 1751.

According to Naves,[65] the α- and γ-irones possess a *cis* (2,6) configuration; the substituents on the double bond in the side chain are also in the *cis* position.[66] In the nomenclature which he proposed for the various irones, Naves [67] calls the *cis* (2,6) isomers simply "Irones," and the *trans* (2,6) isomers "Isoirones." "Neo" compounds possess the *trans* ($2^1,2^2$) form.

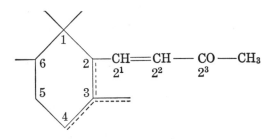

(For the structural formulas of α-, β-, and γ-irone, see Vol. II of the present work, p. 466.)

α-Irone: *cis* (2,6), *cis* ($2^1,2^2$), α-irone

Iso-α-irone: *trans* (2,6), *cis* ($2^1,2^2$), α-irone

Neo-α-irone: *cis* (2,6), *trans* ($2^1,2^2$), α-irone

Neo-iso-α-irone: *trans* (2,6), *trans* ($2^1,2^2$), α-irone

β-Irone: *cis* ($2^1,2^2$), β-irone *

Neo-β-irone: *trans* ($2^1,2^2$), β-irone.

The γ-irones correspond to the α-irones, only the symbol being changed.

d-γ-Irone

Ruzicka et al.

Earlier preparation (cf. Vol. II of the present work, p. 470): d_4^{15} 0.939, α_D +22° 0′, n_D^{15} 1.505. (This product still contained about 10 per cent of α-irone.)

Later preparation: [68] d_4^{20} 0.9368, α_D +8° 0′, n_D^{20} 1.5006.

Derivatives: [69] Phenyl-4-semicarbazone m. 178°; dinitro-2,4-phenylhydrazone m. 130°–131°; thiosemicarbazone m. 127.5°–128.5°.

[65] *Ibid.* **31** (1948), 893, 1103.
[66] Naves and Bachmann, *ibid.* **30** (1947), 2222, 2233, 2241.
[67] *Ibid.* **32** (1949), 970. For illustration of models see *ibid.*, 613.
* On the basis largely of spectroscopic studies, Naves (*Bull. soc. chim.* [5], **18** [1951], 243) has more recently questioned whether β-irone may not actually possess the configuration of neo-β-irone, viz., *trans* ($2^1,2^2$), β-irone.
[68] Bächli, Seidel, Schinz and Ruzicka, *ibid.* **32** (1949), 1744.
[69] *Ibid.*

Naves et al.

"Neo-γ-irone" [*cis* (2,6), *trans* (2^1, 2^2), γ-irone].

Earlier preparation:[70] d_4^{20} 0.9348, $[\alpha]_D^{20}$ +25° 7', n_D^{20} 1.5012.

New preparation:[71] d_4^{20} 0.9355, $[\alpha]_D^{20}$ +7° 36', n_D^{20} 1.5019.

Derivatives:[72] Phenyl-4-semicarbazone m. 178°–179°; dinitro-2,4-phenyl-hydrazone m. 146°–146.5°; thiosemicarbazone m. 169.5°–170°.

Dihydro Compound (obtained with Raney Nickel)

Ruzicka et al.:[73] Semicarbazone m. 199°–200°; dinitro-2,4-phenylhydrazone m. 108°–109°.

Naves et al.:[74] Semicarbazone m. 199.5°–200°; dinitro-2,4-phenylhydrazone m. 109°–110°.

d-α-Irone

Ruzicka et al.[75]

Natural irone was isomerized, with formic acid, to a mixture of α- and β-irones, and the α- form separated by means of the phenyl-4-semicarbazone m. above 151°.

d_4^{20} 0.9358, α_D +114° 0', n_D^{20} 1.5013.

(This product still contained about 5 per cent of β-irone.)

Derivatives: Phenyl-4-semicarbazone m. 153°–154°; dinitro-2,4-phenyl-hydrazone m. not constant.

Earlier preparation: Phenyl-4-semicarbazone m. 160°–161°; thiosemicarba-zone m. 180° (cf. Vol. II of the present work, p. 469).

Naves et al.[76]

"α-Irone" [*cis* (2,6), *cis* ($2^1,2^2$), α-irone].

d_4^{20} 0.9349, $[\alpha]_D^{20}$ +226° 0', n_D^{20} 1.5003.

Derivatives: Phenyl-4-semicarbazone m. 157.5°–158°; dinitro-2,4-phenyl-hydrazone m. 125.5°–126°; *p*-bromophenylhydrazone m. 169°–170°; thio-semicarbazone m. 182.5°–183°.

Earlier preparation: Phenyl-4-semicarbazone m. 162°–163° (cf. Vol. II of the present work, p. 469).

Dihydro Compound (obtained with Raney Nickel)

Ruzicka et al.:[77] Semicarbazone m. 171°–172°; dinitro-2,4-phenylhydrazone m. 128.5°–129°. Probably *cis* (2,6) configuration.

[70] Naves, *ibid.* **31** (1948), 912.
[71] *Ibid.*, 2047.
[72] *Ibid.*, 2049; **32** (1949), 603. Cf. Tables, *ibid.*, 2193, and "Proceedings of the Scientific Section of the Toilet Goods Association" (1949), No. 11.
[73] Bächli, Seidel, Schinz and Ruzicka, *Helv. Chim. Acta* **32** (1949), 1744.
[74] Naves and Bachmann, *ibid.* **30** (1947), 2231. Naves, *ibid.* **31** (1948), 913, 2050; **32** (1949), 971.
[75] Bächli, Seidel, Schinz and Ruzicka, *ibid.* **32** (1949), 1744.
[76] Naves, *ibid.* **32** (1949), 599, 612.
[77] Bächli, Seidel, Schinz and Ruzicka, *ibid.* **32** (1949), 1744.

Naves et al.: [78] Semicarbazone m. 172.5°–173° and m. 203.5°; dinitro-2,4-phenylhydrazone m. 130°–131° and m. 106°–106.5°.

l-α-Irone

Ruzicka et al.[79]

Natural irone was isomerized with alcoholic potassium hydroxide; β- form separated by means of its semicarbazone, α- form by means of its phenyl-4-semicarbazone. The remaining product still contained a small percentage of β-irone.

d_4^{20} 0.9314, α_D −79° 30′, n_D^{20} 1.4973.

Derivatives: Phenyl-4-semicarbazone m. 164°–165°; dinitro-2,4-phenylhydrazone m. 103°–104°.

Naves et al.[80]

"*l*-Neo-α-irone" [*cis* (2,6), *trans* ($2^1,2^2$), α-irone].

d_4^{20} 0.9347, α_D −8° 12′, n_D^{20} 1.5013.

Derivatives: Semicarbazone m. 164°–165°; phenyl-4-semicarbazone m. 181.5°–182°; dinitro-2,4-phenylhydrazone m. 153°–154°; thiosemicarbazone m. 188.5°–189°.

Dihydro Compound (obtained with Raney Nickel)

Ruzicka et al.: [81] Semicarbazone m. 143.5°–144.5°; dinitro-2,4-phenylhydrazone m. 114°–115°. Probably *trans* (2,6) configuration.

d-β-Irone

(occurs in genuine natural irone only in traces)

Ruzicka et al.

1. Natural irone was isomerized with alcoholic potassium hydroxide, and the β- form separated by means of its semicarbazone:

d_4^{15} 0.9485, α_D +41° 0′, n_D^{15} 1.5205.

Derivatives: Semicarbazone m. 167°–168°; thiosemicarbazone m. 165°–166°; phenyl-4-semicarbazone m. 160°–161°.

(Cf. Vol. II of the present work, p. 469.)

2. Natural irone was isomerized with concentrated sulfuric acid: [82]

d_4^{20} 0.9444, α_D +11° 18′, n_D^{20} 1.5178.

Derivatives: Dinitro-2,4-phenylhydrazone m. 131°–132°.

[78] Naves and Bachmann, *ibid.* **30** (1947), 2231. Naves, *ibid.* **31** (1948), 893, 1103.
[79] Bächli, Seidel, Schinz and Ruzicka, *ibid.* **32** (1948), 1744.
[80] Naves, *ibid.* **31** (1948), 1280, 1876; **32** (1949), 599, 971.
[81] Bächli, Seidel, Schinz and Ruzicka, *ibid.* **32** (1949), 1744.
[82] Bächli, Seidel, Schinz and Ruzicka, *ibid.*

Naves et al.[83]

Natural irone was isomerized with concentrated sulfuric acid:
d_4^{20} 0.9456, $[\alpha]_D^{20}$ +20° 0′, n_D^{20} 1.5180.

Derivatives: Dinitro-2,4-phenylhydrazone m. 135°–136°; phenyl-4-semi-carbazone m. 167°–168°; thiosemicarbazone m. 167.5°–168°.

Köster [84]

Natural irone was isomerized with concentrated sulfuric acid:
d_4^{18} 0.9472, α_D +48° 24′, n_D^{25} 1.5160.

Derivatives: Semicarbazone m. 166°–167°; thiosemicarbazone m. 166°–167°.
(Cf. Vol. II of the present work, p. 469.)

Dihydro Compound (obtained with Raney Nickel)

Ruzicka et al.: [85] Semicarbazone m. 161°–162°; dinitro-2,4-phenylhydrazone m. 104°–105°.

Naves et al.: [86] Semicarbazone m. 157°–158°; dinitro-2,4-phenylhydrazone m. 103°–104°.

Tetrahydroirone

Ruzicka et al.

Tetrahydroirone was regenerated from its semicarbazone m. 203°–204° (cf. Vol. II of the present work, p. 471): [87]
d_4^{24} 0.9173, α_D +35° 0′, n_D^{25} 1.4721.

Natural irone was hydrogenated, with platinic oxide (PtO_2) in acetic ester solution, to tetrahydroirol, and the latter reoxidized with chromic acid (CrO_3) to tetrahydroirone.

Stereoisomeric Tetrahydroirones: [88]

	Semicarbazone (m.)	Dinitro-2,4-phenyl-hydrazone (m.)	p-Nitrophenyl-hydrazone (m.)
I.	203°–204°	116°–117°	139°–140°
II.	160°–161°	76°–77°	...
III.	162°–164°	135°–136°	...
IV.	154°–155°	81°–83°	...

I and II were obtained by hydrogenation of the original irone mixture, III and IV from an irone isomerized by boiling with sulfuric acid (20%). I probably has the *cis* (2,6) configuration, II probably the *trans* (2,6) configuration.

[83] Naves, *ibid.* **31** (1948), 912; **32** (1949), 600; cf. Tables, *ibid.*, 971.
[84] *Ber.* **77** (1944), 559.
[85] Bächli, Seidel, Schinz and Ruzicka, *Helv. Chim. Acta* **32** (1949), 1744.
[86] Naves, *ibid.* **31** (1948), 1875; cf. Table, *ibid.* **32** (1949), 971.
[87] Ruzicka, Seidel and Firmenich, *ibid.* **24** (1941), 1434. Ruzicka, Seidel and Brugger, *ibid.* **30** (1947), 2168.
[88] Seidel, Schinz and Ruzicka, *ibid.* **32** (1949), 2113, compilation.

Naves et al.[89]

Natural irone was hydrogenated, with platinic oxide (PtO_2) in glacial acetic acid solution at 60°, to tetrahydroirol, and the latter reoxidized with chromic acid (CrO_3) to tetrahydroirone:

Semicarbazone m. 201°–202°; from this the tetrahydroirone regenerated: d_4^{20} 0.9218, $[\alpha]_D$ +39° 39′, n_D^{20} 1.4743.

Derivatives: Dinitro-2,4-phenylhydrazone m. 130°–130.5°; *p*-nitrophenylhydrazone m. 142°–143°; no semicarbazone obtained.

Conclusion

As was pointed out above, Ruzicka and his collaborators found that the natural irones present in orris concrete consist of about 75 per cent of γ-irone, and about 25 per cent of α-irone. The quantity of β-irone present in the concrete is very small. Naves and his co-workers, on the other hand, first claimed that the natural irone mixture consists chiefly of α-irone. Later, they conceded that the quantity of γ-irone may be as high as 53 per cent in some samples.

Using his own nomenclature, Naves [90] suggests that the concrete of orris contains the following irones:

Neo-γ-irone [91]

Another γ-irone,[92] probably resulting from isomerization; dinitro-2,4-phenylhydrazone m. 126°–127°.

α-Irone [93]

Iso-α-irone [94]

Neo-α-irone [95]

β-Irone,[96] in very small quantities.

USE OF ORRIS CONCRETE, ABSOLUTE AND RESINOID

The most important of all products derived from orris rhizomes is the *concrete;* it imparts strong, lasting, and alluring notes, reminiscent of violet,

[89] Naves, *ibid.* **31** (1948), 1875.
[90] *Ibid.* **32** (1949), 2675.
[91] Ruzicka, Seidel, Schinz and Pfeiffer, *ibid.* **30** (1947), 1807. Naves, *ibid.* **31** (1948), 2047. Naves and Bachmann, *ibid.* **32** (1949), 402.
[92] Naves, *ibid.* **32** (1949), 2192.
[93] Naves and Bachmann, *ibid.* **30** (1947), 2222. Ruzicka, Seidel, Schinz and Pfeiffer, *ibid.* **30** (1947), 1807. Re optical activity (+226°), see Naves, *ibid.* **32** (1949), 2616. Re racemization, see Naves, *ibid.* **31** (1948), 1104, 1873; **32** (1949), 612.
[94] Naves, *ibid.* **31** (1948), 1287.
[95] *Ibid.*, 1876.
[96] Ruzicka, Seidel, Schinz and Pfeiffer, *ibid.* **30** (1947), 1807.

to perfumes, cosmetics and high-grade soaps. In preparations where a higher solubility in alcohol is required, the *absolute* of orris will give excellent results. However, this latter product commands a very high price; it belongs among the most expensive raw materials available to the perfumer.

The *resinoids* of orris, of softer odor than the concrete, are much lower priced and produce good effects in soaps and in any preparation where a lasting odor is desired.

SUGGESTED ADDITIONAL LITERATURE

Y. R. Naves, "Progress in the Knowledge of the Irones" (A Chronological Summary of the Bibliography), *Perfumery Essential Oil Record* **41** (1950), 121.

R. Louis Joly, "Les Possibilités de la Culture de l'Iris sur les Hauts-Plateaux Algériens," *Ind. parfum.* **4** (1949), 449.

OIL OF SAFFRON

Steam-distilling saffron, the well-known spice derived from the stigma of *Crocus sativus* L. (fam. *Iridaceae*), in a current of carbon dioxide, Kayser [1] obtained small quantities of a light colored, mobile oil with a strong and characteristic saffron odor. On exposure to air, the oil readily absorbed oxygen and turned viscous and dark.

The principal constituent of the oil is *safranal* (cf. Vol. II of this work, p. 348).

According to the author's knowledge, the oil has never been produced on a commercial scale.

[1] *Ber.* **17** (1884), 2228.

CHAPTER IX

ESSENTIAL OILS OF THE PLANT FAMILY *ARACEAE*

OIL OF CALAMUS

Botanical and Geographical Origin.—*Acorus calamus* L. (fam. *Araceae*), our common sweet flag, is a perennial growing wild on the edges of swamps, on the banks of rivers and ponds in North America, Europe, and Asia. It has a horizontal jointed rhizome of spongy texture from ½ to 1 in. thick and sometimes several feet long. The rhizomes of the wild growing plants are collected in spring or late fall, washed, freed of fibrous root, and dried at moderate heat.

The dried root (rhizome) has long been employed in medicinal preparations and for the flavoring of liqueurs. It contains a volatile oil of peculiar, but pleasant, slightly sweetish odor, which can be isolated by steam distillation. Prior to World War II commercial supplies of the drug came from the U.S.S.R., Central Europe, Roumania, India, and Japan. Roots from Japan have a somewhat harsher, more camphoraceous odor than the domestic or European material.

Cultivation and Harvest.—Although calamus in the wild state grows in water, it may be cultivated, according to Stockberger,[1] in almost any good, but fairly moist, soil. It usually does well on moderately dry upland soils that will produce fair crops of corn or potatoes. The plants are readily propagated from divisions of old roots. These should be set out in rows, 1 ft. apart, in the fall, and well covered. During the growing season the plants require frequent and thorough cultivation.

The roots are harvested in the fall. They can be readily dug up with a spade or turned out with a plow. The tops, together with about 1 in. of the rootstock, are cut off and used for replanting. The roots are washed and dried artificially at a moderately low degree of heat. The marketable product consists of the thick rootstocks deprived of their small rootlets or "fibers." These may be removed before drying, but more easily afterward, since they break off more readily when dry and brittle. These so-called "stripped" roots are more aromatic than those which have been peeled.

According to Stockberger,[2] yields at the rate of 2,000 lb. of dried roots per acre have been obtained.

The annual importation figures of calamus root into the United States are small, but they do not take into consideration the importation of oil of

[1] "Drug Plants under Cultivation," *U. S. Dept. Agr., Farmers' Bull.* No. 663 (1935), 15.
[2] *Ibid.*

109

calamus from the U.S.S.R. and Roumania, which represent a large quantity of root material.

Distillation and Yield of Oil.—The rhizomes should not be peeled prior to drying, because peeling results in considerable losses of oil by evaporation and resinification. Highest yields of oil are obtained from dried unpeeled rhizomes that have been granulated immediately before they are charged into the still.

According to Gildemeister and Hoffmann,[3] unpeeled dried European calamus roots yield from 1.5 to 4.8 per cent of oil, whereas the Japanese material yields up to 5 per cent of oil. Distilling dried European roots in Seillans (Var), France, the author obtained 0.94 to 2.2 per cent of oil, and from imported Japanese roots 4.63 per cent of oil. Fritzsche Brothers, Inc., New York, distilled domestic calamus roots and noted a yield of 3.3 per cent of oil. Kofler[4] reported yields of oil ranging from 0.48 to 2.23 per cent from powdered root material. The laboratories of the American Pharmaceutical Association[5] obtained yields varying between 1.1 and 1.4 per cent, by using the Clevenger method in a somewhat modified form.

Physicochemical Properties.—The volatile oil derived from calamus root is a yellow to yellowish-brown, somewhat viscous liquid, with a peculiar, warm, slightly camphoraceous odor, and a burning spicy flavor.

(a) *Oils from European* (*including Russian*) *Root Material.*—Gildemeister and Hoffmann[6] reported these properties for European calamus oils:

Specific Gravity at 15°..............	0.959 to 0.972; in exceptional cases as low as 0.9564
Optical Rotation....................	+9° 0′ to +31° 0′
Refractive Index at 20°.............	1.5028 to 1.5098
Acid Number.......................	Up to 3.7
Ester Number......................	4 to 18
Ester Number after Acetylation......	32 to 50
Solubility.........................	Clearly miscible with 90% alcohol in almost any proportion; only sparingly soluble in dilute alcohol. Clearly soluble in about 15 vol. of 80% alcohol; also soluble in about 1,000 vol. of 50% alcohol

Senov[7] examined calamus oils from the far eastern part of the U.S.S.R. and noted the following properties:

[3] "Die Ätherischen Öle," 3d Ed., Vol. II, 396.
[4] *Pharm. Monatsh.* **16** (1935), 209.
[5] *Bull. Natl. Form. Comm.* **8** (1940), 224.
[6] "Die Ätherischen Öle," 3d Ed., Vol. II, 397.
[7] *Arch. Sci. Biol. U.S.S.R.* **44** (1936), No. 3, 173 (188, in English).

Specific Gravity at 15°......... 0.9616 to 0.9738
Specific Optical Rotation........ +9° 39′ to +23° 26′
Refractive Index............... 1.5211 to 1.5289
Acid Number.................. 1.2 to 2.0
Ester Number................. 10 to 12
Solubility..................... Insoluble in 70% alcohol

Shipments of Russian calamus oil analyzed by Fritzsche Brothers, Inc., New York, had properties varying within these limits:

Specific Gravity at 15°/15°...... 0.952 to 0.955
Optical Rotation............... +12° 48′ to +15° 0′
Refractive Index at 20°........ 1.5020 to 1.5031
Saponificat'on Number.......... 4.7 to 7.5
Solubility..................... Soluble in 5 vol. and more
     of 90% alcohol

Oils distilled in Southern France (Seillans, Var), under the author's supervision, from European root material exhibited the following properties:

Specific Gravity at 15°......... 0.960 to 0.974
Optical Rotation............... +15° 50′ to +18° 40′
Refractive Index............... 1.5045 to 1.5070
Saponification Number.......... 6.8 to 7.5
Solubility..................... Soluble in 0.5 and more vol.
     of 90% alcohol

(b) *Oils from Japanese Root Material.*—According to Gildemeister and Hoffmann,[8] the oils derived from Japanese calamus root usually have a higher specific gravity and are more soluble in 80 per cent alcohol than the European oils. These authors reported the following values for Japanese calamus oil:

Specific Gravity at 15°.............. 0.973 to 1.023
Optical Rotation................... +7° 20′ to +26° 30′. In a few cases laevoro-
    tatory Japanese oils have been observed:
    −5° 36′ to −11° 25′
Refractive Index at 20°............. 1.511 to 1.528
Acid Number..................... Up to 2
Ester Number.................... 2 to 8
Ester Number after Acetylation (five
  determinations)................. 15 to 34
Solubility........................ Soluble in 1 to 10 vol. of 80% alcohol; the di-
    luted solution occasionally shows opales-
    cence. Soluble in 1 vol. and more of 90%
    alcohol

[8] "Die Ätherischen Öle," 3d Ed., Vol. II, 397.

Oils distilled under the author's supervision in Southern France (Seillans, Var) from imported Japanese calamus root had these properties:

Specific Gravity at 15°......... 0.975 to 0.985
Optical Rotation.............. +2° 8' to +13° 44'
Refractive Index.............. 1.5051 to 1.5090
Saponification Number......... 3.7 to 12.1
Solubility.................... Soluble in 1.5 vol. and more of 80%
                        alcohol; some oils are soluble only
                        in 6 to 7 vol. of 80% alcohol

(c) *Oils from North American Root Material.*—Oils of calamus distilled by Fritzsche Brothers, Inc., New York, from domestic calamus root exhibited the following values:

Specific Gravity at 15°/15°...... 0.950 to 0.974
Optical Rotation.............. +13° 48' to +15° 0'
Refractive Index at 20°........ 1.5013 to 1.5069
Saponification Number......... 8.4 to 10.7
Solubility.................... Soluble in 0.5 to 5 vol. and more of
                        90% alcohol

The properties of the domestic oil approach those of the European, rather than of the Japanese oil.

(d) *Oils from Indian Root Material.*—Rao, Sudborough and Watson,[9] (I), and Kelkar and Rao [10] (II) distilled the dried rhizomes of Indian *Acorus calamus* L., and obtained oils with these properties:

	I	II
Specific Gravity at 15°/15°............	1.0694	1.076
Optical Rotation.....................	+6° 12'	−1° 30'
Refractive Index.....................	n_D^{25} 1.5030	n_D^{30} 1.5461
Acid Number........................	1.4	2.4
Saponification Number................	5.1	4.1
Saponification Number after Acetylation	16.6	15.7
Methoxy Content.....................	...	36.7%
Solubility at 8°.....................	Soluble in 1.5 vol. of 70% alcohol	...

Two lots of imported Indian root distilled commercially by Fritzsche Brothers, Inc., New York, showed the following properties:

	I	II
Specific Gravity at 15°/15°..	1.083	1.081
Optical Rotation..........	−0° 52'	Inactive
Refractive Index at 20°.....	1.5522	1.5510
Acid Number.............	2.8	2.6

[9] *J. Indian Inst. Sci.* **8A** (1925), 149.
[10] *Ibid.* **17A** (1934), 25.

	I	II
Saponification Number......	7.5	10.6
Solubility................	Soluble in 0.5 vol.	Soluble in 0.5 vol.
	of 80% alcohol.	of 80% alcohol
	Opalescent in	and more
	10 vol.	

(e) *Oils from Javanese Root Material.*—Two oils of calamus distilled in the Botanical Garden of Buitenzorg (Java) and analyzed by Schimmel & Co.[11] had the following properties:

	I	II
Specific Gravity at 15°........	1.0783	1.0771
Optical Rotation.............	+0° 53′	+0° 51′
Refractive Index at 20°.......	1.55043	1.55065
Ester Number..............	12	...
Solubility..................	Soluble in 1 to 1.5 vol.	
	of 70% alcohol, with	
	slight separation of	
	paraffins	

These oils differed from the European oils by their higher specific gravity, much lower optical rotation, higher refractive index, and better solubility.

Chemical Composition.—Early attempts at elucidating the chemical composition of calamus oil by Martius,[12] Schnedermann,[13] Gladstone,[14] and Kurbatov [15] gave practically no results and need not be discussed here. Moreover, some of the oils examined by these workers were probably adulterated. Since the beginning of the century, however, the oil has been studied quite thoroughly by a number of researchers, among them chiefly Schimmel & Co.,[16] von Soden and Rojahn,[17] Thoms and Beckstroem [18] (who investigated the high boiling fractions of a Japanese oil), Asahina [19] (Japanese oil), Semmler and Spornitz [20] (Russian oil), Asahina and Imai [21] (high boiling fractions of a Japanese oil), Ruzicka and collaborators,[22] Kelkar and Rao [23] (Indian oil), Rao and Subramaniam [24] (Indian oil), and Qudrat-i-Khuda et al.[25] (Indian oil).

[11] *Ber. Schimmel & Co.*, April (1909), 21.
[12] *Liebigs Ann.* **4** (1832), 264, 266.
[13] *Ibid.* **41** (1842), 374.
[14] *J. Chem. Soc.* **17** (1864), 1.
[15] *Ber.* **6** (1873), 1210. *Liebigs Ann.* **173** (1874), 4.
[16] *Ber. Schimmel & Co.*, October (1899), 8.
[17] *Pharm. Ztg.* **46** (1901), 243.
[18] *Ber.* **34** (1901), 1021; **35** (1902), 3187. *Ber. deut. pharm. Ges.* **12** (1902), 257.
[19] *Apoth. Ztg.* **21** (1906), 987.
[20] *Ber.* **46** (1913), 3700.
[21] *J. pharm. chim.* [7], **11** (1915), 299.
[22] *Helv. Chim. Acta* **5** (1922), 348, 358.
[23] *J. Indian Inst. Sci.* **17A** (1934), 25.
[24] *J. Chem. Soc.* (1937), 1338.
[25] *J. Indian Chem. Soc.* **16** (1939), 583.

The presence of the following compounds has been reported by these authors:

d-α-Pinene. Identified in the lowest boiling fractions of a Russian oil by Semmler and Spornitz. Nitrosochloride m. 108°.

Camphene. Characterized by hydration to isoborneol m. 212° (Semmler and Spornitz).

Cineole. Presence reported in calamus oils from the roots of wild-growing plants of the Voronezh District (U.S.S.R.) by Chernukhin.[26]

Camphor. Identified by Semmler and Spornitz. Oxime m. 115°.

Calamene. A sesquiterpene $C_{15}H_{24}$ (cf. Vol. II of this work, p. 112), observed in the fraction b_{12} 130°–135° of a Russian oil by Semmler and Spornitz.

Two Hydrocarbons(?) $C_{15}H_{22}$. From a Japanese calamus oil, Thoms and Beckstroem isolated two hydrocarbons of the empirical molecular formula $C_{15}H_{22}$; b_{19} 146° and b_{22} 151°, d_{18} 0.9330 and d_{12} 0.9336, $[\alpha]_D^{18}$ +34° 50′ and $[\alpha]_D^{22}$ −13° 18′, respectively. No solid derivatives could be obtained.

Later Semmler and Spornitz expressed the opinion that the hydrocarbon $C_{15}H_{22}$ is not a natural constituent of the oil, but an artifact originating by dehydration of a sesquiterpene alcohol $C_{15}H_{24}O$ (see Calamenenol, below).

Calamenol (Calamenenol). The probably tertiary sesquiterpene alcohol $C_{15}H_{24}O$ was originally named calamenol. Later Semmler and Spornitz changed the name calamenol to calamenenol, and reserved the designation calamenol for a sequiterpene alcohol $C_{15}H_{26}O$, which has still to be found in the oil (re Calamenenol, see Vol. II of the present work, p. 282). Recently, Treibs [27] again applied the term calamenol to the tertiary alcohol $C_{15}H_{24}O$, which is perhaps a dehydration product of calameone $C_{15}H_{26}O_2$.

Asaronaldehyde. First isolated by Thoms and Beckstroem with bisulfite solution from the high boiling fraction of a Japanese calamus oil. This 2,4,5-trimethoxybenzaldehyde is a crystalline solid m. 114° (cf. Vol. II of this work, p. 366).

Eugenol. Identified by the same authors. Benzoyl compound m. 70.5°–71°.

Methyleugenol. Reported also in a Japanese oil by Asahina, who characterized this phenolic ether by oxidation to veratric acid.

Asarone. An important constituent of the oil (cf. Vol. II of this work, p. 535). This 1,2,5-trimethoxy-4-propenylbenzene occasionally separates in the form of crystals m. 62°–63° from old oils containing a high percentage of it. Asarone was first noted in the high boiling fractions of a Japanese calamus oil by Thoms and Beckstroem.

Calamol. An allyltrimethoxybenzene, isomeric with asarone (cf. Vol. II of this work, p. 540). Calamol is quite an important component of Indian calamus oil.

[26] *Trans. Sci. Chem. Pharm. Inst. Moscow* **19** (1928), 196 (201, in English). *Chem. Abstracts* **24** (1930), 206.
[27] *Chem. Ber.* **82** (1949), 532.

Calameone. First observed in the high boiling fractions of a calamus oil by Schimmel & Co., and by von Soden and Rojahn, and called "calamus camphor." Later renamed "calameone" by Thoms and Beckstroem. The crystals melt at 168°–169° (for details, see Vol. II of this work, p. 279). According to Böhme,[28] calameone $C_{15}H_{26}O_2$ is a bicyclic sesquiterpene glycol, containing two tertiary hydroxy groups and one double bond. On dehydration calameone yields a hydrocarbon $C_{15}H_{22}$, viz., calamenene.

Recently, Treibs [29] proved that calameone and calamenene have these structures:

$$-2H_2O \longrightarrow$$

Calameone   Calamenene

Azulene(?). In the highest boiling fraction Kurbatov noted the presence of a deep blue oil which was probably an azulene.

Fatty Acids. Extracting the high boiling fractions of a Japanese oil with a 2 per cent aqueous solution of sodium carbonate, Thoms and Beckstroem isolated *n-heptylic acid* (amide m. 96°), *palmitic acid* m. 32°, and an unsaturated acid.

As regards the quantitative composition of the oil, Kelkar and Rao [30] investigated an oil that had been distilled in India from dried rhizomes of *Acorus calamus* L. (yield 2.8 per cent) and found that the oil consisted of the following:

	Per Cent		Per Cent
Asarone.............	82.0		
		α-Pinene and Camphene	0.2
Calamenol...........	5.0		
Calamene............	4.0		
Calameone...........	1.0	Palmitic Acid	
Methyleugenol.......	1.0	n-Heptylic Acid	No percentage given
Eugenol.............	0.3	Asaronaldehyde	
		Butyric Ester(?)	

More recently Sorm and Herout [31] investigated the chemical composition of an oil of *Acorus calamus* L. of German origin and arrived at results

[28] *Arch. Pharm.* **278** (1940), 1.
[29] *Chem. Ber.* **82** (1949), 532.
[30] *J. Indian Inst. Sci.* **17A** (1934), 25.
[31] *Collection Czech. Chem. Commun.* **13** (1948), 177. *Chem. Abstracts* **43** (1949), 3807. Cf. *Ind. parfum.* **3** (1948), 396.

partly confirming and supplementing, partly contradicting, the above-described findings of the earlier researchers. For this reason the work of Sorm and Herout will be reviewed here separately. They reported the presence of the following compounds in calamus oil:

Terpenes(?). The lower boiling fractions b_8 42°–70° of the oil, after separation of acidic and phenolic substances, contained terpenes which polymerized upon standing and were not further examined.

d-Camphor. Present in small quantities only.

An Aldehyde(?) $C_{10}H_{16}O$. A terpenic aldehyde $C_{10}H_{16}O$ was observed in the oil. It gave a semicarbazone m. 133° and appeared to be of the citral type. The aldehyde possesses a characteristic odor, and readily polymerizes.

Terpene Alcohols(?). A mixture of tertiary monocyclic alcohols $C_{18}H_{18}O$ (terpineol type), containing one double bond per molecule.
    The above-named substances were responsible for the characteristic odor of the oil.

Calamene. This sesquiterpene $C_{15}H_{24}$, d_{20} 0.9226, n_D^{20} 1.5040, consisted of a mixture of α-calamene (a bicyclic sesquiterpene with two double bonds) and β-calamene (a tricyclic sesquiterpene with one double bond).

Acoroxide. A compound $C_{15}H_{24}O$, which probably possesses two double bonds and a carbonylic oxygen, was named acoroxide by Sorm and Herout. It was easily hydrogenated to $C_{15}H_{28}O$, which contained no active hydrogen and did not form a semicarbazone.

Calamone. Sorm and Herout also isolated a ketone, calamone $C_{15}H_{26}O$, b_{44} 96°–99°, which yielded a semicarbazone m. 185°–187°.

Calameone. The presence of calameone $C_{15}H_{26}O_2$, m. 168°, in the oil was confirmed by Sorm and Herout.

Acorone and Isoacorone. The same workers also found that the oil contains two isomeric diketones $C_{15}H_{24}O_2$, viz., acorone m. 100°–101°, and isoacorone m. 96°–97°. In 1949 Sorm and Herout [32] reported that these two sesquiterpenic diketones occur in the oil in enolization equilibrium, and separated them chromatographically. Acorone yields a disemicarbazone m. 211° (decomp.). Chemical reactions and infrared spectra indicate that acorone possesses the **structural formula**

in which the 5-position is favored for the second carbonyl group.

[32] *Collection Czech. Chem. Commun.* **14** (1949), **723**. *Chem. Abstracts* **44** (1950), 9384.

Use.—In India and in the Far East the powdered rhizomes are esteemed as a vermifuge and insecticide.

Oil of calamus is used as an ingredient in flavors, particularly in liqueurs. The oil is employed also in perfumery. Because of its peculiar, warm, and somewhat spicy odor, it blends well into compositions of the heavier oriental type.

CHAPTER X

ESSENTIAL OILS OF THE PLANT FAMILY *PALMAE*

OIL OF COCONUT

The crude fatty oil expressed or extracted from the nuts of *Cocos nucifera* L. (fam. *Palmae*) contains a number of fatty acids and other compounds of unpleasant odor and flavor, which have to be removed in order to make the fatty oil palatable. For this purpose the fatty acids are usually first eliminated; the residual fatty oil is then treated with superheated steam. The volatile oil thus obtained has a peculiar, rather disagreeable odor; it contains a number of carbinols and ketones, aside from some fatty oil carried over with the superheated steam.

Haller and Lassieur,[1] and Schimmel & Co.[2] reported the presence of the following compounds in the volatile oil obtained by steam distillation of crude fatty coconut oil:

d-2-Nonanol (*d*-Methyl *n*-Heptylcarbinol). For details see Vol. II of this work, p. 154.

d-2-Hendecanol (*d*-Methyl *n*-Nonylcarbinol). Cf. Vol. II of this work, p. 156.

Methyl *n*-Amyl Ketone. Cf. Vol. II of this work, p. 375.

Methyl *n*-Heptyl Ketone. Cf. Vol. II of this work, p. 376.

Methyl *n*-Nonyl Ketone. Cf. Vol. II of this work, p. 377.

Methyl *n*-Undecyl Ketone. Cf .Vol. II of this work, p. 378.

An Unidentified Aldehyde.

The volatile oil of coconut is not used as such in the perfume or flavor industries, but for the isolation of the compounds listed above. These, in turn, are employed as components of synthetic (imitation) essential oils and as starting material for the preparation of various synthetic aromatics.

---

[1] *Compt. rend.* **150** (1910), 1013; **151** (1910), 697.
[2] *Ber. Schimmel & Co.* (1925), 43.

CHAPTER XI

ESSENTIAL OILS OF THE PLANT FAMILY *CYPERACEAE*

OIL OF *CYPERUS ROTUNDUS* L.

Cyperus rotundus L. (fam. *Cyperaceae*) is a grass which grows abundantly as a weed in moist areas of India, East and West Africa, Japan, and China. The air-dried tubers have a pleasant, violet-like odor, and are used in native perfumes, incense, and medicinal preparations.

On steam distillation the dried tubers yield from 0.5 to 1.0 per cent of volatile oil. Although this has not been produced commercially, it has been the subject of several investigations during the past twenty-five years.

Physicochemical Properties.—Oils distilled by Rao, Panicker and Sudborough,[1] in India, exhibited these properties:

Specific Gravity at 15.5°/15.5°. . . . . 0.9829 to 0.9907
Optical Rotation at 25°. . . . . +20° 6′ to +42° 48′
Refractive Index at 25°. . . . . 1.5126 to 1.5156
Acid Number. . . . . 2.1 to 3.4
Saponification Number. . . . . 11.7 to 16.1
Saponification Number after Acetylation. 66.5 to 98.1

Oils distilled by Hegde and Rao[2] from Madras and Mysore tubers had the following properties:

Specific Gravity at 30°/30°. . . . . 0.9847 to 1.0009
Specific Optical Rotation at 30°. . . . . −11° 48′ to +35° 30′
Refractive Index at 30°. . . . . 1.4980 to 1.5132
Acid Number. . . . . 1.1 to 11.3
Ester Number. . . . . 4.8 to 20.1
Ester Number after Acetylation. . . . . 63.3 to 100.8

Two oils distilled by Kimura and Ohtani[3] in Japan (where the tubers are called "Kobushi") had these properties:

	I	II
Specific Gravity	d_{15}^{15} 0.9871	d_{20}^{20} 0.9718
Specific Optical Rotation	$[\alpha]_D^{15}$ +74° 28′	$[\alpha]_D^{20}$ +84° 41′
Refractive Index	n_D^{16} 1.5036	n_D^{20} 1.5076
Acid Number	2.94	1.76
Saponification Number	16.55	10.62
Saponification Number after Acetylation	82.71	66.54

[1] *J. Ind. Inst. Sci.* **8A** (1925), 39.
[2] *J. Soc. Chem. Ind.* **54** (1935), 388T.
[3] *J. Pharm. Soc. Japan* **48** (1928), Abstracts (in German), 128. The Japanese term "Kobushi" also applies to *Magnolia kobus* DC.

Chemical Composition.—The following compounds have been identified in the volatile oil derived from the tubers of *Cyperus rotundus:*

l-α-Pinene. Small quantities only (Hegde and Rao).

Cineole. Traces only (Hegde and Rao).

Phenols (?). Small quantities; not identified (Kimura and Ohtani).

Cyperene. A tricyclic sesquiterpene $C_{15}H_{24}$, amounting to as much as 32 per cent of the oil (cf. Vol. II of this work, p. 749).

Cyperol. A tricyclic sesquiterpene alcohol $C_{15}H_{24}O$, amounting to as much as 49 per cent of the oil (cf. Vol. II of this work, p. 759).

α-Cyperone. A bicyclic sesquiterpene ketone $C_{15}H_{22}O$. The chief constituent, present to the amount of 33 to 54 per cent (cf. Vol. II of this work, p. 453).

Use.—According to the author's knowledge, oil of *Cyperus rotundus* is not produced on a commercial scale.

CHAPTER XII

ESSENTIAL OILS OF THE PLANT FAMILY *MORACEAE*

OIL OF HOPS

Essence de Houblon   *Aceite Esencial Lupulo*   *Hopfenöl*
Oleum Humuli Lupuli

Introduction.—Hops, also called "Humulus," "Lupulus," or "Fructus Lupuli," is the dried strobile (ovate membranous cone, somewhat conical catkins) of the female plants of *Humulus lupulus* L. (fam. *Moraceae*). The cones bear glandular trichomes at the base of each scale, surrounded by a pale yellow granular powder, called "Lupulin." The lupulin grains are plainly visible and can easily be shaken from the flowers, after the latter have reached maturity toward the end of July. At first transparent and yellow in color, the lupulin grains become opaque as the plant matures, until they resemble flower of sulfur. The quantity of lupulin produced in each hop cone amounts to one-tenth to one-sixth of the weight of the cone.

Lupulin contains resins and essential oil, imparting to beer, ale, stout, porter and other malt beverages their characteristic aroma and bitter flavor. Lupulin is the most important constituent of hops for the flavoring of beer.

The practice of using hops for the flavoring of malt beverages (malt alone produces insipid beverages) goes back to early times. In 768 A.D., King Pepin the Short donated hops gardens to the monastery of St. Denis; subsequently, many monasteries became famous for their brews. According to Smith,[1] hopped beer was in general favor in Germany by 1320–30 A.D. From Germany hop culture spread to the Netherlands, France, Sweden, and Bohemia. Today the leading hop-producing countries abroad are Germany (Bavaria), Czechoslovakia (Bohemia), France (Alsace and West Flanders), Belgium (East Flanders), Holland, and England, the best qualities of hops originating from Bavaria and Czechoslovakia. As regards North America, the growing of hops began in the New Netherlands as early as 1629, and in Virginia in 1648, but did not become important until about 1800. During the middle of the last century the industry shifted to the midwest, and finally to the Pacific Coast States. Today the world's largest producers of hops are northern California, Washington, and Oregon. The northern part of New York State also supplies substantial quantities of hops.

Botany, Planting, and Harvesting.—Hops are dioecious perennials, closely allied to hemp and nettles among the commonly known plants. New

---

[1] "Varietal Improvement in Hops," *U. S. Dept. Agr.,* Yearbook Separate No. 1598 (1937).

shoots are produced each year. The European type has been identified as *Humulus lupulus* L. (fam. *Moraceae*), but a native American type sometimes has been called *Humulus americanus* Nutt.[2] These two species include all commercial hop varieties.

According to Hoerner and Rabak,[3] hops are produced most successfully in regions with a mild climate, where abundant early rainfall is followed by warm dry weather as the crop approaches maturity. As regards soil, rich alluvial lands or deep sandy or gravelly loams are preferred.

In general, the cultivation of hops resembles that of pole beans. Hops are commonly propagated from "root" cuttings and not from seed, because seedlings show little uniformity in the type of hops produced and tend to vary greatly as to time of ripening. Also, seedlings require more than one season to give satisfactory yields. In the United States, the common practice is to plant the cuttings or sets in rows equidistant each way. As a rule, the hills are from 6½ to 7 ft. apart. Hops may be grown on either poles or trellises; they reach a height of 25 to 30 ft., coiling clockwise around the supports.

Hops are dioecious or unisexual; that is, the male and female flowers are borne on separate plants. In most countries abroad, male plants are not permitted to grow in a yard, but in this country it is a common practice to allow one male plant in a field to every hundred female plants. For beer-brewing only the cones of the female plants are desired; they develop without fertilization. However, the male plants serve to stimulate production of larger and heavier female plants, and in greater quantity. Fertilized hop plants develop seeds, which contribute to the weight of the cones, but are undesirable in beer-brewing. In lupulin content, hops of the seedless type do not differ materially from the seeded hops.

Hops should be picked when fully mature. Unripe or immature hops are deep green in color, soft and pliable, lacking in resiliency and elasticity. The lupulin in unripe hops is not fully developed and contains less resins and essential oil than that in ripe hops. Fully matured hops possess an agreeable aroma and a maximum content of desirable constituents, on which their brewing value depends. They are usually bright yellowish-green in color, sticky, crisp or papery to the touch, and noticeably resilient (Hoerner and Rabak). Hops are picked either by hand or by machine. In the former case, the harvesters have to be supervised strictly; being paid on a pound basis they have a tendency to include much undesirable material, such as leaves and stems, to which the brewing industry objects. Lately, very efficient stationary and movable hop-picking machines have been de-

---

[2] "Gray's Manual of Botany," 8th Ed. (1950).

[3] "Production of Hops," *U. S. Dept. Agr., Farmers' Bull.* No. 1842 (1940). Cf. *U. S. Dept. Agr., Tech. Bull.* No. 16 (1928), 32.

veloped, which greatly facilitate the harvest and produce clean hops. Leaves and stems contain undesirable extractive matter, which imparts an objectionable taste to the brewed beverages.

Freshly picked hops contain from 65 to 80 per cent of moisture, which must be reduced to about 12 per cent; otherwise heating will take place while the hops are being stored preparatory to baling. Such heating is likely to cause a brownish color, a change in the desirable resinous constituents, and especially an alteration of the aroma (essential oil), resulting in a sour or musty odor. In practice, the drying temperature must not be too high. In certain sections where the atmospheric temperature in summer is commonly above 100° F. the crop may be dried at the temperature of the natural air in 18 to 20 hr. by the use of forced draft. This can be done only in regions where the outside air is extremely dry. In more humid sections temperatures of 145° to 150° F. are frequently necessary and have been found satisfactory. If temperatures above 165° are required, the hops are apt to become dark and the lupulin deteriorates in quality.

After drying, the hops are moved to a cooling house or cooler, where they are piled in huge heaps, and allowed to stand for ten to fourteen days, to undergo a curing or sweating process. During this period the moisture content of the hops is equalized, and they become tough and pliable, acquiring a finer taste and better aroma. During the curing process the hops should be handled as little as possible to prevent undue breakage, which affects their appearance and results in loss of lupulin. After completion of the curing process the hops can be baled and shipped to the breweries. (For further details concerning the production of hops in the United States, see the above-cited bulletin by Hoerner and Rabak.)

As regards the cultivation of hops in Europe, the reader may be interested in some observations which the author made in Belgium:

Hops constitute one of the most important of Belgium crops. The plant, which has perennial roots, sometimes grows to a height of 8, 10, or 12 m., creeping and climbing about poles or along iron wires stretched between posts, as described below. Hops are propogated with slips cut from the underground parts. Planting is done in March or April, only female plants being employed (only these bear cones).

The plants may be grown:

1. On long poles. These poles are stripped of their bark (to avoid insect infestation) and treated with creosote. They are generally 8 to 12 m. tall, 8 or 10 cm. thick at the base, and placed upright in rows 2 m. apart—a distance which allows for the penetration of light and air to the plants. From 3 to 5 hop plants are trained to climb about each pole.

2. On galvanized iron wires. These are stretched between two poles placed 8 or 10 m. apart and rather sharply slanted, both to make the wire more taut and to withstand the pressure of the wind. The wires are strung out, like the strings of a harp, the interval between them being about 2 m. Along the length of the wire, wooden pegs are hammered into the ground, about 1.4 m. from each other. From these pegs, wires are stretched up (some 7 or 8 m.) to the overhead wire. It is up these wires that the hop plants are trained to twist and grow.

Hop plantations are generally established in the neighborhood of coppices (poplar groves, e.g.), which protect them from strong winds. Hops are expensive to plant and maintain, demanding constant care and a great deal of hand labor.

Harvesting requires dry and clear weather. Picking lasts from the beginning of September into October. If harvested from poles, the plant stalks are cut, about 1 to 1.2 m. from the ground, the pole is pulled up, maneuvered into a horizontal position, and the entwining hops are gathered. If harvested from wires, the supporting wire is cut, and the plants are carefully removed.

After the plants have been gathered, they are transported to barns or sheds. The planter's family then pluck the cones—a tedious and slow task, which keeps them busy all day. An expert man or woman may pick from 25 to 30 kg. in a day. The cones are put into baskets, which are then emptied into driers, heated with coke or a small amount of coal. About 5 kg. of green (fresh) hops are required per kilogram of dried commercial hops.

A plantation sometimes lasts twenty years; but it may be profitable to renew it after eight or ten years. It must at all times be well fertilized and cultivated.

Composition of Lupulin.—As was pointed out above, the most important constituent of dried hop cones is lupulin, a glandular yellow to brown substance containing an oleoresin which consists of resins and essential (volatile) oil. The resins impart to fermented beverages their characteristic bitter taste, while the essential oil is responsible for the characteristic aroma.

The resins are divided into two major groups, viz., the soft resins and the hard resin. The soft α- and β-resins contain two crystallizable bitter substances of acidic character, viz., α-lupulinic acid or humulone, and β-lupulinic acid or lupulone, respectively. Humulone has the empirical molecular formula $C_{21}H_{30}O_5$, lupulone the formula $C_{26}H_{38}O_4$. These acidic substances, also known as "Hop-bitters," are not carboxylic acids, but owe their acidic properties to enol formation. Their structural formulas have been elucidated by Wieland and his collaborators,[4] by Wöllmer,[5] Walker,[6] and more recently by Verzele and Govaert.[7] The quantities of humulone and lupulone occurring in hops vary considerably, ranging up to 10 per cent for the humulone, and being about 6 per cent for the lupulone. Both substances can be purified by crystallization from petroleum ether. Crystalline humulone melts at about 64°, and has an α acid content of approximately 95 to 98 per cent (determined by titration). White crystalline lupulone melts at 92°–93°. The soft resins are extracted during boiling of hops in the wort, and impart the desired bitter taste to beverages. Humulone and lupulone are highly bacteriostatic against gram-positive bacteria (Hansens[8]).

In 1950 Cook and Harris[9] isolated, from English hops, a new constituent of the petroleum ether-soluble hop resins, viz., humulinone $C_{21}H_{30}O_6$, a white crystalline substance m. 74°.

The hard resin, also called γ-resin, is an oxidation product, composed of hydroxy- and poly- derivatives of humulone, lupulone and certain constituents of the *essential oil*. According to Dyr,[10] the mixture represents different stages of chemical alteration, beginning with the α- and β-bitter acids, and ending with the final oxidation, polymerization or hydrolysis phase. The hard resin has no significant effect upon the taste and aroma of finished beverages.

Aside from the soft and hard resins, the lupulin also contains an essential oil which is responsible for the characteristic odor of the hop cones. On drying and aging of the hops, this oil is readily oxidized and polymerized. When stored over a prolonged period, dried hops lose much of their oil,[11] partly by evaporation of the lower boiling constituents, partly by polymerization of some components into hard resin (γ-resin, which is odorless and tasteless), and partly by degradation of certain high boiling constituents into compounds with a disagreeable odor reminiscent of isovaleric acid and rancid cheese. The latter compounds give a most unpleasant odor to beer. It is, therefore, imperative to use only freshly dried hops for the brewing

[4] *Ber.* **58** (1925), 102, 2012; **59** (1926), 2352. Cf. Windisch et al. *Wochschr. Brau.* **44** (1927), 453, 473, 485, 497; **46** (1929), 101, 111, 124. *Chem. Abstracts* **22** (1928), 2026; **23** (1929), 4011. Beyaert and Cornand, *Congr. intern. inds. fermentation, Confs. et communs.* (1947), 236.

[5] *Ber.* **49** (1916), 780; **58** (1925), 672.

[6] *J. Inst. Brew.* **30** (1924), 712.

[7] *Bull. soc. chim. Belg.* **58** (1949), 432. Cf. Carson, *J. Am. Chem. Soc.* **73** (1951), 4652.

[8] *Congr. intern. inds. fermentation, Confs. et communs.* (1947), 302. *Chem. Abstracts* **42** (1948), 7928.

[9] *J. Chem. Soc.* (1950), 1873.

[10] *Chem. Obzor* **20** (1945), 168. *Chem. Abstracts* **42** (1948), 7379.

[11] According to Salač [*Kvas* **64** (1936), 307. *Chem. Abstracts* **33** (1939), 7038], the loss amounts to about one-third of the amount originally present in the hops.

of malt beverages. The same may be said of the distillation of the essential oil from hops. In the brewing of the wort, most of the essential oil is lost by evaporation, with the result that finished beverages will have the desired bitter taste imparted by the soft resins, but very little of the aroma of the hops. To restore the lost aroma, essential oil distilled from freshly dried hops is occasionally added to the beverage, after brewing of the wort (see below).

Lupulin contains also a tannin, humulotannic acid, which is hydrolyzable into glucose and a substance known as "Hop-red."

Summarizing the chief value of hops in the brewing of malt beverages, it can be said that hops (principally the lupulin):

1. Imparts the desired bitter taste
2. Adds aroma, although most of the volatile oil is lost during brewing of the wort
3. Acts as preservative against certain microorganisms
4. Acts as a clarifying precipitation agent
5. Helps to retain foam.

Distillation, Yield, and Quality of Oil.—As can be readily seen from the foregoing, only freshly dried hops should be used for distillation purposes. It would be even better to employ nothing but freshly harvested, undried hops. This, however, is feasible only in the immediate areas of production. The older the dried hops, the lower is the yield and the poorer the quality of the oil. On prolonged storage of the hops the more volatile components of the essential oil are lost by evaporation, and a part of the oil is resinified to hard (γ-) resin. Simultaneously, the luparol, a phenolic ether present in the high boiling portions of the oil, gradually undergoes decomposition, with the formation of isovaleric acid and a phenol, among other products. The isovaleric acid imparts a most unpleasant "cheesy" odor to old hops, which is carried over into the distillate, on distillation of the hops. Oils derived from old hops usually exhibit an abnormally high acid number, an undesirable feature, since the free acids must be removed to make the oil acceptable to the trade.

Rabak[12] suggested using fresh lupulin (instead of fresh hops with the lupulin powder contained therein) for production of the oil. By doing so, Rabak obtained yields of oil slightly more than three times higher than he obtained from fresh whole hops. The oils from fresh Californian lupulin and from fresh Californian hops were very similar, but obviously differed considerably from the foreign oils, because the latter are always distilled

---

[12] *Am. Perfumer* **22** (1927), 6.

from dried hops. Fresh lupulin is now readily available during the hops harvest in the growing regions of the Pacific Coast as a result of the introduction of mechanical harvesters. It was mentioned above that during picking of the hops the lupulin powder detaches itself readily from the cones. If the hops are hand picked, as in Europe, some of the lupulin is lost on the ground; if harvesting machines are employed any lupulin falling off the bracts can easily be collected. Whether fresh lupulin or fresh hops cones (with the attached lupulin) should be used for distillation is a matter of opinion. In the author's experience, lupulin powder causes foaming and "baking" in the still, which may become annoying, whereas steam distillation of the cones offers no special problem.

The usual practice now is to submit freshly dried hops to distillation with direct steam. This produces a normal yield and quality of oil. If old hops are used, the quantity of direct oil is much smaller than with freshly dried hops, much of the oil being dissolved and suspended in the distillation water. The latter then has to be redistilled or extracted with volatile solvents; the indirect oil thus obtained will be a heavy dark liquid with a very high acid number (chiefly isovaleric acid) and a disagreeable odor. If the indirect oil is added to the direct oil, the total oil will also have an abnormally high acid number and specific gravity, and an unpleasant odor. Such oils must then be rectified (redistilled) or otherwise reconditioned to yield an acceptable quality. Up to 65 per cent of oil may be lost in the process of rectification.

Some producers use water distillation (cf. Vol. I of the present work, pp. 112, 120, 142) for the isolation of the essential oil from the hops and submit the distillation waters to automatic redistillation (cohobation) during the process. With freshly dried hops this method gives fairly good results, except for the fact that the long contact of boiling water with the immersed hops causes hydrolysis of some constituents of the essential oil. The products of hydrolysis, particularly the acids, pass into the distillation water and, on cohobation, into the oil. If old hops are used, the total crude oil will be of such poor quality (dark color, high specific gravity, very high acid number, "cheesy" odor, etc.) that rectification may become quite difficult.

In general, distillation of hops must be carried out carefully. If the rate (speed) of distillation is too high, particles of the resins will be carried mechanically into the distillate and impart a dark color and high acid number to the oil. On the other hand, if distillation is conducted too slowly, resinification and hydrolysis of the essential oil in the still will take place.

Yield and quality of hops oil depend not only upon the age of the hops or lupulin and the method of distillation, but also upon a number of other factors, among them geographical origin and climatic conditions. Freshly dried hops from Bavaria (Hallertau) and Bohemia (Saaz) give the best yield and quality of oil, but being in great demand for the brewing of high-grade beer, these types of hops are far too expensive for the distillation of oil. In general, therefore, European producers use Belgian and Alsatian hops for distillation purposes. Depending upon the age of the dried hops, the yield of oil varies from about 0.2 to 0.8 per cent, the average being 0.4 to 0.5 per cent. According to Rabak,[13] the essential oil occurs to the extent of 0.2 to 0.5 per cent in freshly dried hops, depending upon the variety, origin, method of drying, and conditions of age and storage. Distilling fresh Californian (undried) lupulin, fresh (undried) hops, and dried hops (two years in storage), Rabak [14] obtained 0.72, 0.23, and 0.12 per cent, respectively, of essential oil. Nebovidsky and Horel [15] reported yields of oil varying between 0.2 and 0.37 per cent from Czechoslovakian hops that had not been sulfured. (It should be mentioned, in this connection, that hops or lupulin are occasionally sulfured, but such material is useless for distillation.) These yields refer to rectified oils. Nebovidsky and Horel used old hops for their experiments; the crude oils separated so much resin that they had a deep rusty color and an acrid odor, and had to be rectified. Distilling dried hops from Belgium, France, and Germany—some of the lots were freshly dried, others several years old—the author of the present work obtained from 0.14 to 0.87 per cent of crude oils. Most of these contained much resinous matter, and a substantial amount of free acids; their color was so dark, their odor so acrid, that they had to be rectified. Rectification yielded from 34 to 64 per cent of normal oils. Determining the essential oil content of freshly dried California, Oregon, and Washington hops in a Clevenger apparatus, the laboratories of Fritzsche Brothers, Inc., New York, obtained yields of 0.7, 0.6, and 0.6 per cent, respectively, of oil.

Physicochemical Properties.—Like its odor, the physicochemical properties of a hops oil depend chiefly upon the age of the hops (or lupulin) from which the oil is distilled, the method of distillation, and the age of the oil itself. In many cases the crude oils must be rectified to produce oils of normal odor and properties. An oil distilled from freshly dried hops is usually a thin liquid of light color, with a pleasant characteristic hops aroma. With the passage of time the color darkens to red-brown, the oil becomes viscous, the specific gravity increases, the solubility in alcohol decreases, and the aroma takes on a "cheesy" character, reminiscent of isovaleric and butyric acids; oils distilled from old hops exhibit similar qualities. These changes are caused by polymerization of the myrcene,

---

[13] *Wallerstein Laboratories Communications* **7** (1944), 173.
[14] *Am. Perfumer* **22** (March 1927), 6.
[15] *Chimie & industrie* **29** (1933), Special Number, 1208. Cf. *Perfumery Essential Oil Record* **25** (1934), 14.

one of the principal constituents of the oil, and by decomposition of the luparol, a phenolic ether, into a phenol and isovaleric acid.

Gildemeister and Hoffmann [16] reported these properties for oil of hops:

Specific Gravity at 15°..........	0.855 to 0.899
Optical Rotation................	$-1° 0'$ to $+2° 27'$
Refractive Index at 20°..........	1.4852 to 1.4936
Acid Number...................	0.5 to 10.0
Ester Number..................	13 to 40
Ester Number after Acetylation...	18 to 46
Solubility.....................	Very difficultly soluble in alcohol. Older oils are not clearly soluble even in 95% alcohol (the result, probably, of polymerization of myrcene)

Louveau [17] steam-distilled hops of different geographical origins; he examined the oils which separated directly from the distillate, and the water-soluble oils, the latter recovered by extraction of the aqueous portion with petroleum ether and removal of the solvent. Oil (I) was distilled from Bavarian hops, oil (II) from Bohemian hops, oil (III) from Burgundian hops. The letters (a) refer to the direct oils, the letters (b) to the indirect or water-soluble oils.

	Ia	Ib	IIa	IIb	IIIa	IIIb
Yield of Oil............	0.30%	0.07%	0.28%	0.06%	0.35%	0.04%
Specific Gravity at 15°..	0.8617	0.9101	0.8673	0.9265	0.8715	0.9208
Optical Rotation........	$+0° 18'$	...	$-0° 4'$	...	$-0° 10'$	...
Refractive Index........	1.4850	1.4910	1.4852	1.4922	1.4883	1.4968
Acid Number..........	9.1	25.6	11.5	33.8	8.5	34.3
Ester Number..........	21.0	45.5	24.5	58.1	20.3	32.2

Distilling unsulfured Czechoslovakian hops, Nebovidsky and Horel [18] obtained oils (yield 0.2 to 0.37 per cent), some of which had an agreeable, some a disagreeable, odor, and properties varying within these limits:

Specific Gravity at 20°......	0.831 to 0.861
Refractive Index at 20°.....	1.4740 to 1.4912
Acid Number..............	1.5 to 8.2
Ester Number.............	23.1 to 39.1

Steam-distilling two lots of Alsatian hops that had been harvested and dried several months previously, the author obtained 0.87 and 0.74 per cent of two crude oils which had the following properties, respectively:

[16] "Die Ätherischen Öle," 3d Ed., Vol. II, 495.
[17] *Rev. marques parfum. savon.* **10** (1932), 420, 456.
[18] *Chimie & industrie* **29** (1933), Special Number, 1208. Cf. *Perfumery Essential Oil Record* **25** (1934), 14.

Specific Gravity at 15°...... 0.906 and 0.934
Refractive Index at 20°..... 1.4948 and 1.5018
Acid Number.............. 27.6 and 37.3
Ester Number............. 19.6 and 21.9
Solubility................. Soluble in 0.5 vol. of 95% alcohol; turbid with
more alcohol

Rectification of the two crude oils yielded 63.2 and 55.5 per cent, respectively, of two rectified oils, possessing these properties:

Specific Gravity at 15°...... 0.896 and 0.912
Refractive Index at 20°..... 1.4928 and 1.4971
Acid Number.............. 6.1 and 6.4
Ester Number............. 34.7 and 12.5
Solubility................. Soluble in 0.5 vol. of 95% alcohol; opalescent
with more alcohol

Genuine hop oils of various origin examined in the laboratories of Fritzsche Brothers, Inc., New York, had properties varying within the following limits:

Specific Gravity at 15°/15°.. 0.829 to 0.895, occasionally as high as 0.914
Optical Rotation........... −1° 23' to +2° 12'
Refractive Index at 20°..... 1.4691 to 1.4908, occasionally as high as 1.4939
Acid Number.............. Up to 7.0
Ester Number............. 14.9 to 61.5
Solubility................. Usually turbid in 10 vol. of 95% alcohol

Rabak [19] described three hops oils distilled from fresh Californian lupulin (I), from fresh California hops (II), and from dry Californian hops that had been in storage for two years (III):

	I	II	III
Specific Gravity at 20°........	0.8312	0.8265	0.8737
Optical Rotation.............	−0° 44'	−0° 44'	...
Refractive Index at 20°.......	1.4735	1.4720	1.4733
Acid Number................	0.91	1.06	7.3
Ester Number..............	41.3	41.4	78.0

The odor of the oils was pleasant, strongly aromatic, and characteristic of hops.

Chemical Composition.—The first investigation of the chemical composition of hop oil dates back to 1822, but none of the work carried out in the course of sixty years by Payen and Chevallier,[20] Wagner,[21] Personne,[22] Kühnemann,[23] and Ossipoff [24] gave any tangible results. It was only during the last part of the nineteenth century that the first important findings

[19] *Am. Perfumer* **22** (March 1927), 6.
[20] *J. Pharm.* **8** (1822), 214, 538.
[21] *J. prakt. Chem.* **58** (1853), 351.
[22] *Compt. rend.* **38** (1854), 309.
[23] *Ber.* **10** (1877), 2231.
[24] *J. prakt. Chem.* [2], **28** (1883), 447.

were reported by Chapman.[25] Since then the oil has been investigated quite thoroughly by Semmler and Mayer,[26] Deussen,[27] Rabak,[28] Chapman,[29] and more recently by Sorm and his collaborators.[30]

The presence of the following compounds has been reported in the oil:

Formaldehyde. Characterized by color reaction in the saponified oil (Rabak).

Dipentene. Reported by Chapman [31] in the lowest boiling fraction of the oil.

β-Myrcene. In the same fraction Chapman noted the presence of a low boiling olefinic terpene which, on hydration, yielded an ester with an odor reminiscent of lavender oil. Later, Semmler and Mayer identified this terpene as β-myrcene (cf. Vol. II of the present work, p. 8). Myrcene is one of the most important constituents of the oil, causing part polymerization of the oil on aging.

Linaloöl and Linalyl Isononylate. Noted by Chapman [32] in the middle fractions of the oil. The linaloöl occurs in these fractions partly free, partly as ester, probably with isononylic acid.

Geraniol. Also reported by Chapman as a constituent of the oil.

Myrcenol. According to Rabak, this olefinic terpene alcohol occurs in the oil partly free, partly esterified with enanthic, caprylic, and pelargonic acids.

Methyl Nonyl Ketone. Years ago Chapman [33] isolated from the fraction b_4 87°–97° of hops oil a ketone b_3 74°–76° of agreeable odor. He assigned the empirical molecular formula $C_{13}H_{22}O_2$ to this ketone and named it "Luparone." Separating the pure compound chromatographically, Sorm, Mleziva and Arnold [34] recently proved that the "Luparone" of Chapman in reality is methyl nonyl ketone.

Luparol. A new phenolic ether $C_{16}H_{26}O_2$, b_2 122°–124°, optically inactive, with a weak but pleasant odor. Its constitution has not yet been elucidated (cf. Vol. II of the present work, p. 766. Note, however, that luparol is a phenol ether, not a phenol, as stated erroneously in Vol. II). On decomposition, luparol yields a phenol, among other products, and isovaleric acid. The latter causes the disagreeable, "cheesy" odor of old hops and old hop oils.

Luparenol. An unsaturated sesquiterpene alcohol $C_{15}H_{24}O$, b_3 125°–128°, containing one double bond. The constitution of luparenol is still unknown (cf. Vol. II, p. 762).

Humulene. Years ago Deussen [35] suggested that this sesquiterpene $C_{15}H_{24}$ is closely related to α-caryophyllene. This has recently been confirmed beyond doubt by

[25] *J. Chem. Soc.* **64** (1895), 54, 780.
[26] *Ber.* **44** (1911), 2009.
[27] *J. prakt. Chem.* [2], **83** (1911), 483. *Liebigs Ann.* **388** (1912), 149.
[28] *J. Agr. Research, U. S. Dept. Agr., Washington* 2 (1914), 115.
[29] *J. Chem. Soc.* **83** (1903), 505; (1928), 1303. Cf. *J. Inst. Brew.* **35** (1929), 247.
[30] *Collection Czech. Chem. Commun.* **14** (1949), 693, 699, 716, 723.
[31] *J. Chem. Soc.* **83** (1903), 505.
[32] *Ibid.* Cf. *J. Inst. Brew.* **35** (1929), 247.
[33] *J. Chem. Soc.* **67** (1895), 54; (1928), 1303.
[34] *Collection Czech. Chem. Commun.* **14** (1949), 693.
[35] *J. prakt. Chem.* [2], **83** (1911), 483; [2], **120** (1928), 133.

Sorm and his collaborators [36] who showed that humulene contains three ethylenic linkages and is, therefore, monocyclic. Hydrogenation gave the saturated hexahydrohumulene $C_{15}H_{30}$, b_{13} 120°–122°, d_4^{20} 0.8637, n_D^{20} 1.4723, whereas treatment with perbenzoic acid yielded humulene trioxide $C_{15}H_{24}O$, m. 122.5°. Ozonolysis of humulene furnished α,α-dimethylsuccinic acid, which had been obtained earlier by Chapman [37] when he submitted humulene to oxidation with chromic acid.

Comparing the infrared spectrum of α-caryophyllene (from clove oil) and that of its hexahydro derivative with those of humulene (from hops oil) and of its hexahydro derivative, respectively, Herout, Streible, Mleziva and Sorm [38] found them to be identical. Therefore, they proposed that the name caryophyllene, which indicates bicyclic hydrocarbons, in the case of the α-isomer be replaced by the term "humulene" which is monocyclic.

Other sesquiterpenes, $C_{15}H_{24}$. Aside from humulene, Sorm and his co-workers [39] noted the presence, in the volatile hops oil, of natural *farnesene*, an acyclic sesquiterpene with four double bonds, two of which are conjugated (2,6-dimethyl-10-methylene-2,6,11-dodecatriene), and a β-caryophyllene type which is bicyclic and contains one double bond.

Acids, Free and Esterified. Among the acids present in the oil, free and as esters, Rabak identified free formic, valeric and enanthic acids; and esterified formic, acetic, butyric, caprylic, pelargonic, and capric acids.

According to Rabak,[40] oil of hops has the following quantitative composition:

> Myrcene.............. 30 to 50%
> Humulene............. 15 to 25%
> Esters of Myrcenol...... 20 to 40%

The high ester content reported by Rabak, however, is not quite in accord with the ester numbers usually observed in hop oils. Nebovidsky and Horel [41] reported the composition of Czechoslovakian hop oils as:

> Myrcene.............. 30 to 50%
> Sesquiterpenes.......... 15 to 25%

the balance being made up of the other compounds described above.

[36] *Collection Czech. Chem. Commun.* **14** (1949), 693, 699, 716.

[37] *J. Chem. Soc.* **83** (1903), 513.

[38] *Collection Czech. Chem. Commun.* **14** (1949), 716. In 1950 Wolfrom and Mishkin [*J. Am. Chem. Soc.* **72** (1950), 5350] proposed a structural formula for humulene (α-caryophyllene), which, however, was shortly afterwards challenged by Clemo and Harris [*Chemistry Industry* (1951), 50. *J. Chem. Soc.* (1951), 22]. At the time of the printing of the present volume, a lively controversy regarding the configurations of humulene and β-caryophyllene is going on among several groups of researchers, and various structural formulas have been tentatively advanced. For details, see *Perfumery Essential Oil Record* **42** (1951), 326; *Chem. Abstr.* **45** (1951), 8482, 9485.

[39] *Collection Czech. Chem. Commun.* **14** (1949), 699.

[40] *J. Agr. Research, U. S. Dept. Agr., Washington* **2** (1914), 115.

[41] *Chimie & industrie* **29** (1933), Special Number, 1208. Cf. *Perfumery Essential Oil Record* **25** (1934), 14.

Louveau,[42] who investigated an oil distilled from Bavarian hops, arrived at still other conclusions:

Myrcene................ About 22%
Sesquiterpenes.......... About 56%

the balance consisting of the other constituents of the oil.

According to Sorm, Mleziva and Arnold,[43] the essential oil of Bohemian hops contains chiefly myrcene, pelargonic esters, $MeCOC_9H_{19}$, a crystalline triterpene $C_{30}H_{50}$, m. 34°, and another triterpene m. 60°, α $+17°$ 0′.

Use.—Very small quantities of hop oil are employed in the flavoring of certain liqueurs, and in some perfume compositions, to which the oil imparts tonalities most difficult to identify. However, the proper application and dosage of the oil require great experience and skill, in order to achieve the desired results.

The principal use of hop oil is in the flavoring of malt beverages, particularly beer. In the foregoing it has been mentioned that during the long-continued boiling of the wort, most of the essential oil contained in the hops evaporates, or is altered and lost. Lüers [44] reported that two batches of beer brewed from the same type of malt, but from two different qualities of hops, exhibited a marked difference in taste (due to the "hop bitters"), but no difference in odor. To restore the lost hop aroma, some brewers add oil of hops to the cooled beverage, after brewing. They claim that a true hop-flavored beverage is one that has not only the bitter taste of the hops, but the aroma as well. However, brewers are not in accord as to the proper and most effective procedure for combining and retaining the aroma in the beverages. Czechoslovakian experts, for instance, claim that owing to its insolubility, addition of oil of hops to the finished beer gradually causes haziness in the beverage, which should be of sparkling clarity. Various methods for overcoming this difficulty have been devised, the most recent one being that of Rabak.[45] He recommended shaking 1 volume of oil in 5 volumes of 95 per cent ethyl alcohol; the clear supernatant solution will contain about 85 per cent of the oil. This alcoholic essence contains only the more soluble and aromatic alcohols and esters of the oil. Addition of 3 to 5 oz. of the essence to 100 barrels of beverage imparts a pronounced hop aroma to the beer.

[42] *Rev. marques parfum. savon.* **10** (1932), 420, 456.
[43] *Collection Czech. Chem. Commun.* **14** (1949), 693.
[44] *Wochschr. Brau.* **44** (1927), 588.
[45] *Wallerstein Laboratories Communications* **7** (1944), 173.

SUGGESTED ADDITIONAL LITERATURE

Albert Couvreur, "Essence de Houblon," *Ind. parfum.* **1** (1946), 274.

T. W. Campbell and G. M. Coppinger, "The Synthesis and Absorption Spectra of some Analogs of Humulone," *J. Am. Chem. Soc.* **73** (1951), 1849.

J. F. Carson, "The Hydrogenation of Lupulone and Humulone," *J. Am. Chem. Soc.* **73** (1951), 1850.

CHAPTER XIII

ESSENTIAL OILS OF THE PLANT FAMILY *ARISTOLOCHIACEAE*

(*Top Left*) Production of orris root in the Apennine Mountains, near Florence, Italy. Hoeing in an orris field. (*Top Right*) Orris root, Italy. Peeling of the orris root in the villages near the fields. *Photos Fritzsche Brothers, Inc., New York.* (*Bottom*) Storage of peeled and dried orris root in a warehouse in Florence, Italy. *Photo A. Piazzesi, Florence, Italy.*

(*Top Left*) *Valeriana officinalis. Photo Missouri Botanical Garden, St. Louis, Mo.* (*Top Right*) Gathering of Easter lilies (*Lilium candidum*) near Seillans (Var), France. *Photo Fritzsche Brothers, Inc., New York.* (*Bottom Left*) Calamus plants (*Acorus calamus*) growing wild on the bank of a river near Feketeviz (Pozsony County), Hungary. *Photo Dr. Jules de Bittera, Budapest, Hungary.* (*Bottom Right*) A hops plantation in Bavaria, Germany. *Photo Fritzsche Brothers, Inc., New York.*

OIL OF CANADIAN SNAKEROOT
(*Asarum canadense* L.)

Essence de Serpentaire du Canada   *Canadisches Schlangenwurzelöl*
Aceite Esencial Serpentaria   *Oleum Asari Canadensis*

Asarum canadense L. (fam. *Aristolochiaceae*), a native of North America, is a low perennial herb growing wild in partly shaded, moist, and loamy sections of our woodlands. The plant has a horizontal rhizome, from 5 to 17 cm. long, and 2 to 4 mm. thick, with several fibrous rootlets, about 7 cm. long and 1 mm. thick. The rhizomes and rootlets contain an essential oil of pungent flavor and somewhat spicy odor which can be isolated by steam distillation of the dried root material.

The root, commonly called "Canadian snakeroot"[1] or "wild ginger," is gathered in the spring and early summer by herb collectors in Virginia, North Carolina, Kentucky, and Tennessee. After removal of the fibrous rootlets, the rhizomes are dried and sold to the drug trade.

Prior to distillation, the rhizomes have to be triturated. Distillation with live steam requires about 24 hr. The distillation waters should be cohobated. The yield of oil averages 3 per cent.

Physicochemical Properties.—Oil of Canadian snakeroot is a yellow to yellowish-brown liquid with a strong, pleasant, and spicy odor and flavor, somewhat reminiscent of ginger.

Oils produced by Fritzsche Brothers, Inc., New York, had properties varying within these limits:

Specific Gravity at 15°/15°....... 0.947 to 0.998
Optical Rotation................ Inactive to −11° 20′
Refractive Index at 20°.......... 1.4843 to 1.5015, occasionally as high as 1.5082
Acid Number................... 1.9 to 7.5
Saponification Number.......... 68.1 to 116.7, occasionally as low as 47.5
Ester Number after Acetylation... 92. 4 to 144.2
Solubility..................... Soluble in 1.5 to 2.5 vol. of 70% alcohol and more

---

[1] Not to be confused with *Aristolochia serpentaria* L. ("Virginia snakeroot") or *A. reticulata* Nutt. ("Texas snakeroot"), which along with *Asarum canadense* L., belong to the family *Aristolochiaceae*.

Chemical Composition.—The chemical composition of the volatile oil derived from *Asarum canadense* L. was investigated by Power,[2] and by Power and Lees [3] who reported the presence of the following compounds:

α-Pinene. Identified by means of the nitrolpiperidine m. 118°–119°. The terpene occurs in the oil probably as *d*- and *l*-α-pinene.

d-Linaloöl. Characterized by oxidation to citral and preparation of the naphtho-cinchoninic acid compound m. 195°–198°.

l-Borneol. Oxidation to camphor, the latter identified as oxime m. 115°–116°.

l-α-Terpineol. Characterized by means of dipentene dihydroiodide m. 80°; also by oxidation to the ketolactone $C_{10}H_{16}O_3$, m. 62°.

Geraniol. Identified by preparation of the diphenylurethane m. 81°–82°.

Eugenol. Power and Lees first noted the presence of a phenol $C_9H_{12}O_2$. Later Kleber [4] reported that he identified eugenol by means of its benzoate.

Methyleugenol. Characterized by oxidation to veratric acid, and by preparation of the bromoeugenol methyl ether dibromide m. 78°–79°.

A Lactone(?). Power and Lees observed in the oil a lactone of the empirical molecular formula $C_{14}H_{20}O_2$.

Azulene(?). The same authors noted the presence of a blue oil (perhaps an azulene) of unknown composition. It contained oxygen and exhibited the characteristics of an alcohol.

Fatty Acids. Power and Lees also observed *acetic acid, palmitic acid* and other fatty acids in the oil.

The *quantitative* composition of the oil is approximately as follows:

α-Pinene	2%
Esters, calculated as $C_{10}H_{17}\cdot COOCH_3$	27.5%
Free Alcohols, calculated as $C_{10}H_{18}O$	13.3%
Total Alcohols, calculated as $C_{10}H_{18}O$	34.9%
Phenol Ethers, Calculated as Methyleugenol (Zeisel's Method)	36.9%
High Boiling Constituents, including Azulene, etc.	About 20%

Use.—Oil of Canadian snakeroot is used chiefly in flavors, to which it imparts warm and spicy notes. In medicinal preparations, tonic mixtures

[2] *Proc. Am. Pharm. Assocn.* **28** (1880), 464. *Pharm. Rundsch.*, New York, **6** (1888), 101.
[3] *J. Chem. Soc.* **81** (1902), 59.
[4] Private communication of the late Dr. C. Kleber, Clifton, N. J. Gildemeister and Hoffmann, "Die Ätherischen Öle," 3d Ed., Vol. II, 530.

and infusions, it is employed as a feeble aromatic. Oil of Canadian snake-root blends well with orris; hence its use in certain perfume compositions.

SUGGESTED ADDITIONAL LITERATURE

Chester J. Cavallito and John H. Bailey (Winthrop Chemical Co., Inc., Rensselaer, N. Y.), "Antibacterial Substances from *Asarum canadense.* Isolation, Physical Properties, and Antibacterial Action," *J. Am. Chem. Soc.* **68** (1946), 489.

OIL OF *ASARUM EUROPAEUM* L.

Asarum europaeum L. (fam. *Aristolochiaceae*) is a perennial herb growing wild in the shade of deciduous forests from Europe to Siberia. The plant requires a rich and humid soil. In Hungary the roots are collected and sold to the drug trade. On steam distillation the dried roots yield about 1 per cent of a viscous brownish oil with a strong aromatic odor and a burning pepper-like flavor. The oil is heavier than water (specific gravity 1.018 to 1.068); on standing it occasionally deposits crystals of asarone.

Little is known about the physicochemical properties of the oil.

As regards its chemical composition, the presence of the following compounds in Hungarian oils has been reported by Gerö,[1] and by Bruckner and Széki: [2]

A Terpene(?) (1–2%). According to Bruckner and Széki, the oil contains from 1 to 2 per cent of a terpene $C_{10}H_{16}$, b_{23} 62.5°. A few years earlier Gerö had observed *terpinene* in the oil.

l-Bornyl Acetate (12–15%). Bruckner and Széki found that the Hungarian oil of *Asarum europaeum* differs from the German oil by the presence of *l*-bornyl acetate in the former.

A Sesquiterpene(?) (10–12%). The Hungarian oil also contains a probably tricyclic sesquiterpene $C_{15}H_{24}$, b_3 78°, d_{15} 0.940 (Bruckner and Széki).

Methyleugenol (15–20%). Characterized by oxidation to veratric acid (Bruckner and Széki).

Asarone (30–35%). The chief constituent, m. 63°. The presence of this phenolic ether in the oil was first reported by Schmidt,[3] (who named it asarone), and later confirmed by Gerö, and by Bruckner and Széki (cf. Vol. II of this work, p. 535).

[1] *Riechstoff Ind.* **3** (1928), 176, 195, 214. [3] *Liebigs Ann.* **53** (1845), 156.
[2] *J. prakt. Chem.* [2], **134** (1932), 107.

Diasarone. Observed in the Hungarian oil by Gerö (cf. Vol. II of this work, p. 537).

Asaronaldehyde (2–3%). First found in the oil by Gerö, later confirmed by Bruckner and Széki (cf. Vol. II of this work, p. 366).

Resinified Substances (10–12%). Reported by Bruckner and Széki.

In the Hungarian oil which he investigated, Gerö also noted the presence of an *ether-like compound* $C_{11}H_{18}O$, b_{20-22} 155°–163°, as well as a *sesquiterpene* and a *sesquiterpene alcohol*.

The oil derived from the roots of *Asarum europaeum* L. is not produced on a commercial scale. According to Orient,[4] the oil is poisonous, causing hyperaemia of all organs, and inflammation of the kidneys and the uterus.

[4] *Pharm. Monatsh.* **11** (1930), 173.

CHAPTER XIV

ESSENTIAL OILS OF THE PLANT FAMILY *CHENOPODIACEAE*

OIL OF CHENOPODIUM
(Oil of American Wormseed)

Essence de Semen-contra d'Amerique or *Essence d'Ansérine Vermifuge*
Amerikanisches Wurmsamenöl
Aceite Esencial Chenopodium (Quenopodio)
Oleum Chenopodii Anthelmintici

Oil of chenopodium is the volatile oil derived by steam distillation from the overground parts of the flowering and fruiting plant, *Chenopodium ambrosioides* L. var. *anthelminticum* (L.) A. Gray (fam. *Chenopodiaceae*). High-grade oils contain not less than 75 per cent, by weight, of ascaridole. The anthelmintic properties of the oil are due to this terpenic oxide.

Botany and Areas of Production.—*Chenopodium ambrosioides* L. var. *anthelminticum* (L.) A. Gray, a coarse weed, grows wild in the eastern and southern parts of the United States. In certain areas (notably Maryland) it is cultivated. The plant owes its powerful, offensive odor to the volatile oil present in the glandular hairs of the seeds (fruit), stems, and leaves. The stalks contain very little oil.

Chenopodium oil has been in use since the American Civil War. Methods of production were originally quite primitive: the plants were boiled in iron pots equipped with soapstone lids. The oil condensed against these lids, and dripping back, was skimmed off. It was sold mainly in Baltimore —whence the old name "Baltimore Oil."

Maryland remains the chief producer of chenopodium oil, the area of production being concentrated largely in a roughly circular area of a twenty-mile radius in Carroll, Frederick, Howard, and Montgomery counties, with Woodbine as the center of distillation. The plant is also cultivated elsewhere in the United States, but to no great extent. Attempts have been made to raise it in Brazil.

There appear to be two types of *Chenopodium ambrosioides* L. var. *anthelminticum,* one designated "A," the other "B." The latter is the smaller plant, and has a reddish stem; the buds and flowers are more wide than long, and the seeds average 1 mm. or more in width. According to Weiland, Broughton and Metzger,[1] of the two types, "B" contains the heavier percentage of ascaridole (the active principle of the essential oil)

[1] "Wormseed Oil Production," *Agr. Expt. Sta., Univ. Maryland Bull.* No. 384 (1935).

and yields the higher percentage of oil per unit weight of plant distilled. It also matures earlier.

Cultivation.—The plant grows well in almost any kind of soil, but a good sandy loam is to be preferred. Most of the plantings in Maryland are located on loam or gravelly loam soils, generally high in potassium, and comparatively loose and easily worked. The country there is fairly hilly, well drained, with occasional patches of flat land or steep slopes.

Seedbeds are usually laid on new land or along fence rows which have lain fallow for some years. They are prepared as for corn or tomatoes. Brush should be burnt over the ground to exterminate weeds, and the ground, after manuring, plowed to a loose, mellow bed. Planting is done in February, with stock consisting of shattered seed collected during the previous harvest. Two tablespoonfuls of seed suffice for about a hundred square feet. It appears quite probable that careful seed selection might result in strains yielding a higher percentage of oil.

In June the young plants, 6 to 8 in. high, can be transplanted. They are removed from the plant bed and set out, 14 to 15 in. apart, in rows 3 ft. apart. Stockberger [2] recommends transplanting between May 15 and June 15, when the seedlings are 4 to 5 in. tall, with spacing of 10 in. between rows. Most growers employ transplanters.

Fields must be kept free of weeds by shallow cultivation throughout the growing season; this necessitates a good deal of hand labor. Wormseed is quite a soil-exhausting plant, and cereal planted in the fall, after the wormseed harvest, will usually yield an inferior crop.

Experiments with fertilizers have been carried on by Weiland, Broughton and Metzger.[3] Their tests included a nitrogen, phosphorous, and potash series, and a rate of application series. Greatest increase in ascaridole (about 20 per cent) was obtained as a result of using a high proportion of potash. A well-balanced phosphorous-nitrogen ratio appears to assure proper maturation of the plant—an important feature, since delayed maturation tends to lower the ascaridole content of the oil. Weiland, Broughton and Metzger found that the proportions of nitrogen, phosphorous, and potash should be 3:12:6 or 2:9:5, if wormseed is to be cultivated on manor or chester soils, but appreciably higher in potash if the crop is to be grown on other types of soil. Rate of application should be from 300 to 500 lb. per acre, depending upon fertility of the soil and amount of stable manure employed.

Harvesting.—Hogstad [4] observed that the plant develops its highest oil content during the pollination period. The oil at this time, however, is very

[2] "Drug Plants Under Cultivation," *U. S. Dept. Agr., Farmers' Bull.* No. 663 (1935).
[3] "Wormseed Oil Production," *Agr. Expt. Sta., Univ. Maryland Bull.* No. 384 (1935).
[4] *Am. J. Pharm.* **96** (1924), 809.

low in ascaridole, and consists largely of *p*-cymene. Hogstad found that the oil from flowering herb contains from 6 to 10 per cent of ascaridole, whereas that from herb with partly ripe seed contains from 6 to 20 per cent, and that from fully ripened seed 50 to 56 per cent, with very little *p*-cymene. Solubility of the oil in 70 per cent alcohol improves as the content of ascaridole increases. Thus, the riper the seed, the higher the ascaridole content, and the better the solubility of the oil.

Weiland, Broughton and Metzger [5] carried the work of Hogstad further and noted that a substantial portion of the ascaridole forms at the end of the flowering period. The highest content of ascaridole is to be found in plants matured to the point where most of the seeds have turned black. Plants allowed to stand until they have turned brown and have lost some of their leaves are likely to exhibit a diminished content of ascaridole. If too ripe, much seed may be lost by shattering. The exact moment for harvesting is thus a delicate problem: distillers advise allowing the plants to stand until the seed has matured. But the growers, fearing loss of seed by shattering and aware that the oil content of the plant decreases when the crop has passed the stage of maturity, prefer to harvest much earlier.

Practically all of the crop is harvested by hand, the wooden stalks being cut with small axes, sharp hoes, or straight-blade corn knives; only a few of the larger growers use mowing machines or converted grain binders. Cutting the branches separately eliminates the handling of bulky and useless woody stalks; a smaller still will then suffice for processing such material.

After being cut, the plants are left in the fields to dry. This requires from a few days to a week, depending upon the weather. Loss of weight of the plant by drying amounts to approximately 50 per cent.

One acre of chenopodium produces about six tons of fresh, or three tons of dried, plant material. Weiland, Broughton and Metzger [6] showed that drying of the cut plants results in a marked increase in ascaridole content, not entirely attributable to loss of low-boiling constituents through evaporation. These investigators concluded that ascaridole is synthesized from *p*-cymene not only during plant growth (as had been previously suggested by Hogstad), but also during the drying process—possibly by enzyme action.

When fully dried, the plant material is hauled to the distilleries, of which there are about eighteen in Maryland, some rather primitive, some quite up-to-date. The largest and most modern distillery is located in Woodbine. Not all of the distilleries operate during the harvesting period, since the larger ones can generally handle the entire crop. Many of the growers do

[5] "Wormseed Oil Production," *Agr. Expt. Sta., Univ. Maryland Bull.* No. 384 (1935).
[6] *Ibid.*

not have their own stills, but pay to still owners a fixed rate, per pound of oil distilled, for the privilege of using their equipment. When distillation is completed, the growers either sell their oil to the still owners or carry it home, with the hope of disposing of it later at a better price.

Distillation.—Production of a high-grade chenopodium oil depends upon several factors:

1. Rainfall. Rain in early summer, followed by dry and sunny weather during maturation, seed formation and particularly harvesting of the plant, generally causes a high yield of oil with a high ascaridole content. On the other hand, rain during seed formation, and particularly during harvesting, will result in a low yield of oil, of inferior quality.

2. Maturity of the plant when cut. The riper the seed, the higher the yield and quality of oil.

3. Method of distillation. Fifty or sixty years ago, chenopodium stills were somewhat primitive and equipped with such poor condensers that the distillate flowed comparatively warm. The oils, however, were of good quality, and clearly soluble in 70 per cent alcohol. Then, suddenly, inferior oils, with a low specific gravity, and soluble only in 80 per cent alcohol, appeared on the market. Even most thorough analysis of these oils could detect no adulteration, and for some time no satisfactory explanation for the inferiority of the new oils could be advanced. Schimmel & Co.[7] then carried out distillation experiments in their own plant and observed the rather startling fact that too-efficient cooling of the condensate produced oils of poor solubility and of low specific gravity. It was then surmised that the distillers in Maryland might have installed more modern equipment, with a view to obtaining higher oil yields through more thorough cooling of the distillate.

At low temperatures, the difference between the specific gravity of chenopodium oil and that of the condensed (distillation) water is so small that oil and water separate only incompletely, and with difficulty. The heavier portions of the oil tend to remain suspended in the water, and partly run off as a milky, oil-in-water emulsion. As a result, the yield of direct oil is low. The direct oil, moreover, is of low specific gravity and poor solubility, and deficient in ascaridole, its most soluble, important and heaviest constituent. It would be easy to return the milky distillation waters to the still, and redistill them together with the next batch of plant material, but the very labile ascaridole would then be decomposed and the oil would be abnormal. The secret of the superiority of the oils distilled in the older type of still lay, therefore, in the fact that, at slightly elevated tempera-

[7] *Ber. Schimmel & Co.,* April (1908), 108.

tures, the difference between the specific gravity of the oil and that of the condensed (distillation) water was sufficiently great to permit an easier separation of water and oil than is possible with more efficient condensers. (Cf. Vol. I of this work, p. 139.) In the case of chenopodium oil, at elevated temperatures of the condensate, the spent water runs clearer, since it contains little oil in suspension. The oil, moreover, is richer in ascaridole, hence of higher specific gravity and greater solubility in 70 per cent alcohol. Ascaridole, the chief constituent of chenopodium oil, decomposes on prolonged boiling with water, and forms compounds of lower specific gravity, insoluble in 70 per cent alcohol.

For production of an oil of high quality, Gildemeister and Hoffmann [8] suggested that the distillation water be discarded entirely and that the temperature of the condensate be kept rather high. However, Weiland, Broughton and Metzger [9] showed that the water layers generally contain some oil which, unless recovered, represents an appreciable loss. They recommend collecting the aqueous layers and pumping them into a special retort, for separate, *rapid* redistillation—i.e., apart from any fresh plant material. The oil of cohobation contains up to 85 per cent of ascaridole. Pauly [10] found that practically pure ascaridole is obtained by redistillation (cohobation) of waste liquids from distillation of the herb. If the suggestion of Weiland, Broughton and Metzger is followed, a 15 per cent increase in yield of oil, as well as an oil of better quality, may be obtained —which would certainly justify installation of a simple cohobation still. Unfortunately, some distillers do not seem to be interested in acting upon this suggestion.

Distillation of wormseed, in a modern plant, proceeds as follows:

Approximately 1,000 lb. of dried plants are packed tightly into a still of about 1,300-gal. capacity. The plant material is not comminuted prior to distillation. Hinged iron covers, balanced with counter weights, are tightly clamped on the still by means of winged bolts. Live steam, of about 100 lb. pressure, and generated in a separate boiler, enters the still through a perforated steam coil at the bottom. A grid prevents direct contact of the plant material with the steam coil. Distillation of one batch takes about 30 min. if the plant material is well dried, longer if the plants are wet.

The oil separator, holding about 50 gal., is provided with a siphon, which leads the distillation water into a separate still for redistillation (cohobation), whereby about 10 per cent of additional oil is obtained. The distil-

[8] "Die Ätherischen Öle," 3d Ed., Vol. II, 538.
[9] "Wormseed Oil Production," *Agr. Expt. Sta., Univ. Maryland Bull.* No. 384 (1935).
[10] Ph.D. Thesis, University of Wisconsin, 1931.

late flows at a temperature ranging from 120° to 130° F., depending upon prevailing atmospheric temperature and upon the temperature of the creek water used for condensation. Russell [11] found that the most complete separation of oil and water is obtained by keeping the temperature of the distillate at 140° to 163° F. He obtained more oil (of superior quality) by rapid distillation with a warm condenser than by slow distillation with a cold condenser. He reports no difference in the quality or yield of oil distilled at a pressure of from 80 to 100 lb. per square inch; but he obtained oils of low gravity by distillation at 40 to 60 lb. pressure.

In order to check the findings of the various investigators, the author of the present work suggested a number of experiments [12] to Mr. E. W. Pickett in Woodbine, Maryland. These were carried out in the course of the distillation season, in the fall of 1942. The results fully confirmed the findings of earlier workers and proved that keeping the temperature of the distillate in the condensers between 150° and 160° F. (instead of the usual 115° to 120° F.) raises the yield of oil by more than 10 per cent, and slightly increases the ascaridole content of the oil.

Yield of Oil.—The yield of oil depends upon several factors, among them, weather conditions, the stage of maturity of the plant, and the method of distillation. Yields up to 2 per cent (from dried plant material) have been claimed, but in practice a yield of 1 per cent, or perhaps slightly higher, is considered normal. One acre of chenopodium produces, on the average, from 50 to 60 lb. of oil per year.

Total Production.—The total yearly production of oil of chenopodium in Maryland depends chiefly upon the weather; in normal years it varies between 60,000 and 80,000 lb. In exceptionally favorable years (e.g., in 1940) it amounted to almost 140,000 lb.

Use of Spent Plant Material.—After completion of a charge, the exhausted plant material is hoisted from the still, dumped into a truck, and either spread on the fields to maintain fertility, or fed to cattle. For the latter purpose, the spent herb must be dried immediately after distillation, to prevent formation of mold. The installation of fast driers has been suggested. Weiland, Broughton and Metzger [13] found that animals can eat large amounts of the exhausted and shredded herb without suffering any toxic effects. They recommend its use in mixed feeds, or to supplement the feeding of forage crops.

Physicochemical Properties.—Oil of chenopodium is a colorless to yellowish liquid with a pungent, most disagreeable, camphoraceous odor, characteristic of the seed. The flavor is bitter and burning.

[11] *J. Am. Pharm. Assocn.* **11** (1922), 255.
[12] For details see *Drug Cosmetic Ind.* **52** (March–April, 1943).
[13] "Wormseed Oil Production," *Agr. Expt. Sta., Univ. Maryland Bull.* No. 384 (1935).

The properties of genuine chenopodium oils distilled in Woodbine, Maryland, and examined by Fritzsche Brothers, Inc., New York, in 1949, varied within these limits:

Specific Gravity at 25°/25°.... 0.937 to 0.990
Optical Rotation at 25°....... −4° 20′ to −12° 27′
Refractive Index at 20°....... 1.4741 to 1.4778
Ascaridole Content (Method of
   Cocking and Hymas)....... 71.6 to 91.0%
Solubility at 25°............. Soluble in 2 to 10 vol. of 70% alcohol,
    often with a haze or slight turbidity,
    sometimes with turbidity, occasionally with actual separation of oil droplets

Not all of the oils included in the above figures can be considered of best quality. Practical experience suggests that oils of highest grade should meet the following requirements:

Specific Gravity at 25°....... Not less than 0.960
Optical Rotation at 25°....... Not less than −8° 0′
Refractive Index at 20°....... Not less than 1.4750
Ascaridole Content (Method of
   Cocking and Hymas)....... Not less than 75%
Solubility at 25°............. Soluble in 8 vol. or less of 70%
    alcohol, with not more than slight turbidity

Even oils with a high ascaridole content are often opalescent to slightly turbid in 8 vol. of 70 per cent alcohol. For a time it was thought that this might be due to an excessive amount of resinous matter in the oil, but this theory has since been disproved (see below).

A Brazilian chenopodium oil distilled exclusively from seed and analyzed by Fritzsche Brothers, Inc., New York, had the following properties:

Specific Gravity at 25°/25°.... 0.981
Optical Rotation at 25°....... −0° 20′
Refractive Index at 20°....... 1.4765
Ascaridole Content (Method of
   Cocking and Hymas)....... 91.6%
Solubility.................. Soluble in 2.5 vol. and more
    of 70% alcohol

The oil was of exceptionally good quality.

A second sample from the same source showed the following properties:

Specific Gravity at 25°/25°.... 0.982
Optical Rotation............. −0° 7′
Refractive Index at 20°....... 1.4762

Ascaridole Content (Method of
  Cocking and Hymas)....... 84.0
Solubility.................. Soluble in 2.5 to 3 vol. and
                             more of 70% alcohol

The optical rotation figures of these two Brazilian oils are very low owing to the fact that these samples were distilled from seed material exclusively.

Oil of chenopodium should be stored in a cool room and protected from direct sunlight. Under the influence of light and heat the ascaridole content of the oil gradually diminishes. The oil must be handled with great care and should never be heated above 100° C., because at that temperature it is liable to decompose with explosive violence.

Analysis.—The most important phase of the analysis of chenopodium oil is the determination of the ascaridole content. Details of the procedure are given in Vol. I of this work, p. 298. (In a footnote on p. 299 of that volume it is mentioned that the empirical factor 0.00665 used in the official British Pharmacopoeia procedure for converting the cubic centimeter of tenth-normal sodium thiosulfate into per cent weight of ascaridole is actually too high by about 10 per cent. Recently Lepetit [14] suggested that 0.00605 be used as a factor, replacing the factor 0.00665 of the British Pharmacopoeia, and 0.0084 of the French Codex.)

In 1948, Halpern [15] reviewed the various methods which have been proposed for the determination of the ascaridole content of chenopodium oil, and investigated the possibility of utilizing the oxidative action of ascaridole on ascorbic acid as an assay procedure. However, Halpern did not find any evidence of a stoichiometric relationship between the reactants.

The specific gravity, optical rotation, and refractive index of wormseed oil are determined in the usual way. In general, the higher the ascaridole content of an oil, the higher is its specific gravity, and the better its solubility. However, it should be kept in mind that *old* oils also exhibit high specific gravities and good solubility, while the ascaridole content decreases.

The solubility in alcohol is not a reliable criterion of the ascaridole content. As was pointed out above, even pure oils with a normal ascaridole content may occasionally be opalescent to slightly turbid in 8 volumes of 70 per cent alcohol. Gildemeister and Hoffmann [16] expressed the opinion that poor solubility of a chenopodium oil may be explained by the presence of substantial quantities of resinous matter, such as was observed by Schimmel & Co. on fractionation of a pure oil of their own production (see

[14] Thesis, University of Paris. Cf. *Perfumery Essential Oil Record* **40** (1949), 195.
[15] *J. Am. Pharm. Assocn.* **37** (1948), 161.
[16] "Die Ätherischen Öle," 3d Ed., Vol. II, 545.

below). In order to determine whether any relationship exists between solubility in alcohol and resinous matter in the oil, the laboratories of Fritzsche Brothers, Inc., New York [17] assayed the evaporation residues of five American samples by heating the oils at 100° C. for a period of 4 hr. in a glass evaporation dish. It was found that the evaporation residues of these five genuine oils ranged from 0.9 to 1.2 per cent only. Some of the five oils were clearly soluble in 70 per cent alcohol, others exhibited slight turbidity. There appeared to be no consistent relationship between the solubility of these oils and the amount of residue left upon evaporation.

This conclusion is in accord with certain observations of Nelson,[18] who determined the *distillation* (not the *evaporation*) residues of a number of chenopodium oils. In a series of fractionations of normal and aged oils, Nelson obtained distillation residues ranging from 0.9 to as much as 9.1 per cent. All of these oils were clearly soluble in 8 volumes of 70 per cent alcohol. On the other hand, two oils with distillation residues of only 2.8 and 3.1 per cent exhibited slight turbidity in 8 volumes of 70 per cent alcohol. Two oils distilled from chenopodium plants growing *wild* in Florida had distillation residues of only 2.2 and 2.4 per cent, but were not completely soluble in 70 per cent alcohol.

In general, slight turbidity in 8 volumes of 70 per cent alcohol should not be considered abnormal. However, partial turbidity in 8 volumes of 70 per cent alcohol, with separation of droplets of oil, indicates an oil of poor quality.

In an attempt to determine ascaridole content by fractionation, Schimmel & Co.[19] fractionated several chenopodium oils of widely different physical properties, and arrived at these results:

1. A normal oil (d_{15} 0.9708) contained 62 to 65 per cent of ascaridole, about 22 per cent of p-cymene, and 4 to 6 per cent of distillation residue.

2. An oil of low specific gravity (d_{15} 0.9426) contained 45 to 50 per cent of ascaridole, about 38 per cent of hydrocarbons, and 4 to 6 per cent of distillation residue. The poor solubility of this oil was probably due to its high content of terpenes.

3. A pure oil of Schimmel's own distillation contained 65 to 70 per cent of ascaridole, only 20 per cent of hydrocarbons (p-cymene), and as much as 12.5 per cent of resinous distillation residue. The oil exhibited poor solubility in 70 per cent alcohol, the result, in the opinion of the investigators, of its high content of resinous matter. (It is also possible that the high distillation residue observed in this oil was the result of distillation with steam of relatively high pressure.)

[17] Unpublished reports.   [19] *Ber. Schimmel & Co.*, April (1908), 118.
[18] *J. Am. Chem. Soc.* **42** (1920), 1204.

Chemical Composition.—The first investigation of chenopodium oil was undertaken almost a century ago by Garrigues,[20] but did not lead to any conclusive results. It was only in 1908 that Schimmel & Co.[21] determined the composition of ascaridole, the chief constituent of the oil. A few years later Wallach [22] succeeded in establishing the structural formula of ascaridole. Other investigations of the chemical composition of chenopodium oil are those undertaken by Nelson,[23] and by Henry and Paget.[24] The following compounds have been identified in oil of chenopodium:

Dimethylene Oxide(?). From the forerun of large quantities of the terpene fraction, Henry and Paget isolated a few cc. of a substance $C_4H_8O_4$, b. 56°–57°, which was probably sym-dimethylene oxide.

p-Cymene. That p-cymene occurs in the low boiling fractions, b. 172°, of chenopodium oil was first reported by Schimmel & Co., and later confirmed by Henry and Paget. Oxidation gave p-hydroxyisopropylbenzoic acid and p-propenyl-benzoic acid m. 159°–160°.

Δ^3- or Δ^4-Carene(?). According to Schimmel & Co., the p-cymene was accompanied by small quantities of a terpene, which reacted like sylvestrene, but was probably Δ^3- or Δ^4-carene (cf. Vol. II of this work, p. 32).

l-Isolimonene(?). In 1920 Nelson reported the presence of l-limonene in a hydrocarbon fraction of the oil (preparation of a tetrabromide m. 104°–105°). Later Henry and Paget questioned Nelson's conclusion, and expressed the opinion that the compound which he had taken to be l-limonene was more probably l-isolimonene b. 177°–178°, d_{15} 0.847, $[\alpha]_D^{15}$ −57°0′, n_D^{20} 1.484; tetrabromide m. 117°, inactive.

l-Limonene. At the same time Henry and Paget identified l-limonene in the terpene fraction of the oil, by means of the tetrabromide m. 104°, and by oxidation of the l-limonene to hydroxyterpenylic acid and levulinic acid.

α-Terpinene. The same authors also established the presence of α-terpinene by preparation of the nitrosite m. 155°.

d-Camphor. In the fraction boiling just below the main fraction Schimmel & Co. identified d-camphor by means of the semicarbazone m. 236° and of the oxime m. 118°. The occurrence of camphor in oil of chenopodium was confirmed by Wirth,[25] by preparation of its semicarbazone m. 237°. (In the opinion of Henry and Paget, however, the compound does not exist in the oil.)

Ascaridole. The content of ascaridole in chenopodium oil varies with the quality of the oil, high-grade oils containing not less than 75 per cent. The compound has a most obnoxious, nauseating odor. It is unstable to heat, and liable to explode at temperatures above 100° C. Nelson has shown that ascaridole undergoes

[20] *Am. J. Pharm.* **26** (1854), 405.
[21] *Ber. Schimmel & Co.*, April (1908), 112.
[22] *Liebigs Ann.* **392** (1912), 59.
[23] *J. Am. Chem. Soc.* **42** (1920), 1204. *Ibid.* **33** (1911), 1405.
[24] *J. Chem. Soc.* **119** (1921), 1714; **127** (1925), 1649.
[25] *J. Am. Pharm. Assocn.* **9** (1920), 139.

molecular rearrangement when heated to 150°. It forms no known solid derivatives by which it can be characterized. (For details, cf. Vol. II of this work, p. 715.)

Methyl Salicylate. Henry and Paget found that the oil contains methyl salicylate (less than 0.5 per cent). Identified by means of the benzoyl compound of the ester, m. 83°; salicylic acid m. 156°.

Butyric Acid. The same authors established the presence of butyric acid in the oil (analysis of the silver salt).

Ascaridole Glycol. In the distillation residues Henry and Paget observed ascaridole glycol as chief component.

Safrole(?). According to Gildemeister and Hoffman,[26] safrole is possibly a constituent of American chenopodium oil. On the other hand, Henry and Paget were unable to identify the compound.

In the distillation waters of American chenopodium oil, Pauly [27] observed acetaldehyde, acetone, methyl alcohol, ethyl alcohol(?), ammonia, and methylamine.

Use.—Chenopodium oil is one of the best-known anthelmintics, used successfully against several types of intestinal parasites in man and animals, against roundworms, tapeworms, and hookworms, e.g. However, great care must be exercised in the administration of the oil, as it is very dangerous if given in excessive doses. The toxic effects are partly the result of local irritation of the alimentary tract (particularly the liver and kidneys) and partly of direct depressant action on the circulatory and respiratory systems. The oil may be fatal if taken in excess. Symptoms of poisoning are delayed in appearing. They consist of nausea, vomiting, headache, and drowsiness, and, finally, convulsions and coma. Administration of the oil, therefore, should not follow any period of starvation, since poorly nourished animals and humans appear especially susceptible to its toxic effects. The dosage of wormseed oil and the method of administration should always be left to the physician.

SUGGESTED ADDITIONAL LITERATURE

Yu. S. Khavkin, "Oil of Chenopodium." *Ukrain. Gosudarst. Inst. Eksptl. Farm. Kharkov Konsul'tats. Materialy* No. 6 (1939), 165. *Chem. Abstracts* **36** (1942), 2997.

A. Schmotkin and E. Schmied, "Cultural Tests on *Chenopodium ambrosioides* L. var. *anthelminticum.* The Value and Determination of the Volatile Oil." *Schweiz. Apoth. Ztg.* **81** (1943), 221. *Chem. Abstracts* **38** (1944), 216.

G. Sanna and A. Marchi, "Determination of Ascaridole in Chenopodium Oil," *Boll. Chim. Farm.* **89** (1950), 447. *Chem. Abstracts* **45** (1951), 2146.

26 "Die Ätherischen Öle," 3d Ed., Vol. II, 543.
27 *Pharm. Arch.* **7** (1936), 1.

CHAPTER XV

ESSENTIAL OILS OF THE PLANT FAMILY *RANUNCULACEAE*

OIL OF NIGELLA DAMASCENA L.

On steam distillation the seeds of *Nigella damascena* L.[1] (fam. *Ranunculaceae*) yield from 0.35 to 0.5 per cent of a yellow oil exhibiting a beautiful blue fluorescence. The odor of the oil is characteristic of strawberries, occasionally reminiscent also of ambrette seed oil.

According to Gildemeister and Hoffmann,[2] the essential oil derived from the seed of *Nigella damascena* has these properties:

Specific Gravity at 15°.............. 0.895 to 0.915
Optical Rotation.................. +1° 4' to −7° 48'
Refractive Index at 20°............ 1.49970 to 1.5582
Acid Number..................... 1.1
Ester Number.................... 14.0
Ester Number after Acetylation..... 17.7
Solubility....................... Not completely soluble in 90% alcohol; soluble in absolute alcohol in any proportion

The chief constituent of the oil (which causes its fluorescence) is *damascenine* (for details see Vol. II of this work, p. 654). Extracting the oil with a solution of tartaric acid and decomposing the tartrate with sodium carbonate, Schneider[3] obtained 9 per cent of damascenine. Kaufmann and Rothlin[4] developed a relatively simple synthesis of damascenine.

According to the author's knowledge, oil of *Nigella damascena* is not produced on a commercial scale.

[1] Commonly known in the United States as "Love-in-a-mist."
[2] "Die Ätherischen Öle," 3d Ed., Vol. II, 553.
[3] *Pharm. Zentralhalle* **31** (1890), 173, 191. Cf. *Ber. Schimmel & Co.*, October (1899), 40. Cf. Pommerehne, *Arch. Pharm.* **237** (1899), 475.
[4] *Ber.* **49** (1916), 579.

CHAPTER XVI

ESSENTIAL OILS OF THE PLANT FAMILY *EUPHORBIACEAE*

OIL OF CASCARILLA

Essence de Cascarille   Aceite Esencial Cascarilla   Cascarillöl
Oleum Cascarillae

Introduction.—Cascarilla is the dried bark of a small tree or shrub, *Croton eluteria* Bennett (fam. *Euphorbiaceae*), indigenous to the Bahamas, the chief producer of the spice. The bark has an agreeable, aromatic odor and a very bitter, spicy taste, for which reason it is employed in stomachic bitters. The odor becomes particularly noticeable when the bark is allowed to burn slowly. Some smokers have tried to flavor their tobacco with small quantities of cascarilla bark, but it is said to produce intoxication and vertigo.

On distillation the dried bark yields from 1.5 to 3 per cent, on the average 2 per cent, of a volatile oil. The latter, a yellow to greenish liquid, possesses a warm spicy odor reminiscent of nutmeg, cardamom, clove, and thyme, with a top-note of *p*-cymene and dipentene.

Physicochemical Properties.—Gildemeister and Hoffmann [1] reported these properties for cascarilla bark oil:

Specific Gravity at 15°.............	0.898 to 0.925
Optical Rotation....................	+1° 0′ to +13° 0′
Refractive Index at 20°............	1.489 to 1.496
Acid Number......................	2 to 9
Ester Number.....................	5 to 12
Ester Number after Acetylation......	54 to 72
Solubility........................	Easily soluble in 90% alcohol

Genuine cascarilla bark oils distilled by Fritzsche Brothers, Inc., New York, had properties varying within the following limits:

Specific Gravity at 15°/15°..........	0.897 to 0.918
Optical Rotation...................	−1° 40′ to +8° 54′
Refractive Index at 20°............	1.4880 to 1.4930
Saponification Number..............	8.4 to 17.1
Ester Number after Acetylation......	65.3 to 84.9
Solubility........................	Soluble in 0.5 vol. of 90% alcohol

Chemical Composition.—The earliest investigations of the chemical composition of cascarilla bark oil, carried out more than a century ago, need

[1] "Die Ätherischen Öle," 3d Ed., Vol. III, 197.

169

not be discussed here, because they gave no positive results. Later researches by Gladstone,[2] Brühl,[3] and particularly by Fendler,[4] yielded more conclusive data. These authors reported the presence of the following compounds in cascarilla oil:

A Terpene(?). In the lowest boiling fraction (b. 155°–157°, d_{20} 0.845, α_D^{21} +2° 6′) of the oil. The monohydrochloride and the dibromide were oily substances. Nitrosochloride m. 91°–92°, nitrolpiperidine m. 112°. The properties of this terpene and its derivatives led Fendler to conclude that it was not identical with pinene.

p-Cymene. Characterized in the fraction b. 170°–173° by oxidation to hydroxyisopropylbenzoic acid.

l-Limonene(?). The same fraction probably also contained small quantities of *l*-limonene (Fendler).

Dipentene(?). In the fraction b. 172° Gladstone observed a hydrocarbon which, in the later opinion of Brühl, was dipentene.

Eugenol. Identified by Fendler in the oil, after the acids (see below) had been removed. Benzoyl compound m. 71°. The quantity of eugenol isolated by Fendler amounted to 0.3 per cent of the oil.

Sesquiterpenes(?). The same author noted the presence of two sesquiterpenes b. 255°–257°, and b. 260°–265° in the oil, but did not succeed in identifying them, because they yielded no crystalline derivatives.

A Sesquiterpene Alcohol(?). The same applies to a sesquiterpene alcohol $C_{15}H_{24}O$, which Fendler observed in the fraction b. 280°–290°.

Cascarillic Acid. According to Fendler, the acidic reaction of the oil is a result of the presence of about 2 per cent of acids, which he isolated by fractional distillation and separated into a liquid acid, and a crystalline residual acid. The former, $C_{11}H_{20}O_2$, was isomeric with undecylenic acid. Fendler named it cascarillic acid; m. −18°, b. 270°, d_{20} 0.9324; amide m. 78°.

Palmitic Acid and Stearic Acid. The above mentioned crystalline residual acid melted at 58° and consisted of a mixture of 80 per cent of palmitic acid, and 20 per cent of stearic acid.

Use.—Because of its high price, oil of cascarilla is used only in high-grade flavoring preparations—aromatic bitters in particular.

[2] *J. Chem. Soc.* **17** (1864), 1.
[3] *Ber.* **21** (1888), 152.
[4] *Arch. Pharm.* **238** (1900), 671. Cf. Thoms, *Apoth. Ztg.* **14** (1899), 562.

CHAPTER XVII

ESSENTIAL OILS OF THE PLANT FAMILY *MALVACEAE*

OIL OF AMBRETTE SEED

Essence de Graines d'Ambrette   *Moschuskörneröl*
Aceite Esencial Ambrette de los Granos
Oleum Abelmoschi Seminis

Abelmoschus moschatus Moench, syn. *Hibiscus abelmoschus* L. (fam. *Malvaceae*), a native of tropical East India, is cultivated in the Seychelles Islands,[1] on Nossi-Bé (Madagascar), on some of the West Indian Islands, and particularly in the warm and humid regions of Ecuador and Colombia, the seed in the case of the latter two countries being shipped from Guayaquil. In the course of World War II, efforts were made in the State of São Paulo (Brazil) and in various parts of Central America to cultivate *Abelmoschus moschatus* without, however, due consideration to the fact that the use of the seed and the essential oil derived from it is very limited.

According to information gathered by the author while surveying essential oil production on Nossi-Bé (Madagascar), seed is sown directly, 1 by 1 m. apart, into well-prepared ground at the beginning of the rainy season. After six months the fruit, which encloses the seed, is cut with knives. It is then dried in the sun on concrete floors. The fruit bursts open, the seed falls to the ground and is collected.

The seed contains a volatile oil with a strong, peculiar, and lasting odor, reminiscent of musk. Years ago the seed as such was employed in pharmaceutical preparations, but today it is used mostly for the purpose of distillation in European and North American essential oil houses. Prior to distillation the seed must be crushed. Aside from the volatile oil, it contains a large amount of fatty acids which, on distillation, are carried over together with the volatile oil. The crude ambrette seed oil is therefore a concrete mass, resembling concrete of orris root, and consisting mostly of higher fatty acids, chiefly palmitic acid. To prepare a liquid oil for the perfume industry, the fatty acids have to be removed from the concrete oil, which is achieved by various methods—such as treatment with dilute alcohol, or precipitation of the fatty acids by means of their calcium or lithium salts. Depending upon the amount of fatty acids present, the yield of oil from the seed varies from 0.2 to 0.6 per cent.

---

[1] Re cultivation of the plant see *J. agr. trop.* **5** (1905), 17. *Ber. Schimmel & Co.*, April (1905), 59.

Physicochemical Properties.—The melting point of the crude (concrete) oil of ambrette seed is in direct ratio to the quantity of fatty acids present. Gildemeister and Hoffmann [2] reported these properties for the crude oil:

> Specific Gravity at 40°...... About 0.89
> Specific Gravity at 50°...... About 0.88
> Acid Number.............. 75 to 140
> Ester Number............. 66 to 130

According to the same authors, liquid ambrette seed oil, from which the fatty acids have been removed, exhibits the following properties:

> Specific Gravity at 15°........... 0.905 to 0.917
> Optical Rotation................ Usually slightly dextrorotatory, up
>   to +1° 35'; seldom laevorotatory,
>   up to −2° 24'
> Refractive Index at 20°.......... 1.474 to 1.480
> Acid Number.................. 0.4 to 2.5
> Ester Number.................. 137 to 190
> Ester Number after Acetylation... 199.7 (one determination on an oil
>   with an ester number of 167.4)
> Solubility....................... Soluble in 2.5 to 8 vol. and more of
>   80% alcohol

One oil described by Gildemeister and Hoffmann had somewhat different properties:

> Specific Gravity at 15°........... 0.9298
> Optical Rotation................ −1° 34'
> Refractive Index at 20°.......... 1.48519
> Acid Number.................. 0.7
> Ester Number.................. 139.8
> Solubility....................... Not clearly soluble in 80% alcohol
>   even in 10 vol.; soluble in 0.5 vol.
>   and more of 90% alcohol

Two liquid ambrette seed oils produced under the author's supervision in Southern France (Seillans, Var) exhibited these values:

	I	II
Specific Gravity at 15°......	0.908	0.908
Optical Rotation..........	+0° 30'	+0° 12'
Refractive Index at 20°.....	1.4701	1.4691
Acid Number..............	2.8	1.4
Ester Number.............	189.5	190.9
Solubility.................	Soluble in 0.5 vol. of 90% alcohol; cloudy with more	Soluble in 0.5 vol. and more of 90% alcohol

[2] "Die Ätherischen Öle," 3d Ed., Vol. III, 220.

Shipments of pure (liquid) ambrette seed oils examined by Fritzsche Brothers, Inc., New York, had properties varying within the following limits:

Specific Gravity at 15°/15°....	0.902 to 0.920
Optical Rotation.............	+0° 12′ to +2° 46′
Refractive Index at 20°.......	1.4695 to 1.4768
Acid Number................	Up to 2.8
Ester Number...............	143.7 to 196.0
Ester Number after Acetylation (Three Determinations).....	206.3 to 213.7
Solubility...................	Soluble in 0.5 vol. of 90% alcohol, often opalescent with more. Sometimes soluble in 2 to 4 vol. of 80% alcohol and more

Chemical Composition.—We owe our knowledge of the chemical composition of ambrette seed oil chiefly to the work of Kerschbaum,[3] who established the presence of the following compounds in the liquid oil:

Farnesol. This sesquiterpene alcohol is the principal constituent of the liquid oil (cf. Vol. II of this work, p. 258).

Ambrettolide. This lactone is responsible for the characteristic musk-like odor of the oil (cf. Vol. II of this work, p. 689).

Decyl Alcohol. Small quantities only (cf. Vol. II of this work, p. 156).

As regards the crude (concrete) oil, it contains chiefly *palmitic acid,*[4] m. 61°, and in addition *acetic acid* in ester form, and *ambrettolic acid,* also in ester form (cf. Vol. II of this work, p. 595).

In the distillation water of the oil, Schimmel & Co.[5] identified *furfural.*

Use.—The liquid oil of ambrette seed is a valuable adjunct in high-grade perfume compositions, to which it imparts strong and characteristic musk-like notes. The oil possesses a much smoother odor than synthetic musk ambrette. The crude (concrete) oil can be used in cosmetics. Because of its powerful, lasting odor, it must be dosed most carefully.

[3] *Ber.* **46** (1913), 1732; **60** (1927), 902.
[4] Gildemeister and Hoffmann, "Die Ätherischen Öle," 3d Ed., Vol. III, 221.
[5] *Ber. Schimmel & Co.,* October (1899), 36.

(*Top*) Production of oil of chenopodium (American wormseed oil) in Maryland. A modern distillery in Woodbine, Maryland. (*Bottom*) Chenopodium (American wormseed oil), Maryland. Discharge of the spent plant material from a steam still. *Photos Fritzsche Brothers, Inc., New York.*

(*Top*) Close-up of oak moss (*Evernia prunastri*) growing on branches of an oak tree. (*Bottom*) Collection of oak moss (*Evernia prunastri*) in the mountains of Tuscany, near Florence, Italy. *Photos A. Piazzesi, Florence, Italy.*

CHAPTER XVIII

ESSENTIAL OILS OF THE PLANT FAMILY *USNEACEAE*

CONCRETE AND ABSOLUTE OF OAK MOSS

Botanical and Geographical Origin.—Volatile oils occur not only in flowering plants, but also in some of the cryptogams. However, only a few members of the latter group can be utilized for the extraction of their fragrance on a commercial scale. Most important among them are the lichens *Evernia prunastri* (L.) Ach., and *E. furfuracea* (L.) Mann (fam. *Usneaceae*). These grow as epiphytes on the trunks of the oak, and certain fruit and pinaceous trees, particularly in southern and central Europe. When dried and stored for a period of time, these lichens develop a peculiar mossy, earthy odor, the carriers of which can be extracted with volatile solvents, yielding the so-called resinoids, concretes and absolutes of "Oak Moss." In its strict sense the name "Oak Moss" refers only to *Evernia prunastri* (L.) Ach., the true oak moss or "Mousse de chêne," which grows chiefly on the bark of the oak. *Evernia furfuracea* (L.) Mann thrives on the bark of firs and pines in humid forests and is commonly called "Sprout Lichen," "Tree Moss," or "Mousse d'arbre." Commercial lots of so-called oak moss frequently represent mixtures of several lichens, and it is not always easy to distinguish the species. True oak moss, collected from oak trees, has the most pronounced and finest odor. It may be identified by a light green color on one side, and a whitish color on the other. True oak moss is soft to the touch. Tree moss, on the other hand, collected from pinaceous trees, has a gray color on one side, and a black-gray color on the other. It is hard and rough to the touch and has a resinous odor. Lichens collected from fruit trees and acacias are of gray-green color; their quality stands between that of true oak moss and tree moss.

Producing regions lie is southern and central Europe. The best quality of true oak moss comes from the Apennines and the Piedmont in Italy, from Dalmatia, Southern France, and from the oak forests of Fontainebleau near Paris. Lichens originating from Czechoslovakia, Hungary, and from Central France (Cévennes and Ardèche) are usually of second quality. This applies particularly to lichens from Central France, which consist chiefly of *Evernia furfuracea*, and perhaps some *Usnea barbata* (L.) Wigg., our common "Bearded Usnea" or "Old Man's Beard," another ordinary tree moss. According to Trabaud,[1] a new producing region was opened some

[1] *Perfumery Essential Oil Record,* Annual Special Number (1936), 95.

years ago in the western part of Morocco, in the great cedar and oak forests of the Atlas Mountains, south of Meknès, at an altitude of about 4,000 ft. This section supplies *Evernia furfuracea* chiefly; center of collection is the Berber village of Azrou, located in the foothills of the Atlas. Not very far distant are the beautiful oak and wild pear forests of Mamora, which produce a good quality of *Evernia prunastri.* Here, the center of collection is Harcha.

In general, the lichen is collected from the bark of the trunk and branches, during the dry season. Prior to shipment the material is usually baled and pressed. On arrival in the extraction plant it should be stored in a cool and dry place; otherwise fermentation may take place and spoil the odor of the moss.

Extraction.—Odoriferous substances occur in the lichens in such small quantities that they cannot be isolated by steam distillation; therefore, extraction with volatile solvents must be resorted to. This, however, is not a simple matter, and requires a great deal of experience. Yield and quality of the extracts depend upon the botanical and geographical origin of the lichens, upon the type of solvent used, and the temperature and duration of extraction. (For details, see Vol. I of the present work, pp. 200 ff.)

Extraction can be carried out (a) with nonalcoholic solvents, such as benzene and petroleum ether, or (b) alcoholic solvents, such as ethyl alcohol and methyl alcohol. The composition of the products obtained will depend upon the type of solvent employed; with alcohols certain chemical reactions will take place (see below).

(a) *Benzene or Petroleum Ether as Solvent.*—Benzene is now the solvent most commonly used for extraction of the lichens. It gives a higher yield of concrete, with more perfume, colored matter and resins than that obtained by extraction with petroleum ether. In the case of true oak moss, benzene extracts 2 to 4 per cent of concrete, petroleum ether only 1.5 to 3.0 per cent. With tree moss, benzene yields about 5 per cent of concrete, petroleum ether from 2 to 4 per cent (Naves and Mazuyer [2]). According to Trabaud,[3] lichen from Morocco, when extracted with petroleum ether, yields only one-third to one-half of the quantity of concrete obtained by extraction with benzene. The same author [4] also noted that *Evernia furfuracea* from Morocco, on extraction with benzene, gives concretes with a much larger quantity of crystalline substances (chiefly lichen acids) than

[2] "Les Parfums Naturels," Paris (1939), 314.
[3] *Perfumery Essential Oil Record,* Annual Special Number (1936), 95.
[4] *Drug Cosmetic Ind.* **65** (1949), 591.

the concretes prepared from *Evernia furfuracea* originating in central France.

To facilitate extraction with benzene or petroleum ether, most manufacturers moisten the dried lichen with lukewarm water, about 24 hr. prior to extraction, then drain off excess water before pumping the solvent into the extractors. This treatment has the effect of enlarging the plant tissues and rendering them more permeable to the solvent. Some manufacturers extract the lichen at room temperature, others by heating the solvent almost to the boiling point at the beginning of the extraction process. Obviously, this produces extracts of different properties, and affects the yield also.

In general, the concretes derived by extraction with petroleum ether are more fluid and of finer odor than those obtained with benzene. The latter are solid, waxy masses, containing a considerable amount of crystalline substances; their color is darker than that of the petroleum ether extracts. (For the extraction of lichens petroleum ether is a much more selective solvent than benzene.)

Several samples of concretes examined by Naves and Mazuyer [5] had these properties:

	Petroleum Ether Concrete	Benzene Concrete
Melting Point	48° and 50°	50° and 52°
Acid Number	68.2 and 56.8	16.1 and 22.4
Ester Number	74.2 and 78.5	42.0 and 38.1

Naves, Sabetay and Palfray [6] described four volatile oils obtained by steam distillation of the concretes at reduced pressure:

	Oils from Petroleum Ether Concretes	Oils from Benzene Concretes
Acid Number	21.5 and 31.4	82.3 and 90.6
Ester Number	16.1 and 22.4	42.0 and 38.1

(Note: Such volatile oils are not commercial products, but are occasionally prepared in the laboratory for purposes of analysis. Cf. Vol. I of the present work, p. 215.)

Because of their poor solubility in alcohol, the concretes cannot be used in alcoholic perfumes. However, they may be employed for the scenting of soaps, if the dark color of the concretes is not objectionable. To prepare products soluble in 95 per cent alcohol, the concretes are converted into absolutes in the usual way (cf. Vol. I of the present work, p. 211), except that extraction of the concretes is often carried out with *hot* alcohol.

[5] "Les Parfums Naturels," Paris (1939), 316.
[6] *Perfumery Essential Oil Record* **28** (1937), 337.

According to Naves and Mazuyer,[7] concrete of oak moss yields from 35 to 60 per cent of absolute; concrete of tree moss from 60 to 70 per cent. The author of the present work obtained the following yields:

1. Concrete of *oak moss* prepared by petroleum ether extraction gave 76 per cent of absolute; concrete derived by benzene extraction yielded 68 per cent of absolute:

2. Concrete of *tree moss* prepared by petroleum ether extraction gave 70 per cent of absolute; concrete derived by benzene extraction yielded 80 per cent of absolute.

On extraction with benzene, French oak moss yielded 2.91 per cent of concrete which, in turn, gave 53.25 per cent of absolute. Yugoslavian oak moss, on extraction with benzene, yielded 3.84 per cent of concrete which, in turn, gave 39.1 per cent of absolute.

Absolutes of oak moss and tree moss are very viscous liquids, of dark green color. The absolutes prepared from petroleum ether concretes are usually more fluid than those derived from benzene concretes. The latter absolutes usually contain a considerable amount of crystalline substances.

To obtain absolutes of lighter color, some manufacturers resort to partial decoloration with charcoal. Such treatment, however, entails a considerable loss in odorous compounds. The absolutes thus obtained are of brown color, and turn darker with the passage of time. Colorless concentrates may be prepared by submitting the concretes to distillation with superheated steam at reduced pressure, or to co-distillation with ethylene glycol, also at reduced pressure. The yield of volatile substances thus obtained is from 15 to 20 per cent higher than that obtained by regular steam distillation of the concretes. Owing to the high boiling point of some of the odorous constituents present in the concretes, steam distillation at atmospheric pressure requires too much time and steam to be of practical value. Naves and Mazuyer [8] reported a yield of 3.9 to 5.6 per cent of colorless distillate from petroleum ether concretes, and a yield of 3.0 to 4.8 per cent from benzene concretes. In these experiments Naves and Mazuyer used ethylene glycol and glycerol for co-distillation; these yield better results than distillation with superheated steam.

(*b*) *Alcohols as Solvent.*—Some manufacturers use alcohol (ethyl or methyl alcohol) for extraction of the lichen, obtaining yields of resinoids

---

[7] "Les Parfums Naturels," Paris (1939), 315.
[8] *Ibid.*, 316.

ranging from 8 to 14 per cent. Obviously, this is a much higher yield than that obtained with petroleum ether or benzene. However, the odor of these resinoids differs considerably from that of the concretes and absolutes derived by benzene or petroleum ether extraction. The latter solvents dissolve the odorous principles actually present in the lichen. Treatment with alcohol, on the other hand, causes marked alcoholysis of the depsides present in the lichens. These depsides are generally odorless, and only sparingly soluble in petroleum ether or benzene. Alcoholysis of the depsides, particularly at elevated temperatures, yields esters and other compounds, some of them odorous and soluble. In other words, on treatment of the lichens with alcohol, odoriferous substances originally not present in the lichens are formed. The odor of the resinoids varies according to the nature of the newly formed esters. If methyl alcohol is employed the odor will be somewhat anise-like. The usual procedure is to extract the lichens with hot ethyl alcohol, which gives resinoids of dark green color, waxy in consistency, permeated with crystals, and only partly soluble in cold alcohol. By repeated extraction with certain other solvents the resinoids can be made soluble in cold alcohol. The odor of the resinoids is softer, but not nearly so characteristic as that of the petroleum ether or benzene concretes and absolutes.

Submitting resinoids (extracted from lichens with alcohol) to co-distillation with ethylene glycol at reduced pressure, Naves and Mazuyer [9] obtained from 8 to 13.2 per cent of light-colored volatile oils.

In general, it may be said that the resinoids prepared by alcoholic extraction of the lichens are employed much less widely than the concretes (and absolutes) derived by extraction with petroleum ether or benzene (the latter is now the most widely used solvent). The absolutes reproduce the natural odor of the lichens quite satisfactorily.

Chemical Composition.—The chemical composition of the extracts derived from oak moss and tree moss is complex and differs greatly according to the botanical and geographical origin of the lichens, the nature of the solvent used, and the method of extraction. To understand the problem it is important to be acquainted with the various constituents present in the lichens themselves.

Early investigators in the field isolated a number of compounds, usually of acidic nature, from various lichens, and classified them under the general term "Lichen Acids." Most of these compounds can be obtained in crystalline form. The identity of a number of lichen acids has been estab-

[9] *Ibid.*

lished in the course of the last thirty years, by several researchers, among them Asahina and his collaborators. For reasons of space, only certain aspects of their work, and particularly those connected with *Evernia prunastri* and *E. furfuracea,* can be discussed here. The reader interested in further study is referred to a comprehensive compilation (up to 1934) by Asahina,[10] and to an article specifically on oak moss extracts by Pfau,[11] part of which is incorporated in the following section:

Evernia prunastri contains evernic acid, *d*-usnic acid, atranorin, and chloro-atranorin.

Evernia furfuracea contains atranorin, physodic acid, furfuracinic acid, and chloro-atranorin.

Some of the lichen acids belong to the class of the so-called depsides. These are esters of aromatic hydroxy acids, in which the carboxyl group of an acid is linked to the hydroxy group of another cyclic compound. The ester linkage is quite labile. If it forms the only linkage between two rings, the complex compound is easily hydrolyzed into degradation products containing one ring each. Boiling with alcohol readily causes splitting of the depsides, and a simultaneous ester exchange. On steam distillation, or on extraction of the lichens with a solvent containing hydroxy groups, the lichen acids pass into the extract either as such, or partially decomposed (hydrolyzed). By comparison with the odorous principles, the lichen acids form a much larger part of the lichens; therefore the products of decomposition may constitute a very large part of the distillate or extract. For this reason it is of fundamental importance to be well acquainted with the depsides occurring in oak moss and tree moss, viz., evernic acid, atranorin, barbatinic acid, and chloro-atranorin. Usnic acid and physodic acid do not belong in the depside group. Furfuracinic acid has not yet been investigated.

(a) *Evernic Acid.* On treatment with alcohol, particularly in the presence of small quantities of alkalies, evernic acid undergoes alcoholysis, and everninic ester and orsellinic acid are formed simultaneously. On boiling with water, evernic acid is cleaved into everninic acid and orsellinic acid. The latter two acids readily lose carbon dioxide (even during steam distillation); orcinol monomethyl ether is formed from everninic acid, and orcinol from orsellinic acid:

[10] "Systematization of Lichen Substances," *Acta Phytochim.* (*Japan*) **8**, No. 1 (1934), 33. *Chem. Abstracts* **29** (1936), 147. Cf. Y. Asahina and K. Okazaki, "Lichen Substances: Usnic Acid," *J. Pharm. Soc. Japan* **63** (1943), 618. *Chem. Abstracts* **45** (1951), 5146.

[11] *Riechstoff Ind.* **12** (1937), 179, 208.

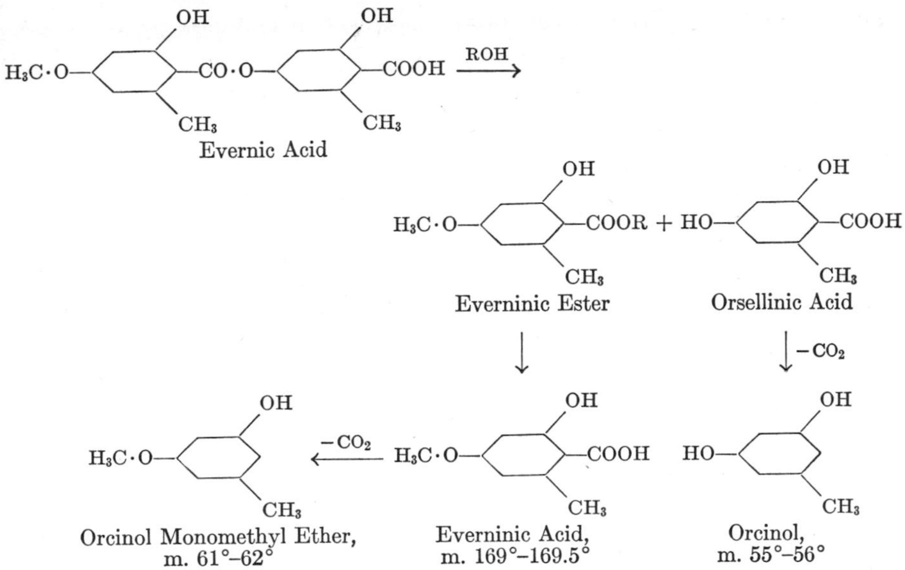

Evernic Acid

$\xrightarrow{\text{ROH}}$

Everninic Ester + Orsellinic Acid

$\downarrow \quad \downarrow -CO_2$

Orcinol Monomethyl Ether, m. 61°–62°   Everninic Acid, m. 169°–169.5°   Orcinol, m. 55°–56°

(*b*) *Barbatinic Acid*, a higher homolog of evernic acid, occurs in the lichen *Usnea ceratina* Ach., small quantities of which are often found accompanying *Evernia prunastri* and *E. furfuracea*. Barbatinic acid, if treated similarly to evernic acid, undergoes these reactions:

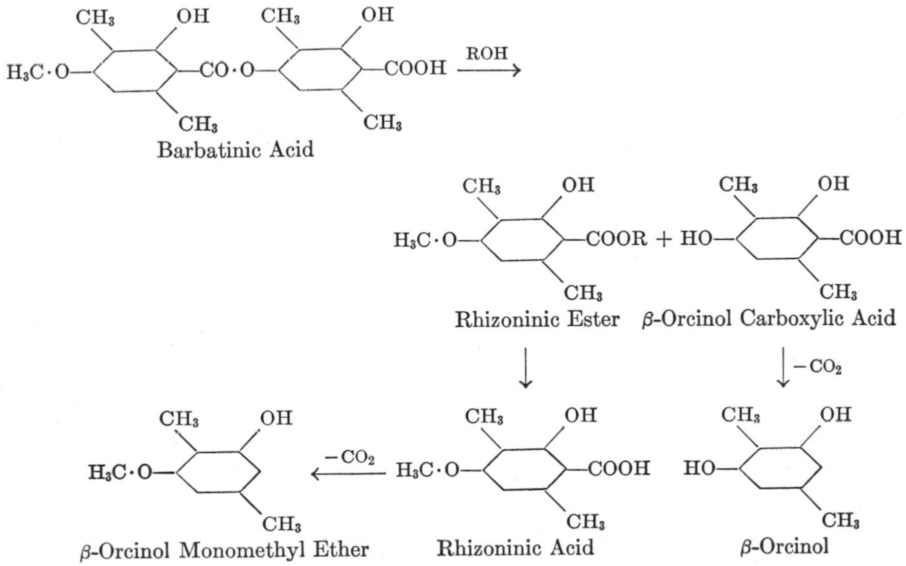

Barbatinic Acid

$\xrightarrow{\text{ROH}}$

Rhizoninic Ester + β-Orcinol Carboxylic Acid

$\downarrow \quad \downarrow -CO_2$

β-Orcinol Monomethyl Ether   Rhizoninic Acid   β-Orcinol

(c) *Atranorin.* Similarly, atranorin undergoes the following reactions:

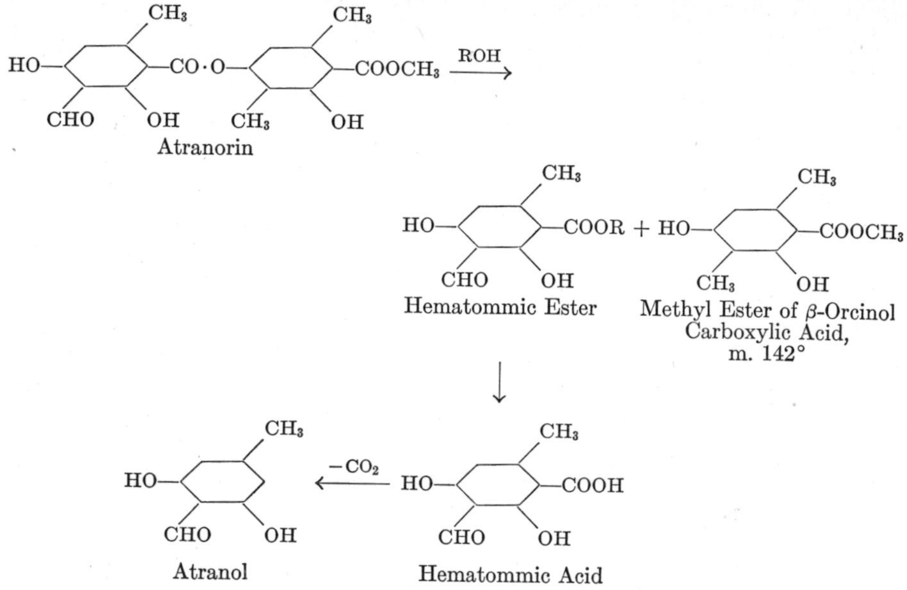

Atranorin

Hematommic Ester

Methyl Ester of β-Orcinol
Carboxylic Acid,
m. 142°

Atranol

Hematommic Acid

(d) *Chloro-atranorin* reacts as follows:

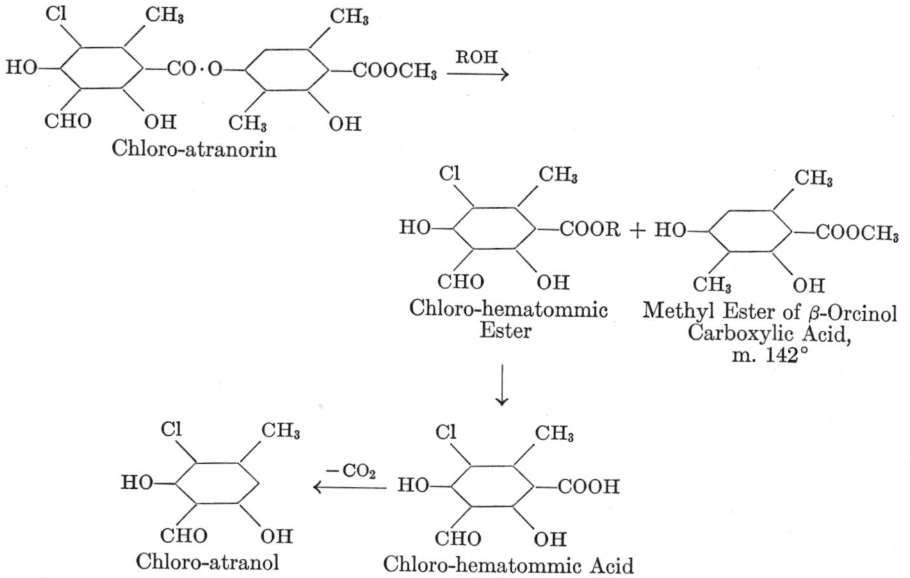

Chloro-atranorin

Chloro-hematommic
Ester

Methyl Ester of β-Orcinol
Carboxylic Acid,
m. 142°

Chloro-atranol

Chloro-hematommic Acid

As a result of the reactions described above (alcoholysis, ester exchange, hydrolysis, and loss of carbon dioxide under the influence of alcohol or hot water) all these substances may be present in the lichen extracts, if alcohol (methyl, ethyl, etc.) is used for extraction. With solvents containing no hydroxy groups (benzene, petroleum ether, etc.) not a single one of the above described degradation products of the lichen substances will be created. As regards the original lichen substances themselves, part of them will be dissolved, the quantity depending upon the nature of the solvent. The nature and percentage of lichen substances depend upon the lichens. *Evernia prunastri*, e.g., has been reported [12] containing from 2 to 3 per cent of evernic acid as chief constituent, 0.1 to 0.3 per cent of atranorin, and 0.1 to 0.2 per cent of chloro-atranorin. In the lichen *Evernia furfuracea* the content of atranorin and chloro-atranorin is higher than in *E. prunastri*. The lichen extracts obviously will also contain the unaltered, *non*-depsidic lichen substances, particularly *d*-usnic acid (about 0.2 to 0.3 per cent of the lichen), and other soluble substances, chlorophyll and waxes among them.

If solvents containing no alcohol are employed for extraction of the lichens, practically all the lichen acids go into solution; therefore they will be present in the concretes. If the concrete is converted into alcohol-soluble absolute by treatment with *cold* alcohol, the lichen acids will remain in the insoluble residue, with the exception of the evernic acid. The latter is quite soluble in cold alcohol; part of it will, therefore, be dissolved and pass into the absolute. Such an absolute will possess an odor similar to that of the original lichen (although evernic acid is odorless).

If ethyl alcohol is used for extraction of the lichens, alcoholysis will take place, and the resinoid will contain not only unaltered lichen acids, but also the ethyl esters of everninic, rhizoninic, hematommic, and chloro-hematommic acids. (Years ago, Gattefossé [13] isolated from oak moss extracts a substance which he named "Lichenol." Later, Pfau [14] proved that "Lichenol" is actually the ethyl ester of everninic acid, m. 73.5°–74°. The same ester, m. 76°, was isolated by Walbaum and Rosenthal [15] from an alcoholic extract of oak moss.) In addition, the resinoid will contain free orsellinic acid, and the methyl ester of β-orcinol carboxylic acid, m. 142°. *These cleavage products are mostly odorless.*

The case is somewhat different if methyl alcohol is used for extraction of the lichens. A number of methyl esters will be formed, that of everninic acid among them. Pfau [16] named this methyl ester *sparassol* (from the fungus *Sparassis ramosa* Schaeff., in which it also occurs). Sparassol pos-

[12] Pfau, *ibid.*
[13] *Parfumerie moderne* **4** (1911), 6.
[14] *Ber.* **57** (1924), 468.
[15] *Ber.* **57** (1924), 770. *Ber. Schimmel & Co.* (1925), 21.
[16] *Ber.* **57** (1924), 468; Späth and Jeschki, *ibid.*, 471.

sesses a pronounced anise-like odor; whence the slight anise-like by-note of the resinoids extracted from the lichens with methyl alcohol.

A comparison of the odor of the concretes obtained by extraction of the lichens by means of benzene or petroleum ether, with that of the resinoids derived by extraction with ethyl alcohol, will show notable differences between them. The resinoids exhibit a more or less characteristic fungus or mushroom odor. How is this to be reconciled with the fact that all ethyl esters formed by cleavage of the lichen acids are odorless (see above)? Pfau [17] investigated this problem, using lichens that had already been exhausted with benzene, and boiling this absolutely odorless material with ethyl alcohol. He obtained a semisolid extract with a strong odor. It appeared that the newly formed odorous principles originated from benzene-insoluble, odorless precursors which, on treatment with hot alcohol, yielded odorous substances. Steam distillation of the extract gave a semisolid volatile oil. The liquid part of the latter contained compounds of strong odor; these were not investigated. The solid, odorless part of the volatile oil consisted of a mixture of the ethyl esters of hematommic acid and chloro-hematommic acid, and of the methyl ester of β-orcinol carboxylic acid. In other words, they were cleavage products of atranorin and chloro-atranorin.

As has been mentioned, some manufacturers produce colorless concentrates, prepared by distillation of the extracts with superheated steam *in vacuo*, or better still, by co-distillation with ethylene glycol *in vacuo*. Owing to the instability of the lichen substances, distillation may cause profound changes in the composition of the distillates. Benzene or petroleum ether extracts will yield distillates quite different from those obtained by distillation of alcoholic extracts. If benzene or petroleum ether extracts are used, the distillate will contain not only the odoriferous substances *originally* present in the lichens, but also orcinol monomethyl ether m. 61°–62°, the methyl ester of β-orcinol carboxylic acid, and small quantities of atranol, β-orcinol monomethyl ether, and chloro-atranol. These compounds are odorless, with the exception of the orcinol monomethyl ether. The latter has such a strong phenolic odor that distillates obtained by the method just mentioned exhibit an odor entirely different from that of the original extract. (In this connection it should be noted that orcinol monomethyl ether was first identified by Walbaum and Rosenthal [18] as a constituent of the volatile oil. In the opinion of Pfau,[19] however, it is doubtful whether this ether actually occurs in the lichens. Pfau found that lichen preparations, from which evernic acid had been removed, on distillation also yielded a volatile oil, in which he could easily identify the ether. Perhaps

[17] *Riechstoff Ind.* **12** (1937), 208.   [19] *Riechstoff Ind.* **12** (1937), 209.
[18] *Ber.* **57** (1924), 771.

the lichen acids are decomposed by the action of enzymes. Under the influence of enzymes in the plant, evernic acid yields everninic acid and orsellinic acid, as well as orcinol monomethyl ether and orcinol. According to Pfau [20] it is quite possible that enzymatic action also occurs, at least to a small extent, in the live lichens, or during the drying process.)

If an alcoholic extract is submitted to steam distillation, the distillate will contain all the above-mentioned alcoholytic cleavage products, particularly the esters of everninic acid. In fact, these esters may be so predominant that the distillates are almost solid. Orcinol monoethyl ether is not formed in this process; therefore these distillates possess a more or less natural, but rather faint odor. In order to remove the sparingly soluble (and odorless) esters of everninic acid, the distillate of the alcoholic extracts should be submitted to a final treatment with cold alcohol or other suitable solvents.

In general, the distillates are difficult to prepare because the yield is very small, and many reactions take place.

So far, we have described chiefly the cleavage reactions taking place in the extraction of lichens with different solvents, and the various cleavage products, most of them odorless or of little odor. However, the lichens also contain a number of highly odorous compounds, although in very small quantities only. From the perfumer's point of view, these odoriferous substances are obviously much more important than the degradation products of the lichen acids.

In 1937, Stoll and Scherrer [21] published the report of a very exhaustive examination of the constituents of the concrete obtained from *Evernia prunastri* by extraction with ether.

Some of the compounds isolated by Stoll and Scherrer from the acidic portions of the extracts are probably degradation products of the lichen acids (see above). Among the acidic substances Stoll and Scherrer identified *everninic acid, orcinol, orcinol monomethyl ether, β-orcinol, methyl ester* of *β-orcinol carboxylic acid, phenols, formic, acetic, stearic, palmitic,* and *oleic acids*. Bases with a pyridine-like odor were also noted in the extracts.

The volatile compounds responsible for the odor of oak moss were found to reside in the neutral part of the extracts, and amounted to only 0.04 per cent. Among the most volatile constituents Stoll and Scherrer isolated:

α- and *β-*Thujone. The chief constituents.

Camphor.

Borneol.

[20] *Ibid.*
[21] *XVIIme Congrès Chim. Ind., Compt. rend.* (1937), 205.

Cineole.

Naphthalene. In varying quantities, depending upon the origin of the oak moss.

Dimethylcyclohexenone(?). The monocyclic ketone $C_8H_{12}O$, observed by Stoll and Scherrer was probably dimethylcyclohexenone. It contained one double bond, and yielded a semicarbazone m. 159°. The odor was reminiscent of bitter almond oil and coumarin.

Methyl Nonyl Ketone(?). This ketone gave a semicarbazone m. 120°.

Other Ketones(?). Not identified.

Geraniol.

Citronellol.

Secondary Terpene Alcohols(?). Not identified.

Vanillin. Traces only.

From the high boiling portions Stoll and Scherrer isolated:

A Lactone(?) $C_{12}H_{20}O_2$ or $C_{13}H_{22}O_2$.

Hydrocarbons $C_{15}H_{28}$.

Hydrocarbons $C_{20}H_{32}$.

Stearyl Alcohol.

Stearaldehyde.

Palmitic Acid. In ester form.

Unsaturated Acids(?).

The content of the above-listed compounds varies considerably according to the origin of the oak moss. Oak moss from Moravia, e.g., contains α- and β-thujone as chief constituents, as well as some camphor, borneol, and cineole (but no naphthalene). Oak moss from Sarajevo contains a high percentage of naphthalene, some of the ketone $C_8H_{12}O$ described above, but very little α- and β-thujone, and no camphor and borneol. Oak moss from Florence and Trieste contains naphthalene and (like all naphthalene-containing oak moss) no camphor and borneol.

Use.—The alcohol-insoluble concretes and resinoids of oak moss and tree moss are used particularly for the scenting of soaps. The products derived from tree moss offer the advantage of lower price. All these products are unsuitable in white soaps, except when used in very small quantities. In preparations where solubility is a requisite, the absolutes should be employed, those made from concretes derived by petroleum ether extraction being of highest quality. The most popular of all products is the absolute of oak moss, obtained from the benzene concrete. It offers the advantage of a true-to-nature odor, combined with a moderate price.

In general, oak moss preparations are not only excellent odor fixatives, but impart to the finished product—whether soap, cosmetic, lotion or handkerchief perfume—a peculiar, earthy, mossy character, the origin of which is often most difficult to trace. Oak moss preparations are indispensable in the creation of chypre and fougère scents. Quite a number of well-known and popular perfumes owe their alluring, exotic odor to a substantial content of oak moss extracts. These extracts have become an important tool in the hands of the experienced perfumer.

SUGGESTED ADDITIONAL LITERATURE

G. A. Perez-Llano, "Lichens—Their Biological and Economic Significance," *Botan. Rev.* **10** (1944), No. 1, 1.

K. Bournot, "Oak Moss," *Am. Perfumer* **32** (June 1936), 65.

J. B. Stark and E. D. Walter, "Isolation of Usnic Acid," U. S. Patent No. 2,522,-547 (1950).

CHAPTER XIX

ESSENTIAL OILS OF THE PLANT FAMILY *PODOCARPACEAE*

OIL OF *DACRYDIUM FRANKLINI* HOOK. F.[1]

A. Huon Pine Wood Oil

Dacrydium franklini Hook. f.[2] (fam. *Podocarpaceae*), the so-called "Huon Pine," a beautiful and tall tree attaining a height of about 100 ft., is one of Tasmania's best known and most valuable pines. It occurs chiefly on the west coast of Tasmania and to a smaller extent in New Zealand, northern Caledonia, in the Malayan Archipelago, Borneo, and Chile.[3] Because of its high content of essential oil, the wood resists attacks of white ants and borers. Moreover, the wood is very durable and has been used extensively for boat building, cabinet making, interior decorating, and carving. Only the heartwood contains essential oil.

The Huon pine wood oil of commerce is produced exclusively from waste wood and sawdust resulting from the milling of logs. Wood chips and sawdust are placed into a battery of stills holding about 2 tons, and are subjected to steam distillation at about 25 lb. pressure per sq. in. Distillation requires approximately 6 hr. The oil is heavier than water and must be collected in suitable oil separators. The yield of oil from air-dried sawdust ranges from 4 to 6 per cent.

Formerly, from 5,000 to 10,000 lb. of oil were produced per year in Tasmania; lately production has declined to about 1,200 lb. per year.

Physicochemical Properties.—The oil derived from the wood of *Dacrydium franklini* Hook. is a colorless or slightly yellowish liquid of mild, pleasant and somewhat spicy odor.

Oils examined by Penfold and Morrison[4] had properties varying within these limits:

> Specific Gravity at 15°/15°...... 1.0438 to 1.0450
> Optical Rotation............... ±0°
> Refractive Index at 20°........ 1.5320 to 1.5323
> Solubility..................... Soluble in 0.6 to 1 vol. and
> more of 70% alcohol

These values resemble those recorded in literature for methyleugenol.

[1] This monograph by A. R. Penfold and F. R. Morrison, Museum of Applied Arts and Sciences, Sydney, Australia.
[2] Baker and Smith, "A Research on the Pines of Australia," Sydney (1910), 397.
[3] *Perfumery Essential Oil Record* **17** (1926), 508.
[4] Own laboratory observations.

Schimmel & Co.[5] analyzed several samples of Huon pine wood oil and reported the following properties:

Specific Gravity at 15°..........	1.0406 to 1.0470
Optical Rotation...............	+1° 21' to −1° 16'
Refractive Index at 20°.........	1.53037 to 1.53446
Solubility.....................	Soluble in 4.3 to 4.8 vol. and more of 60% alcohol
Boiling Range at 770 mm.:	
252° to 255°..................	60%
255° to 260°..................	30%

Chemical Composition.—The oil derived from the wood of *Dacrydium franklini* Hook. has been investigated chiefly by Baker and Smith,[6] by Schimmel & Co.,[7] and the Imperial Institute[8] in London. The oil consists almost entirely of methyleugenol. The following compounds have been identified:

Methyleugenol. The chief constituent, the oil containing from 95 to 97 per cent of methyleugenol. Identified by means of the tetrabromide m. 77°–78°, and by oxidation with potassium permanganate to veratric acid m. 179°–180° (Baker and Smith, Schimmel & Co.).

Eugenol. The oil contains only 0.5 to 1 per cent of eugenol. Identified by preparation of the benzoyl compound m. 70°. In some oils eugenol appears to be absent (Baker and Smith).

Cadinene(?). The high boiling fractions gave a color reaction characteristic of cadinene (Baker and Smith).

Use.—Because of its high germicidal properties, the oil derived from the wood of *Dacrydium franklini* Hook.[9] has been used extensively in the treatment of perionychia, tinea, cuts and wounds, and as a preservative of casein and other nitrogenous products. One interesting application during World War II was its use, in Australia, as a controlling agent in the manufacture of optical glasses—an application the oil owes to its high refractive index. The oil has been used with success in perfumes of the carnation type. Its noncoloring properties are an advantage in the perfuming of transparent soaps.[10]

Huon pine wood oil was one of many Australian essential oils examined during World War II for their efficacy as insect repellents. In common with other oils consisting largely of phenol ethers, it yielded excellent results.

[5] *Ber. Schimmel & Co.* (1928), 23.
[6] "A Research on the Pines of Australia," Sydney (1910), 397.
[7] *Ber. Schimmel & Co.*, October (1910), 135.
[8] *Bull. Imp. Inst.* **22** (1924), 277.
[9] Penfold and Grant, *J. Proc. Roy. Soc. N. S. Wales* **58** (1924), 120; **59** (1925), 348.
[10] *Perfumery Essential Oil Record* **17** (1926), 508.

Huon pine wood oil gave the best protection of all essential oils tested, and was considered to be as effective as dimethyl phthalate.[11] Its use was restricted, however, since it caused irritation of the skin and nausea in a high proportion of sensitive individuals. Pure methyleugenol was found to behave similarly.

In the experience of the authors, Huon pine wood oil offers better protection against sandflies than any other repellent. McCulloch and Waterhouse [12] also pointed out that Huon pine wood oil is at least as promising as Ceylon citronella oil in the prevention of blowfly strike in sheep—a serious menace to the sheep industry of Australia.

B. Huon Pine Leaf Oil

The leaves of *Dacrydium franklini* Hook. f., the "Huon Pine," which grows chiefly in Tasmania, contain about 0.5 per cent of an essential oil which, however, is not produced commercially.

Baker and Smith [13] first examined an oil (d_{15}^{17} 0.8667, α_D +20° 30′, n_D^{25} 1.4815) in which they identified *l-α-pinene, d-limonene,* "dacrydene," and *methyleugenol.*

More recently, Penfold and Simonsen [14] investigated the chemical composition of Huon pine leaf oil and found that it consists chiefly of *l-α*-pinene, *β-pinene, d*-limonene, Δ^4-*carene*, and *phyllocladene* (cf. Tables of Diterpenes, Vol. II of this work, p. 126/7). Penfold and Simonsen confirmed the findings of Baker and Smith in regard to *l-α*-pinene and *d*-limonene, but arrived at the conclusion that the "dacrydene" of Baker and Smith is probably Δ^4-carene.

[11] McCulloch and Waterhouse, "Laboratory Field Tests of Mosquito Repellents," *Australia Council Sci. Ind. Research Bull.* No. 213 (1947), 21, 22, 26.
[12] *Ibid.*
[13] "A Research on the Pines of Australia," Sydney (1910), 399.
[14] *J. Proc. Roy. Soc. N. S. Wales* **63** (1929), 95.

CHAPTER XX

ESSENTIAL OILS OF THE PLANT FAMILY *PINACEAE*

OIL OF *PICEA EXCELSA* LK.

The young twigs and adherent leaves of *Picea excelsa* Lk. (syn. *Picea abies* (L.) Karst. or *P. vulgaris* Lk.), fam. *Pinaceae,* the so-called "Norway Spruce," or spruce, contain an essential oil, small quantities of which are produced in the Tyrol (Puster Valley) and in Yugoslavia (Cerknica). Despite its delightful odor, the oil has not attracted much interest in the trade. Distillation material is available from the end of March to the end of October, when trees are felled or trimmed in order to clear out the forests.

The yield of oil from fresh branches and needles varies from 0.15 to 0.20 per cent. Distillation of one charge requires about 5 hr. Prior to distillation the branches should be cut into small pieces to facilitate packing of the still.

Physicochemical Properties.—Oil of *Picea excelsa* is an almost colorless oil with a most pleasant, refreshing odor resembling that of silver fir oil (*Abies alba* Mill.). Gildemeister and Hoffmann [1] reported these properties for oil of *Picea excelsa:*

Specific Gravity at 15°......	0.874 to 0.888
Optical Rotation..........	$-20°\ 36'$ to $-40°\ 0'$
Refractive Index at 20°.....	1.474 to 1.478
Ester Content, Calculated as	
Bornyl Acetate..........	6 to 12%
Solubility................	Soluble in 3 to 6 vol. of 90% alcohol, occasionally with slight turbidity

Boiling range, according to Bertram and Walbaum: [2]

160°–170°............	20%
170°–185°............	50%
Above 185°..........	Decomposition

Boiling range, according to Umney: [3]

	Per Cent
163°–173°..........	41
173°–176°..........	16
176°–185°..........	13
185°–220°..........	14
Residue.............	16
	100

[1] "Die Ätherischen Öle," 3d Ed., Vol. II, 179.
[2] *Arch. Pharm.* **231** (1893), 296.
[3] *Pharm. J.* **55** (1895), 162.

Two genuine oils of *Picea excelsa* procured by the author in Thal-Assling, Tyrol (I), and in Cerknica, Yugoslavia (II) had the following properties:

	I	II
Specific Gravity at 15°.......	0.882	0.883
Optical Rotation............	−25° 30′	−27° 15′
Refractive Index at 20°......	1.4763	1.4753
Ester Content, Calculated as Bornyl Acetate............	7.8%	9.5%
Total Alcohol Content, Calculated as Borneol..........	11.3%	12.2%
Solubility in 90% Alcohol....	Soluble in 8 vol. with turbidity	Soluble in 7 vol. with slight turbidity
Boiling Range:		
Up to 160°..............	3.0%	2.6%
160°–165°..............	23.0%	8.4%
165°–170°..............	17.0%	22.2%
170°–175°..............	16.0%	26.0%
175°–180°..............	7.5%	13.2%
180°–185°..............	5.0%	4.8%
185°–190°..............	3.5%	2.4%
190°–200°..............	5.2%	3.2%
200°–210°..............	2.4%	2.10%
Above 210° (decomposition products and residue)....	17.4%	15.1%

As in the case of oils of *Abies alba, Pinus sylvestris* and *Pinus mugo* Turra, the boiling ranges observed by the author on genuine oils of *Picea excelsa* produced in recent years differ somewhat from those reported years ago (see above). The reason for this change is still unknown.

Chemical Composition.—The chemical composition of the volatile oil derived from the terminal branches and adherent needles of *Picea excelsa* has been investigated by Bertram and Walbaum,[4] and by Aschan [5] who reported the presence of the following compounds:

Santene. Observed by Aschan in the lowest boiling fractions of German and Swedish oils (cf. Vol. II of this work, p. 79).

l-α-Pinene. In the fraction b. 160°–170°. Identified by means of the nitrolbenzylamine m. 122°–123°, and the nitrosopinene m. 132° (Bertram and Walbaum).

l-Phellandrene. In the fraction b. 170°–175°. Nitrite m. 101° (Bertram and Walbaum).

Dipentene. In the same fraction. Dihydrochloride m. 50° (Bertram and Walbaum).

l-Bornyl Acetate. In the higher boiling fractions (Bertram and Walbaum).

[4] *Arch. Pharm.* **231** (1893), 295.
[5] *Ber.* **40** (1907), 4919.

Cadinene. Also in the higher boiling fractions. Dihydrochloride m. 118° (Bertram and Walbaum).

Use.—Oil of *Picea excelsa* is rarely found on the market. However, the oil could be easily produced in the Tyrol on special request. Because of its very pleasant odor, the oil gives excellent results in all kinds of pine compositions such as bath salts, room sprays, and deodorants.

OIL OF HEMLOCK-SPRUCE

The hemlock and spruce trees are closely related tall evergreens of the family *Pinaceae,* with slender horizontal branches and finely toothed leaves. They grow in many parts of North America from the East Coast to the West Coast. The most important species are:

1. *Tsuga canadensis* (L.) Carr., the so-called "Eastern" or "Common Hemlock" which occurs on the East Coast from Canada to Alabama.
2. *Tsuga heterophylla* (Raf.) Sarg., the "Western Hemlock," "Hemlock-Spruce," "Prince Albert Fir," "Gray Fir," or "Alaska Pine," which occurs on the West Coast from northern California to Alaska, in northern Idaho, and in northwestern Montana.
3. *Picea mariana* (Mill.) B.S.P., syn. *Picea nigra* (Ait.) Lk., the so-called "Black Spruce."
4. *Picea glauca* (Moench) Voss., syn. *Picea alba* Lk., syn. *Picea canadensis* (L.) B.S.P., the "White Spruce."
Like the hemlocks, the spruces are widely distributed in North America.

On steam distillation the young branches and adherent leaves yield an essential oil, substantial quantities of which are produced in the northeastern part of the United States, particularly in northern New York State and in Vermont. Production in the west is negligible.

The method of distillation and the stills employed closely resemble those used for oil of thuja, *Thuja occidentalis* L. In fact, these oils are produced commercially in the same regions, and often by the same farmers (for details see the monograph on "Oil of Thuja," p. 325).

Commercial oil of hemlock or oil of spruce, as it is often called in trade practice, is usually not derived from one single well-defined species of hemlock or spruce, but from mixed branches and leaves of the four species mentioned above, no distinction being made in the collection of the distillation material. As a result of this practice, the physicochemical properties of commercial hemlock or spruce oil vary within rather wide limits (see below).

Yield of Oil.—The yield of oil depends upon several factors, among them the habitat of the trees, their age, the season, and the method of packing the material into the still. Risi and Brule [1] found that branches from isolated, sun-exposed spruce trees yielded 20 per cent more oil than those from trees grown in dense bush. Branches from a twenty-five-year-old spruce tree gave twice as much oil as branches from a forty-five-year-old tree. As regards seasonal yield, the experiments of Risi and Brule showed that there is a first period of high yield during the winter (from the end of January to the end of April), and a second but less pronounced period of good yield in the fall (from the middle of September to the middle of November). The lowest yield was obtained during summer (from May to August). It is noteworthy, particularly to plant physiologists, that the first period of maximum yield precedes the period of strong cambial activity in the spring, whereas the second one follows the formation of summer wood.

As in the case of thuja distillation, the branches should be reduced to small size in order to allow for closer packing of the charge and to prevent the steam from escaping along channels of low resistance. Eleven distillation experiments with spruce carried out in the Province of Quebec by Risi and Brule [2] gave an average oil yield of 0.35 per cent, while four experiments with hemlock yielded only 0.22 per cent of oil. According to the same authors, industrial distillation of hemlock yields from 0.4 to 0.6 per cent of oil, that of spruce from 0.5 to 0.7 per cent of oil. Yields of this order should be considered satisfactory from the commercial point of view.

Physicochemical Properties.—As was mentioned above, the properties of commercial hemlock-spruce oil vary within rather wide limits, because the distillation material used by the oil producers is seldom uniform, being derived from several species. Gildemeister and Hoffmann [3] reported a specific gravity ranging from 0.900 to 0.930 at 15°, and an optical rotation from −14° to −25°.

Commercial hemlock-spruce oils from the northeastern part of the United States (northern New York State, Vermont, etc.) examined by Fritzsche Brothers, Inc., New York, had properties varying within these limits:

[1] *Am. Perfumer* **48** (January 1946), 37.
[2] *Ibid.*
[3] "Die Ätherischen Öle," 3d Ed., Vol. II, 201.

Specific Gravity at 15°/15°.. 0.905 to 0.919
Optical Rotation........... −18° 8' to −26° 10'
Refractive Index at 20°..... 1.4673 to 1.4698
Ester Content, Calculated
  as Bornyl Acetate........ 34.2 to 44.8%, usually above 37.0%
Solubility................. Soluble in 0.5 to 1 vol. and
                    more of 90% alcohol, occa-
                    sionally opalescent with more

Oil of hemlock-spruce is an almost colorless, or slightly yellow, liquid with a very pleasant balsamic odor, reminiscent of pine needles.

Cable [4] described the properties of three commercial hemlock-spruce oils produced between 1909 and 1916:

Specific Gravity at 20°/15°........... 0.9190 to 0.9664
Specific Optical Rotation at 20°....... −14° 51' to −24° 51'
Refractive Index at 20°.............. 1.4721 to 1.4796
Acid Number...................... 1.51 to 18.45
Ester Number..................... 105.09 to 115.41
Ester Number after Acetylation....... 149.51 to 150.83
Ester Content, Calculated as Bornyl
  Acetate......................... 36.78 to 40.39%
Total Alcohol Content, Calculated as
  Borneol........................ 41.55 to 41.74%

The high specific gravity, high refractive index, and particularly the high acid number of these oils indicate that the oils were partly resinified.

As regards the properties of oils derived from well-defined plant species, the following have been reported:

I. Oil of *Tsuga canadensis* (L.) Carr.

Cable [5] examined five samples of oil of *Tsuga canadensis* Carr., the "Eastern Hemlock," distilled in Michigan, Wisconsin, New Hampshire, Tennessee and Virginia (yield 0.29 to 0.65 per cent) which had properties varying within these limits:

Specific Gravity at 20°/15°........... 0.9020 to 0.9234
Specific Optical Rotation at 20°....... −14° 48' to −21° 39'
Refractive Index at 20°.............. 1.4691 to 1.4704
Acid Number...................... 0.33 to 0.70
Ester Number..................... 103.8 to 147.35
Ester Number after Acetylation....... 113.5 to 171.94
Ester Content, Calculated as Bornyl
  Acetate......................... 36.33 to 51.57%
Total Alcohol Content, Calculated as
  Borneol........................ 31.24 to 47.41%

[4] *J. Am. Pharm. Assocn.* **10** (1921), 170.
[5] *Ibid.*

The oil from Wisconsin had a higher ester content and total alcohol content than the four other oils.

More recently, Risi and Brule [6] determined the properties of four samples of oil derived from the "Eastern Hemlock" *Tsuga canadensis* Carr., growing in the Provinec of Quebec, Canada, and found these values:

	Extreme Limits	Average
Specific Gravity at 15°.........	0.9090 to 0.9387	0.9178
Specific Optical Rotation........	−22° 0′ to −24° 24′	−23° 30′
Refractive Index at 20°.........	1.4671 to 1.4766	1.4702
Acid Number..................	0.74 to 2.14	1.31
Ester Number.................	67.6 to 125.3	105.4
Saponification Number..........	68.3 to 126.6	106.7
Boiling Range.................	160° to 165°	162° to 220°
Solubility in 90% Alcohol.......	Soluble in from 0.2 to 0.6 vol.; on the average soluble in 0.3 vol.	

II. Oil of *Tsuga heterophylla* (Raf.) Sarg.

Cable [7] investigated the properties of three oils obtained in Idaho from the "Western Hemlock" *Tsuga heterophylla* Sarg. (yield 0.32 to 0.36 per cent) which had the following properties:

Specific Gravity at 20°/15°.........	0.8444 to 0.8521
Specific Optical Rotation at 20°.....	−6° 44′ to −20° 0′
Refractive Index at 20°............	1.4790 to 1.4840
Acid Number....................	2.57 to 3.4
Ester Number....................	6.7 to 17.25
Ester Number after Acetylation.....	19.6 to 33.4
Ester Content, Calculated as Bornyl Acetate.......................	2.35 to 6.04%
Total Alcohol Content, Calculated as Borneol.......................	5.43 to 9.24%

Lehman and Lynn [8] distilled air-dried needles (oil I) and fresh twigs with adherent fresh needles (oil II) of the "Western Hemlock" *Tsuga heterophylla* Sarg., and obtained 0.12 per cent and 0.09 per cent, respectively, of oils with these properties:

	I	II
Specific Gravity at 25°/25°........	0.9499	0.8741
Specific Optical Rotation at 25°....	Too dark	−17° 20′
Refractive Index at 20°...........	1.4935	1.4804
Acid Number....................	45.74	3.11
Saponification Number...........	78.51	16.51
Ester Content, Calculated as Bornyl Acetate.......................	11.49%	4.69%
Combined Alcohol Content, Calculated as Borneol................	9.01%	3.68%

---

[6] *Am. Perfumer* **48** (January 1946), 37.   [8] *Ibid.* **19** (1930), 1304.
[7] *J. Am. Pharm. Assocn.* **10** (1921), 170.

The oil (II), from the fresh twigs and leaves, was of light color and had a rather unpleasant odor. The oil (I), from the air-dried needles, was viscous, reddish-brown, and exhibited a yellowish-brown fluorescence. The properties show that oxidation by air had profoundly affected this oil while still in the needles (leaves).

III. Oil of *Picea mariana* (Mill.) B.S.P.

Risi and Brule [9] also examined eleven samples of oil derived from *Picea mariana* (Mill.) B.S.P., the "Black Spruce" growing in the Province of Quebec, Canada, and noted the following properties:

	Extreme Limits	*Average*
Specific Gravity at 15°..........	0.9070 to 0.9260	0.9141
Specific Optical Rotation.......	−25° 48′ to −41° 48′	−33° 42′
Refractive Index at 20°........	1.4666 to 1.4722	1.4697
Acid Number................	0.99 to 2.44	1.59
Ester Number................	57.2 to 133.1	97.0
Saponification Number........	59.6 to 135.3	98.6
Boiling Range................	155° to 164°	160° to 221°
Solubility in 90% Alcohol......	Soluble in from 0.4 to 1.2 vol.; on the average soluble in 0.7 vol.	

An oil distilled from *Picea nigra* (Ait.) Lk. (syn. *Picea mariana* [Mill.] B.S.P.) and analyzed by Kremers [10] had these properties:

Specific Gravity at 20°...........	0.9228
Optical Rotation at 20°...........	−36° 22′
Ester Content, Calculated as Bornyl Acetate......................	48.85%
Boiling Range...................	160° to 230°, the principal fraction distilling between 212° and 230°

IV. Oil of *Picea glauca* (Moench) Voss. (syn. *Picea alba* Lk., syn. *Picea canadensis* [L.] B.S.P.).

Komppa [11] distilled young twigs with adherent leaves of the American "White Spruce" *Picea alba* Lk. that had been planted in Finland and obtained 0.3 per cent of an oil with the following properties:

Specific Gravity at 20°/20°...................	0.9251
Specific Optical Rotation at 20°..............	+18° 19′
Refractive Index at 20°.....................	1.4733
Acid Number.............................	1.87
Ester Number.............................	46.67
Ester Content, Calculated as Bornyl Acetate....	16.33%

[9] *Am. Perfumer* **48** (January 1946), 37.
[10] *Pharm. Rundsch.*, New York, **13** (1895), 135.
[11] *Ann. Acad. Sci. Fennicae* [A], **38** (1933), 8. *Ber. Schimmel & Co.* (1935), 62.

The properties of this oil differ greatly from those of the American spruce and hemlock oils. Most striking is the dextrorotation and the low ester content of the finished oil.

Chemical Composition of Hemlock and Spruce Oils.—In the oil of *Picea alba* Lk., just described, Komppa [12] identified:

β-Pinene

Dipentene

l-Limonene

d-Camphor

d-Bornyl Acetate

dl-Fenchyl Alcohol

Cadinene

As regards the American hemlock and spruce oils, Bertram and Walbaum [13] investigated an oil of hemlock and reported the presence of:

l-α-Pinene. Identified by means of the nitrolbenzylamine m. 121°–123°.

l-Bornyl Acetate. The chief constituent of the oil (from 35 to 53 per cent).

A Sesquiterpene(?). Not identified.

More recently Lehman and Lynn [14] examined two oils distilled from the air-dried leaves, and from fresh twigs with adherent leaves of the "Western Hemlock," *Tsuga heterophylla* Sarg. (see above). Lehman and Lynn identified the following compounds in the combined oils, which contained about 65 per cent of terpenes:

α-Pinene. Characterized by oxidation to pinonic acid which yielded a semicarbazone m. 203°.

β-Pinene. Oxidation gave nopinic acid m. 120°.

Camphene. Characterized by hydration to isoborneol m. 206°.

β-Phellandrene. Identified by means of its nitrosite m. 94° (m. 103° on rapid heating).

Cadinene. The oil contains about 10 per cent of cadinene. Identified by preparation of the dihydrochloride m. 117°–118°.

"Picene." A new sesquiterpene which gave a hydrochloride m. 133°. The oil contains about 5 per cent of "picene."

Borneol and Bornyl Acetate. The borneol is present in the oil mostly as acetate.

Benzoic Acid. Contained in the oil partly in free form, partly esterified probably with borneol.

[12] *Ibid.*
[13] *Arch. Pharm.* **231** (1893), 294.
[14] *J. Am. Pharm. Assocn.* **12** (1930), 1304.

The latest and most thorough investigations of the chemical composition of hemlock and spruce oils are those of Shaw, whose papers appeared in 1950 and 1951.

In an essential oil distilled from the foliage and terminal branches of *Tsuga canadensis* (L.) Carr., the "Eastern Hemlock" (yield of oil 0.249%; properties of the oil: d_{20}^{20} 0.9162, α_D^{30} $-12°$ 54', $n_{D_i}^{20}$ 1.4684, acid number 0.76, ester number 130.8, ester number after acetylation 154.1, aldehyde content as citral 0.5%, ketone content as carvone 2.5%), Shaw [15] reported the presence of these compounds:

Terpenes....... Tricyclene (2.2%)
d-α-Pinene (17.6%)
l-β-Pinene (2.9%)
l-Camphene (11.5%)
Myrcene (2.4%)
d-α-Phellandrene (1.8%)
l-Limonene (5.9%)

Alcohols....... A tertiary alcohol b_{10} 189°–192°, d_4^{20} 0.942, α_D $\pm0°$, n_D^{20} 1.4806—(1.3%)

Esters......... l-Bornyl acetate (43.4%)

Ketones........ l-Thujone (1.3%)

Sesquiterpenes.. d-Canadene (0.2%), a new sesquiterpene which appears to be a structural isomer, rather than a diasteriomer, of l-cadinene

Azulenes....... In the highest boiling fractions, but quantity too small to permit identification

In an essential oil distilled from the foliage and terminal branches of *Picea mariana* (Mill.) B.S.P., the "Black Spruce" (yield of oil 0.461 per cent; properties of the oil: d_{20}^{20} 0.9085, α_D $-31°$ 6', n_D^{20} 1.4696, acid number 0.44, ester number 119.7, ester number after acetylation 123.3, aldehyde content as citral 0.3%, ketone content as carvone 1.0%), Shaw [16] observed the following components:

Terpenes....... Santene (2.5%)
Tricyclene (1.0%)
l-α-Pinene (16.0%)
l-β-Pinene (6.5%)
l-Camphene (10.0%)
Myrcene (3.5%)
d-Δ^3-Carene (5.0%)
dl- and l-Limonene (6.5%)
Terpinolene (1.0%)

[15] *J. Am. Chem. Soc.* **73** (1951), 2859.
[16] *Can. J. Research* **28B** (1950), 268.

Alcohols........ *l*-Borneol (1.0%)
An unidentified alcohol b. ~210° (1.0%)
Another unidentified alcohol b_1 ~120° (about 0.5%)

Esters.......... *l*-Bornyl acetate (37.0%)
An unidentified ester b_1 ~120° (about 0.5%)

Ketones........ *dl*-Camphor (1.0%)

Sesquiterpenes.. A compound related to *l*-Cadinene (1.0%)

Residue and Loss 10%

The presence of tricyclene (m. 61°–64°, b. 153°) in the two oils should be of special interest as this is the first report of the occurrence of a tricyclic terpene in nature. Years ago Zienkovski and Moycho [17] reported that tricyclene may be found in camphene prepared by dehydration of isoborneol. Since camphene occurs in oil of hemlock and in oil of spruce it can be assumed that both compounds (camphene and tricyclene) were formed by a similar dehydration of borneol in the living plant. At no time in the investigations carried out by Shaw were conditions sufficiently severe to effect such dehydration of borneol.

Use.—Oil of hemlock-spruce is used as a constituent in pine and cedar blends for the scenting of technical preparations, room sprays, deodorants, and similar products. The oil possesses a very pleasant pine needle odor.

OIL OF *PSEUDOTSUGA TAXIFOLIA* (POIR.) BRITT.

Pseudotsuga taxifolia (Poir.) Britt., syn. *Ps. douglasii* Carr., or *Ps. mucronata* Sudw., or *Tsuga douglasii* Carr., or *Abies douglasii* Lindl., or *A. mucronata* Raf. (fam. *Pinaceae*), the "Douglas Fir," or "Western Fir," is a tall tree widely distributed in the Rocky Mountains and in the mountainous ranges of the Pacific Coast, from California to Oregon and further north.

A. Leaf (Needle) Oil

On steam distillation the young branches and adherent leaves of *Pseudotsuga taxifolia* (Poir.) Britt. yield an essential oil which has been produced experimentally on several occasions. Because of the many varieties and forms in which the Douglas fir occurs in nature, the essential oils de-

[17] *Liebigs Ann.* **340** (1905), 24.

scribed in literature as "Douglas Fir Oils" differ considerably in regard to their physicochemical properties and chemical composition.

Brandel and Sweet[1] distilled fresh twigs and leaves of some trees in Washington and obtained an oil in which they identified *camphene* and *borneol*. The ester content, calculated as bornyl acetate, was 34.6 per cent; the free alcohol content, calculated as borneol, 27.18 per cent.

Oils produced experimentally in California by Schorger[2] (yield 0.163 per cent) had these properties:

Specific Gravity at 15°..............	0.8727 to 0.8759
Optical Rotation at 20°.............	−17° 1′ to −22° 10′
Refractive Index at 15°.............	1.4758 to 1.4780
Acid Number......................	0.65 to 1.1
Ester Number.....................	11.13 to 24.25
Ester Number after Acetylation......	27.5 to 51.78

Schorger found that the Californian oil had the following composition:

Per Cent

Furfural................	Traces
l-α-Pinene..............	25
l-β-Pinene..............	48
l- and *dl*-Limonene......	6
Borneol................	6.5
Esters.................	6.1 (calculated as bornyl acetate)
Sesquiterpenes..........	3 (b_{20} 125°–205°)

The oil did not contain any camphene.

In an oil from the leaves of young *Pseudotsuga douglasii* Carr. trees, grown in Avondale, England, Bennett[3] noted the presence of *dipentene* or *limonene,* traces of *citral,* and perhaps *pinene.* The chief constituent of the oil appeared to be *geraniol.* The total alcohol content (calculated as geraniol) of the oil was 31.5 per cent.

The same author[4] also distilled the leaves of *Pseudotsuga glauca* Mayr., the "Colorado Douglas Fir," or "Blue Fir," grown in East Liss, Hants, England, and obtained 0.31 per cent of an oil which contained 34.5 per cent of esters, calculated as bornyl acetate. The terpenes consisted chiefly of *pinene.*

Alinari[5] investigated an oil derived from the leaves of *Pseudotsuga douglasii* Carr., grown in the Province of Florence, Italy, and found that the oil (yield 1.28 per cent) contained 9.44 per cent of free alcohols, and 6.6 per

[1] *Pharm. Rev.* **26** (1908), 326.
[2] *J. Am. Chem. Soc.* **35** (1913), 1895.
[3] *Perfumery Essential Oil Record* **11** (1920), 218.
[4] *Ibid.*
[5] *Ann. chim. applicata* **16** (1926), 185.

cent of esters, calculated as bornyl acetate. The oil consisted chiefly of *β-pinene*, some *geraniol* and *nerol*, the alcohols occurring in the oil partly free, partly esterified with *acetic acid* and *capric acid*.

More recently Johnson and Cain [6] distilled twigs and leaves of *Pseudotsuga taxifolia* (Poir.) Britt., collected in Washington from August to September, and obtained 0.8 per cent of a yellowish oil with a pleasant odor. The oil had these properties:

Specific Gravity at 20°......................... 0.8696
Specific Optical Rotation at 22°................ −23° 30′
Refractive Index at 20°....................... 1.4732
Acid Number................................ 1.65
Saponification Number........................ 25.4
Saponification Number after Acetylation........ 63.3
Total Alcohol Content, Calculated as Geraniol... 17.2%
Free Alcohol Content, Calculated as Geraniol.... 10.7%

The oil contained 75 per cent of terpenes and 19 per cent of higher boiling constituents, including an alcohol and sesquiterpenes.

Johnson and Cain [7] reported the presence of the following compounds in the oil:

Per Cent

l-α-Pinene.......... 12
l-β-Pinene.......... 33
l-Camphene......... 7
Dipentene........... 18
Geraniol............ 12 (partly as acetate, partly as caprate)
Phenols............ 0.07 (chiefly salicylic acid)

According to the author's knowledge, the oil is not produced at present on a commercial scale.

B. Turpentine Oil
(Oil of Oregon Turpentine—Oil of "Oregon Balsam")

Due to wind shakes, old trunks of *Pseudotsuga taxifolia* (Poir.) Britt. contain clefts and crevices a few inches above the ground; they are filled with an oleoresin similar to that produced by the "Balsam Fir" *Abies balsamea* (L.) Mill. (see the monograph on page 232 of the present volume). This "Pitch" or "Oregon Balsam," as it is called in the trade, is actually not a balsam but a true turpentine because it consists only of resin and

[6] *J. Am. Pharm. Assocn.* **26** (1937), 406.
[7] *Ibid.*

volatile oil, and contains no cinnamic acid or benzoic acid. Oregon turpentine is collected either from felled trees or by drilling a hole into a live tree, inserting a tube and permitting the oleoresin to drip into a vessel. An old tree may yield from 1 to 3 gal. of oleoresin.

Oregon turpentine has a darker color than Canada turpentine; unlike the latter it is clearly soluble in alcohol. On exposure to air, Oregon turpentine remains sticky, whereas the Canadian product dries to a solid transparent film. Canada turpentine is more viscous than Oregon turpentine. Unlike the latter, the product from Canada solidifies when mixed with about one-sixth of its weight of heavy magnesia moistened with a little water.

On steam distillation Oregon turpentine yields from 22 to more than 35 per cent of a volatile oil.

Physicochemical Properties of the Oil.—From the data published by Rabak,[8] Frankforter and Frary,[9] Benson and Darrin,[10] Schorger,[11] Mahood,[12] Holmes,[13] and Benson and McCarthy,[14] it appears that the physicochemical properties of the volatile oil obtained by steam distillation of Oregon turpentine vary within these limits:

> Specific Gravity at 15°...... 0.863 to 0.882
> Optical Rotation........... −22° 0′ to −47° 0′
> Refractive Index at 15°..... 1.470 to 1.473

Chemical Composition of the Oil.—Schorger[15] identified the following compounds in the volatile oil of "Oregon balsam," derived from the heartwood (A), and from the sapwood (B):

(A) *l*-α-Pinene. (About 60 per cent of the oil.)

   l-Limonene. (About 5 per cent of the oil.)

   l-α-Terpineol. (In the highest boiling fraction.) This oil contained no β-pinene.

(B) *l*-α-Pinene. (About 17 per cent of the oil.)

   l-β-Pinene. (About 46 per cent of the oil.)

   l-Limonene. Presence possible, but not proved.

[8] *Pharm. Rev.* **22** (1904), 293.
[9] *J. Am. Chem. Soc.* **28** (1906), 1461.
[10] *J. Ind. Eng. Chem.* **3** (1911), 818.
[11] *J. Am. Chem. Soc.* **39** (1917), 1040.
[12] *Am. J. Pharm.* **91** (1919), 345.
[13] *Pharm. J.* **108** (1922), 146. *Am. J. Pharm.* **94** (1922), 354.
[14] *J. Ind. Eng. Chem.* **17** (1925), 193.
[15] *J. Am. Chem. Soc.* **39** (1917), 1040.

In an oil obtained in Oregon from the turpentine of "Douglas Fir" (yield 38 per cent), Benson and McCarthy [16] noted about 45 per cent of *l*-α-pinene and 45 per cent of *l*-β-pinene.

Use.—According to the author's knowledge, oil of Oregon turpentine is not produced on a commercial scale at present. However, the turpentine itself is used in all kinds of technical preparations.

OIL OF *ABIES SIBIRICA* LEDEB.
(Siberian Fir or "Pine" Needle Oil)

Abies sibirica Ledeb. (fam. *Pinaceae*), the so-called "Siberian Fir," grows in wide areas of the U.S.S.R. The young terminal branches, and particularly the adherent leaves (needles) contain an essential oil, large quantities of which are produced in European Russia, the chief producing region being the district of Vyatka. In the trade the oil is often called "Siberian *Pine* Needle Oil," an obvious misnomer. The same is true of the German term "Sibirisches Fichtennadelöl" for oil of *Abies sibirica*, the Siberian "Fichte" (spruce) actually being *Picea obovata* Ledeb.

Total production of the oil has fluctuated greatly. Prior to World War I, it was about 100 metric tons per year; in 1925–26 it amounted to approximately 240 tons; in 1926–27 production declined to about 100 tons.[1] At the time of this writing reliable data are not available.

According to Birukov,[2] distillation of the oil was resumed after World War I, and in 1927 there were more than 400 small village distilleries in operation, each producing from 0.5 to 2 metric tons of oil per year.

The stills [3] used for this purpose are quite primitive, many of them resembling the wooden barrel stills employed in Japan for the distillation of mint (cf. Vol. III of this work, p. 648), but cruder. About 500 kg. of fresh terminal branches and adherent needles are charged into the still above a wooden screen, which supports the material and prevents contact with the boiling water in the kettle beneath the barrel.

Another type consists of a wooden keg or barrel with a separate steam boiler mounted above a fire hearth.

[16] *J. Ind. Eng. Chem.* **17** (1925), 193.
[1] *Chem. Ind.* **49** (1926), 493; **51** (1928), 116.
[2] *Seifensieder-Ztg.* (*Der Parfumeur*) **3** (1929), 53.
[3] For details see an article by Maisit, *Ber. Schimmel & Co.* (1923), 228. Cf. Gildemeister and Hoffmann, "Die Ätherischen Öle," 3d Ed., Vol. II, 190.

The distillers fully realize that the plant material has to be packed into the stills quite tightly in order to obtain a good yield of oil. Maisit [4] reported yields up to 1.25 per cent, but in actual practice the yield averages 0.66 per cent. The most opportune time for distillation is in spring and summer; in winter the yield decreases substantially. Pigulevski et al.[5] distilled the needles of *Abies sibirica* exclusively and obtained from 1.3 to 2 per cent of oil, which contained from 44 to 51 per cent of bornyl acetate. In general, the yield increased from winter to the end of August. Needles one or two years old contained less oil than young needles.

Physicochemical Properties.—The volatile oil derived from the terminal branches and leaves of *Abies sibirica* Ledeb. is a colorless to slightly yellowish liquid with a most pleasant and refreshing odor, characteristic of fir needles.

Gildemeister and Hoffmann [6] reported these properties for Siberian fir needle oil:

Specific Gravity at 15°............. 0.905 to 0.925
Optical Rotation.................. −37° 0′ to −43° 0′
Refractive Index at 20°........... 1.469 to 1.473
Acid Number.................... Up to 2.5
Ester Content, Calculated as Bornyl
  Acetate....................... 29 to 41%
Solubility..................... Soluble in 10 to 14 vol. of 80% alcohol, usually with slight turbidity. Clearly soluble in 0.5 to 1 vol. of 90% alcohol, in very rare cases opalescent

Numerous shipments of Siberian fir needle oil examined by Fritzsche Brothers, Inc., New York, over a period of years had properties varying within the following limits:

Specific Gravity at 15°/15°........ 0.903 to 0.918
Optical Rotation................. −35° 21′ to −41° 44′
Refractive Index at 20°........... 1.4685 to 1.4720
Ester Content, Calculated as Bornyl
  Acetate....................... 28.5 to 42.0%
Solubility..................... Soluble in 0.5 to 1 vol. of 90% alcohol and more, sometimes with opalescence

Oils of the best quality should show a specific gravity of not less than 0.910, an optical rotation of not less than −36°, and an ester content of not less than 35 per cent.

[4] *Ibid.*
[5] *J. Russ. Phys. Chem. Soc.* **55** (1924), 175. *Chem. Zentr.* (1925), I, 239.
[6] "Die Ätherischen Öle," 3d Ed., Vol. II, 194.

Adulteration.—Oil of *Abies sibirica* is occasionally adulterated with various fractions of pine oil and with synthetic isobornyl acetate. Lately, synthetic *dl*-bornyl acetate has become available at sufficiently low prices to permit use of this ester as an adulterant of Siberian fir needle oil.

Chemical Composition.—The chemical composition of Siberian fir needle oil was investigated by Golubev,[7] Hirschsohn,[8] Schimmel & Co.,[9] Schindelmeiser,[10] Wallach,[11] Aschan,[12] Wallach and Grosse,[13] and Gildemeister and Köhler.[14] The following compounds have been reported as constituents of the oil :

Santene. In the lowest boiling fractions (below 145°) of the oil. Nitrosochloride
m. 109°–111°; nitrosite m. 124°–125°. The oil contains from 3 to 4 per cent of
santene (Aschan).

l-α-Pinene. Identified by means of its nitrolbenzylamine m. 122°–123° (Schimmel &
Co.).

β-Pinene. Reported by Gildemeister and Köhler.

l-Camphene. The oil contains about 10 per cent of *l*-camphene. Fractionation yields
this terpene in crystalline form m. 39°–41° (Golubev, Schindelmeiser, Wallach).

α-Phellandrene. Identified by Schindelmeiser. Nitrite m. 106°–107°.

Dipentene. Identified by the same author. Dihydrochloride m. 49°; dihydrobromide
m. 64°.
According to Schindelmeiser, the oil contains about 5.4 per cent of α-phellandrene and dipentene.

l-Bornyl Acetate. The chief constituent, in the amount of 30 to 40 per cent of the oil.
First reported by Hirschsohn.

Borneol(?). Schimmel & Co. noted the presence, in the oil, of a free terpene alcohol
which was presumably borneol.

Terpinyl Acetate. The same authors furthermore observed in the oil the acetic ester
of another terpene alcohol which was perhaps terpineol.

Bisabolene. In the high boiling fractions of the oil Wallach and Grosse identified
bisabolene. The trihydrochloride melted at 79°–80°.

A Siberian fir needle oil distilled from *Abies sibirica* Ledeb. in the Altai Mountains and examined by Rutovski and Vinogradova [15] had properties

---

[7] *J. Russ. Phys. Chem. Soc.* **20** (1888), 477; **36** (1904), 1096; **41** (1909), 1004.
[8] *Pharm. Zeitschr. Russland* **30** (1892), 593. *Chem. Zentr.* (1892), II, 793.
[9] *Ber. Schimmel & Co.,* October (1896), 76.
[10] *J. Russ. Phys. Chem. Soc.* **35** (1903), 75. *Chem. Zentr.* (1903), I, 835. *Apoth. Ztg.*
19 (1904), 815. *Chem. Ztg.* **31** (1907), 759.
[11] *Nachr. kgl. Ges. Wiss. Göttingen,* Sitzung July 20, 1907.
[12] *Ber.* **40** (1907), 4918.
[13] *Liebigs Ann.* **368** (1909), 19.
[14] *Wallach-Festschrift,* Göttingen (1909), 418.
[15] *Riechstoff Ind.* (1926), 158.

somewhat different from those of the usual commercial oils (d_{20}^{20} 0.9581; ester content, calculated as bornyl acetate, 48.7 per cent; total alcohol content, calculated as borneol, 60.9 per cent). In this oil, Rutovski and Vinogradova identified camphor by conversion to isoborneol m. 210°–211°.

Zalkind and Saboiev [16] investigated an oil obtained by steam distillation of the air-dried bark of *Abies sibirica* Ledeb. In this oil Zalkind and Saboiev noted the presence of *l-α-pinene*, camphene(?), phellandrene(?), *l-bornyl acetate* or *l*-isobornyl acetate(?). Compared with the oil derived from the terminal branches and adherent leaves, the bark oil contained more hydrocarbons and less esters.

Use.—Of all the pine, fir and spruce needle oils, the Siberian fir needle oil is without question the most important one. It is used widely for the scenting of toilet and shaving soaps, bath preparations, room sprays, deodorants, disinfectants, inhalants, and a great variety of similar products.

JAPANESE PINE NEEDLE OIL
("Shin-Yo-Yu")

Japanese pine needle oil is produced by steam distillation of the terminal branches and leaves (needles) of several pinaceous trees—among which *Abies sachalinensis* Masters and *Abies mayriana* Miyabe et Kudo (in Japanese "Aka-Todo-Matsu" and "Ao-Todo-Matsu," respectively) preponderate. If the oil were derived exclusively from these two species of the genus *Abies*, it should be classified as a *fir* needle oil. However, in the collection of the distillation material, as generally practiced in the past, some admixture with leaves and twigs of *Picea jezoensis* Carr. ("Kuru-Ezo-Matsu" in Japanese) was unavoidable. Hence it is more accurate to employ the loose term *"pine* needle oil"* ("Shin-Yo-Yu" in Japanese) to the essential oil obtained from these three pinaceous trees.

Although large quantities of this type of oil are produced in the northern part of Japan, little has been known about it outside of that country; in fact, the oil appeared on the European and American markets only in 1931, when Schimmel & Co.[1] examined the first commercial sample. The follow-

---

[16] *J. Russ. Phys. Chem. Soc.* **60** (1928), 553.
[1] *Ber. Schimmel & Co.* (1931), 86.

ing description is based chiefly upon information which the author was able to obtain recently from reliable sources in Japan.[2]

Occurrence, Producing Regions, and Total Production.—Trees of the genera *Abies* and *Picea* do not grow on Japan's main island (which enjoys a relatively warm climate), but in the cold climate of Hokkaido Island, north of the Tsugaru Strait, and further north in the vast virgin forests on the peninsula of Sakhalin. Since the end of World War II, the former Japanese part of this peninsula has been ceded to the U.S.S.R., and nothing is known about production of the oil there. The Japanese pine needle oil now available on the market is produced exclusively on the island of Hokkaido. Here the trees grow wild in mountain forests; they have also been planted extensively in government-owned woodlands. A survey undertaken in 1945 by the Japanese government indicated that the volume of wood growing in Hokkaido was then about 113,000,000 cu.m. for *Abies*, and 83,000,000 cu.m. for *Picea* species. The average yearly lumber production [3] from 1941 to 1943 inclusive was 1,550,000 cu.m. for *Abies*, and 1,890,000 cu.m. for *Picea* species. About 65 per cent of this was used in building and construction, the balance being employed for the production of pulp in the paper industry, for the shoring of mines, the building of ships, and for use as wire poles. The total quantity of twigs and leaves obtained every year as by-product in the lumber mills has been estimated at 150,000 metric tons for *Abies* species, and 160,000 tons for *Picea*. Since the branches and leaves of *Abies* species yield on the average 1.2 per cent of essential oil, and those of *Picea* 0.4 per cent, the maximum total yearly production of *Abies* oils may be calculated as 1,800 metric tons, and that of *Picea* oil as 640 tons. For practical reasons, however, these maximum figures can never be attained. The trees grow on steep mountain slopes, and for easy transport of the lumber must be felled in winter. Large quantities of twigs and leaves remain in the forests and cannot be used for distillation at present. Total yearly production of pine needle oils in Hokkaido therefore averages only about 120 metric tons. Recently, however, portable stills of simple construction have been designed (see below); once adopted by the lumber industry, they could be set up in the mountain forests, and production of the oil could be increased considerably.

Distillation.—The stationary stills used in the past for distillation of pine needle oils in Hokkaido were of the same type as those employed for the processing of *Mentha arvensis* (cf. Vol. III of the present work, p. 648). However, this older process is apparently being gradually abandoned. A few years ago, the Sapporo Branch of the Forest Experiment Station in Hokkaido devised a very simple, low-priced, and portable still utilizable

[2] Private communication from Dr. Teikichi Hiraizumi, Tokyo.
[3] *Rept. Hokkaido Forest Expt. Sta.*, No. 18 (1944).

even in rough mountain country. It consists of a converted metal drum, 80 cm. high and 55 cm. wide, set up above an open fire hearth; the still top is attached to the retort by a water seal, the latter 10 cm. high (cf. Vol. I of the present work, p. 127). When this type of still gains wide acceptance, production of Japanese pine needle oil will be much facilitated.

The distillation material consists of fresh leaves (needles) and terminal branches about ½ in. thick, in the proportion one to one. From 45 to 50 kg. of this material are charged into the retort, and a quantity of water sufficient to cover the material (about 120 liters) is added. The operation thus actually represents *water* distillation (cf. Vol. I, pp. 112, 120, and 142). Dried wood serves as fuel for the fire beneath the still bottom. The distillation waters are returned to the still for the next operation—i.e., cohobated. Distillation of one charge lasts from 6 to 7 hr., and yields about 800 cu. cm. of oil (1.6 to 1.8 per cent, calculated upon the weight of the charge). This is a much higher yield than that obtained in the wooden barrel stills (see above).

Compared with the *Abies* species, *Picea jezoensis* not only gives a lower yield of oil, but also an oil of poorer quality, and containing less bornyl acetate. For this reason, plant material of *Abies* species ought never to be mixed with leaves and twigs of *Picea*. To prevent any such admixture, government inspectors now encourage producers to cut lower twigs and adherent leaves of live trees during the summer months, and to use only this type of material for distillation (instead of the leaves and twigs of whole trees felled in winter). It should thus be possible to obtain oils of *Abies* exclusively, without any admixed *Picea* oil. The quality of the Japanese pine needle oils will thereby be greatly improved (becoming then, however, a *fir* needle oil—see above).

Physicochemical Properties and Chemical Composition.

(1) Oil of *Abies sachalinensis* Masters
(including Oil of *Abies mayriana* Miyabe et Kudo)

Oil of *Abies sachalinensis*, which in commercial production usually includes oil of *Abies mayriana*, is a colorless to faintly yellow liquid with an odor resembling that of Siberian fir needle oil, but weaker and less lasting. It possesses a lower bornyl acetate content.

Hayashi [4] reported these properties for a sample of the oil:

Specific Gravity at 15°/15°........ 0.8911
Specific Optical Rotation at 20°.... −54° 54′
Refractive Index at 20°........... 1.4762

[4] *Rept. Hokkaido Ind. Research Inst.* No. 11 (1927).

Acid Number.................... 0.56
Ester Number.................. 76.57
Ester Number after Acetylation.... 92.92
Solubility..................... Soluble in 1.74 vol. of 90% alcohol,
                                 in 7.45 vol. of 85% alcohol, and in
                                 14 vol. of 80% alcohol

Boiling Range:
  Up to 158°.................... 3.2%
  158° to 163°.................. 8.6%
  163° to 167°.................. 19.5%
  167° to 171°.................. 16.2%
  171° to 177°.................. 22.4%
  177° to 210°.................. 11.0%
  210° to 220°.................. 3.8%
  220° to 235°.................. 13.2%

According to Hayashi,[5] the oil has the following composition:

	Per Cent
α-Pinene	22
β-Pinene	10
Camphene	15
l-α-Phellandrene	15
Dipentene	3
l-Bornyl Acetate	26
Sesquiterpene	1

Investigating an oil of *Abies sachalinensis* Masters, Miura[6] noted these properties:

Specific Gravity at 15°.............. 0.8962
Optical Rotation................... −33° 39′
Refractive Index at 20°............ 1.4729
Ester Number.................... 76.66
Ester Number after Acetylation...... 85.59

The oil contained about 15 per cent of *α-pinene,* 26 per cent of *camphene,* and 21 per cent of *borneol.*

(2) Oil of *Picea jezoensis* Carr.

Oil of *Picea jezoensis* somewhat resembles oil of *Abies sachalinensis* Masters and oil of *Abies mayriana* Miyabe et Kudo, but is of lower quality, containing much less bornyl acetate.

[5] *Ibid.*
[6] *Proc. Fifth Pacific Sci. Congress* **5** (1934), 3919. *Chem. Zentr.* (1938), I, 4544.

Hayashi [7] reported these properties for a sample of the oil:

> Specific Gravity at 15°/15°.......... 0.8946
> Specific Optical Rotation........... −44° 45′
> Refractive Index at 20°............ 1.4823
> Acid Number..................... 0.38
> Ester Number.................... 21.57
> Yield of Oil...................... 0.51%

According to the same author,[8] the oil has the following composition:

	Per Cent
l-α-Pinene / Camphene	5
β-Pinene......................	...
l-Limonene..................	40
l-Bornyl Acetate.............	7.6
Sesquiterpene................	20–25
Sesquiterpene Alcohol.........	20–25

(3) Commercial Oils

In 1931, Schimmel & Co.[9] examined a commercial sample of oil of *Abies sachalinensis* Masters and noted these values:

> Specific Gravity at 15°........... 0.8959
> Optical Rotation................ −37° 58′
> Refractive Index at 20°.......... 1.47348
> Acid Number.................... 0.4
> Ester Number................... 74.7
> Ester Content, Calculated as Bornyl
>   Acetate...................... 26.1%
> Solubility...................... Soluble in about 3 vol. and more of 90% alcohol, with turbidity

A commercial sample of oil of *Abies sachalinensis* procured by the author during a visit to Japan exhibited the following properties:

> Specific Gravity at 15°/15°........ 0.904
> Optical Rotation................. −36° 45′
> Refractive Index at 20°........... 1.4725
> Ester Content, Calculated as Bornyl
>   Acetate...................... 28.2%
> Ester Number after Acetylation.... 113.9
> Solubility at 20°................. Opalescent in 10 vol. and more of 90% alcohol

[7] *Rept. Hokkaido Ind. Research Inst.* No. 21 (1929).
[8] *Ibid.*   [9] *Ber. Schimmel & Co.* (1931), 86.

The odor of the oil was reminiscent of bornyl acetate, but it had a slight by-note of cuminaldehyde.

Use.—Japanese pine needle oil ("Shin-Yo-Yu") is used in the United States chiefly for the scenting of soaps and technical preparations. Occasionally the oil serves as an adulterant of higher priced fir needle oils.

OIL OF *ABIES ALBA* MILL.

Introduction.—Before discussing oil of *Abies alba* and other essential oils distilled in the Tyrol from coniferous trees it may be well to describe briefly the methods by which these oils are obtained.

In principle, practically all Tyrolean pine needle distilleries operate along similar lines, though they may vary in size or in still capacity. Hence a few introductory remarks about methods of distillation may obviate much repetition in some of the succeeding monographs.

To begin with, a site in the center of an ample supply of raw material is chosen, with a view to minimizing cost of transportation. Important also is low initial investment, allowing for early amortization. Stills must be low-priced, yet efficient, and large enough to permit production of oils of good quality on a commercial scale.

After a distillery has been operated for a number of years in one locality, the plant material in the nearby mountains may become exhausted. The forestry laws in Europe are strict and, in these instances, require a respite of many years, so that trees can recuperate before being trimmed or cut again. The distillery must, therefore, be moved to another location (long-distance transportation of the material makes operation uneconomical).

Plant material growing wild on the surrounding mountains is cut either directly by laborers hired by the distillers, or by individual peasants who work at the task during their spare time. These peasants sell cut plant material to distillers, against cash, whenever they deliver their day's harvest. The paying off of the cutters is done by the foreman of the distillery. The foremen in turn are paid by the owners of the various producing organizations, on a basis of kilograms of oil distilled, the price usually being established before the beginning of the distillation season. The foremen are thus largely responsible for the final success of the distillation, and almost become small producers themselves. Some farmers operate their own stills; but lacking a sales or export organization, such small producers sell their home-distilled oil to exporters or to larger distillers. In general, the bulk of the oil is produced in more or less modern distillation posts distributed throughout the producing regions.

Some of the plant material can be cut all year around (except when snow prohibits transportation). Other material may be cut only at certain periods of the year, when the plant contains the greatest amount of essential oil and gives the best yield. Whatever roads there are on these isolated mountain slopes are difficult to drive over, so that most of the plant material is hauled on horse- or ox-drawn carts. Wherever possible, however, a simple but efficient means of haulage is exploited: a ½-in. cable is stretched from the distillery in the valley up to the mountain forests or the slope where the cut plant material is first assembled. Strong bundles of about 100 lb. are made up. These are then attached with an iron hook to the cable and allowed to slide down to the valley, directly in front of the distillery. If the incline is not sufficiently steep the hooks are replaced by small pulleys. Wherever the distance between the distillery and the cutting ground is too great, several cables are set up, with relay points, at which men transfer the bundles from one cable to the next. In some instances several cables may converge from different hills to one central point of assembly. This is a quick and cheap method of transportation. Care must be exercised not to lead the cables too close to the distillery, since the cables act as excellent lightning rods, and heavy lightning storms occur frequently among the towering peaks and mountains of the Tyrolean Alps.

In general, the distilleries are constructed of wood, which is plentiful and low-priced in these heavily timbered regions. Some buildings contain three floors. The plant material is stored on the third floor. A chopper operated by an electric motor or gasoline engine reduces it to a size suitable for distillation. The motors or gasoline engines are set up outside of the building, or, if inside, must be properly insulated to minimize fire risks. Reduction of the raw material to small size increases the yield of oil, shortens the time of distillation and permits a large quantity of material to be charged into a still. Needles (leaves) are never distilled alone, but always with the twigs and terminal branches on which they grow. It has been found that there is very little difference between oils distilled exclusively from needles and those distilled from terminal branches and twigs with attached needles.

From the chopper on the third floor the reduced plant material slides by gravity into the still or stills on the second floor. The stills—usually two to the building—are of medium size, more or less modern in construction, and usually well insulated with a thick wooden jacket. Some of the older stills are made entirely of wood. Excessive length of distillation is usually the result of the presence of an accumulation of water by condensation within stills improperly insulated. Steam of 3 to 4 kg. per sq. cm. (boiler pressure) gives best results. It is generated in a separate steam boiler located on the ground floor. Exhausted and sun-dried plant material serves as fuel.

There are no general rules for the layout of a distillery, the main object being practicability and economy. Sometimes stills are installed on rollers and metal rails. Thus, after completion of one batch, the still can be moved to an opening in the wall of the building and tilted so that the exhausted plant material falls to the ground outside of the building, for drying in the sun. About one-half or two-thirds of the exhausted material is required to heat the stills. The balance may serve as bedding for cattle; or it may be burned and the ashes used as fertilizer.

In some cases the plant material exhausted by steam distillation is extracted with hot water before it is removed from the still. The aqueous extracts are then drawn off and concentrated in another still. The concentrated extracts constitute the base of the pine needle extracts popular in Europe. They form a dark, semisolid mass, soluble in water, with an odor reminiscent of pine needles, but somewhat masked by a "cooked" off-note. To restore the original perfume, a small quantity of essential oil is added. In such reconstituted form the pine needle extracts are excellent bases for bath preparations. They are said to possess some medicinal value.

A. Leaf (Needle) Oil

Abies alba Mill., syn. *Abies pectinata* DC., or *A. excelsa* Lk., or *A. picea* Lindl., not Mill. (fam. *Pinaceae*), the European silver fir, or "Edeltanne" or "Weisstanne," as it is called in German-speaking countries, grows in Switzerland, the Tyrol, Germany (Black Forest and Thuringia), France (Vosges), Austria, Yugoslavia and other mountainous sections of Europe. It is the tree which produces the so-called "Strassburg Turpentine" ("Thérébenthine d'Alsace" or "Th. des Vosges"), large quantities of which were formerly used in some parts of Europe.

The young twigs and adherent leaves contain an essential oil of delightful odor, substantial quantities of which are produced particularly in Yugoslavia (in Carniola, with Logatec and Cerknica as centers), the Tyrol (Thal-Assling and Puster Valley), Germany (in the Black Forest near Freudenstadt), and in lower Austria (near Neu Lengbach). Under normal conditions, yearly production in Yugoslavia averages 4,000 kg. of oil, in Germany approximately 1,000 kg., and in the Tyrol about 500 kg.

Distillation is carried out throughout the year, particularly in Yugoslavia. During the winter deep snow may prevent collection of distillation material; in this case, accumulated stocks are processed. The plant material is usually obtained when trees are cut. Young branches with adherent leaves (needles) are hacked off the felled trees, tied into bundles of about 100 lb., and either carted to the nearest distillation post or hooked on to long relay cables, on which they slide rapidly from the mountain slopes to the distillery in the valley.

One man can collect and bundle up to 900 kg. of branches per day. Wages of the cutters and transportation to the distillery are the only factors determining the cost of the distillation material. As a rule, only 60 to 70-year-old trees are felled. The strict forestry laws enforced in most parts of Europe require that a new tree be planted for every old tree felled. Natural regrowth also helps to propagate the trees.

Prior to distillation, the twigs are chopped into small pieces by means of special cutting machines, in order to pack the stills tightly. Distillation of dry material lasts about 5 hr. per charge; wet twigs require longer hours, particularly in winter. The exhausted material is dried and used as fuel in the steam boilers.

The yield of oil ranges from 0.25 to 0.35 per cent; dried twigs and leaves obviously yield more oil than wet ones. The poorest yield is obtained in the spring, i.e., during the period of strong cambial activity in the trees.

Physicochemical Properties.—Oil of *Abies alba* is a colorless or slightly yellowish liquid of most pleasant, balsamic odor, reminiscent of fir needles.

Gildemeister and Hoffmann [1] reported the following properties for the volatile oil derived from the twigs and adherent leaves of *Abies alba* Mill. ("Edeltannennadelöl"):

Specific Gravity at 15°.............. The specific gravity depends upon the origin of the oil. In oils from the Tyrol and Switzerland, the gravity ranges from 0.867 to 0.875. Oils from lower and upper Austria may have a gravity as high as 0.886

Optical Rotation................... −34° 0′ to −60° 0′; in exceptional cases as high as −64°. In the opinion of Gildemeister and Hoffmann, oils with such high optical rotations are perhaps adulterated with oil derived from the cones of *Abies alba* (templin oil)

Refractive Index at 20°............. 1.473 to 1.476

Acid Number...................... Up to 2.0

Ester Content, Calculated as Bornyl Acetate........................ 4.5 to 11.0%

Solubility....................... Soluble in 4 to 7 and more vol. of 90% alcohol, occasionally with slight turbidity

Boiling Range..................... 8% of the oil distills below 170°
55% of the oil distills from 170° to 185°

[1] "Die Ätherischen Öle," 3d Ed., Vol. II, 176.

Three genuine oils of *Abies alba* Mill. procured by the author in the Tyrol and Yugoslavia had these properties:

	Eastern Tyrol	Northern Tyrol	Yugoslavia
Specific Gravity at 15°......	0.879	0.880	0.875
Optical Rotation...........	−57° 45′	−45° 17′	−59° 1′
Refractive Index at 20°.....	1.4753	1.4736	1.4744
Ester Number.............	24.3	21.6	19.0
Ester Number after Acetylation......................	33.7	31.2	29.0
Ester Content, Calculated as Bornyl Acetate...........	8.5%	7.6%	6.7%
Total Alcohol Content, Calculated as Borneol........	9.5%	8.8%	8.2%
Free Alcohol Content, Calculated as Borneol..........	2.6%	2.7%	2.8%
Solubility in 90% Alcohol...	Soluble in 6 vol. and more	Soluble in 8 vol., with very slight turbidity	Soluble in 7 vol., with very slight turbidity

The oil from Yugoslavia had the following boiling range:

	Per Cent
Up to 165°......................	25
165° to 170°....................	23
170° to 175°....................	12
175° to 180°....................	6
180° to 185°....................	5
185° to 190°....................	3
190° to 195°....................	2
Above 195° (decomposition products and residue).................	24

Shipments of genuine oil of *Abies alba* Mill. examined by Fritzsche Brothers, Inc., New York, had properties varying within these limits:

Specific Gravity at 15°/15°........	0.873 to 0.880
Optical Rotation.................	−41° 0′ to −48° 3′
Refractive Index at 20°...........	1.4729 to 1.4749
Ester Content, Calculated as Bornyl Acetate.......................	5.2 to 8.9%
Solubility at 20°.................	Soluble in 5 to 10 vol. and more of 90% alcohol, occasionally with slight turbidity
Boiling Range....................	Up to 40% of oil distilled below 165° Up to 22% of oil distilled from 165°–170°

The boiling range of the three genuine oils procured by the author in the Tyrol and Yugoslavia, and that of the numerous oils examined by Fritzsche Brothers, Inc., New York, differed greatly from that reported by Gildemeister and Hoffmann (see above). According to Gildemeister and Hoffmann, these oils would have to be regarded as adulterated, perhaps with turpentine oil or fractions containing laevorotatory pinene.

In an attempt to establish the causes for the discrepancy in the boiling ranges, the author arranged for systematic experiments in the Tyrol whereby twigs and adherent leaves of *Abies alba* Mill. were distilled under various conditions (location, weather, soil, age of the trees, quality of the distillation material, etc.). These experiments were carefully carried out by Messrs. Gebrüder Unterweger, Thal-Assling, Tyrol, who submitted the oils thus obtained to the author [2] for analysis. Examination of the samples proved that a change in the boiling range of genuine oil of *Abies alba* had actually occurred since the days when Schimmel & Co.[3] first determined the properties of this oil. The factors responsible for this change remain a mystery. It should be mentioned that a similar change has also taken place in the boiling range of oil of *Pinus mugo* Turra (*P. pumilio* Haenke).

From the work of Grimm, Langenau and Guenther [4] and from the analytical data of Fritzsche Brothers, Inc., New York, it appears that the specifications for the physicochemical properties of oil of *Abies alba* Mill. should be modified to read as follows:

Specific Gravity at $15°/15°$........ 0.867 to 0.880
Optical Rotation................. $-40° 0'$ to $-67° 0'$
Refractive Index at $20°$.......... 1.4729 to 1.4749
Ester Content, Calculated as Bornyl
   Acetate...................... Up to 9%
Solubility at $20°$................. Soluble in 4 to 10 vol. of 90% alcohol. Occasionally with slight turbidity
Boiling Range................... Up to 55 and more per cent of the oil distills below $170°$; therefore any definite recommendations as to the boiling range would be meaningless

Adulteration.—Oil of *Abies alba* is occasionally adulterated with Siberian fir needle oil, laevorotatory turpentine oil, or fractions thereof.

Chemical Composition.—The chemical composition of the volatile oil derived from the twigs and needles of *Abies alba* Mill. has been investigated chiefly by Bertram and Walbaum,[5] by Schimmel & Co.,[6] and Aschan [7] who reported the presence of the following compounds in the oil:

[2] Grimm, Langenau and Guenther, *J. Am. Pharm. Assocn., Sci. Ed.*, **30** (1941), 209.
[3] *Ber. Schimmel & Co.*, October (1892), 21; April (1893), 29. The properties reported by Gildemeister and Hoffmann are based upon these early observations.
[4] *J. Am. Pharm. Assocn., Sci. Ed.*, **30** (1941), 209.
[5] *Arch. Pharm.* **231** (1893), 291.
[6] *Ber. Schimmel & Co.*, April (1904), 48.
[7] *Ber.* **40** (1907), 4919.

Santene. In the lowest boiling fractions, observed by Aschan (cf. Vol. II of the present work, p. 79).

l-α-Pinene. Identified by means of the nitrolbenzylamine m. 122°–123° (Bertram and Walbaum).

l-Limonene. Characterized by preparation of the tetrabromide m. 104° (Bertram and Walbaum).

l-Bornyl Acetate. In the higher boiling fractions; also reported by Bertram and Walbaum.[8]

Lauraldehyde. Identified by means of the semicarbazone m. 101.5°–102.5° (Schimmel & Co.). This aldehyde, although present in small quantities only, is very important as regards the odor of the oil (cf. Vol. II of the present work, p. 317).

Decylaldehyde. The oil appears to contain also traces of decylaldehyde (Schimmel & Co.).

A Sesquiterpene(?). Not identified (Bertram and Walbaum).

Use.—Of all the pine, spruce and fir needle oils, that of *Abies alba* Mill. possesses perhaps the most pleasant odor, characteristic of the scent pervading sunny, pinaceous forests. In Europe the oil is highly esteemed, being used in all kinds of pine compositions such as room sprays, deodorants, and bath preparations.

The oil is employed also in inhalants for the treatment of colds, and in medicinal preparations against rheumatism and similar ailments.

B. Cone Oil
(Oil of Templin)

On distillation the ripe cones of *Abies alba* Mill. (fam. *Pinaceae*), the "European Silver Fir," yield an essential oil, 1,000 to 6,000 kg. of which are produced every year in Switzerland (Berner Oberland), Germany (Black Forest), the Tyrol (Puster Valley), and Yugoslavia.

The oil is contained chiefly in the seed formed in well-matured cones. Only cones at least one-year-old are, therefore, collected for distillation; this is usually done in August and September. For the purpose, harvesters climb into the trees on ladders and gather the cones in sacks. In most sections permission to collect the cones has to be obtained from the forestry officials, who may impose a nominal fee. In general, the supply of cones is irregular, because the silver fir does not produce a sufficient quantity of cones every year to make collection worth-while.

The seeds, containing most of the essential oil, are surrounded by a very tough skin which prevents the oil from being freed in the course of distilla-

[8] Cf. Hirschsohn, *Pharm. Zeitschr. f. Russland* **31** (1892), 593.

tion. It is, therefore, necessary to break the skin of the seed by mechanical means prior to distillation. For this purpose producers in Switzerland smash the cones with sledge hammers, while distillers in the Tyrol grind them in special small machines, being very careful that all seeds are broken up. In Switzerland the smashed cones are distilled in directly-fired stills (water distillation), 60 kg. yielding about 400 g. of oil. In the Tyrol the crushed cones are distilled in steam stills, 100 kg. yielding about 1,000 g. of oil. Distillation of one batch requires from 5 to 6 hr. Distilling seed exclusively, Schimmel & Co.[9] obtained 2.3 per cent of oil from whole seed, but 12 to 13 per cent of oil from crushed seed.

Physicochemical Properties.—The volatile oil derived from the cones (or from the seed) of *Abies alba* Mill. is a colorless or slightly yellowish liquid of pleasant, balsamic odor, somewhat reminiscent of orange oil.

The oils distilled by Schimmel & Co.[10] from seed exclusively had these properties:

Specific Gravity at 15°............ 0.8629 to 0.8668
Optical Rotation................. −68° 14′ to −76° 38′
Refractive Index at 20°.......... 1.47636 to 1.47812
Acid Number.................... 0.5 to 1.8
Ester Content, Calculated as Bornyl
  Acetate...................... 0.3 to 1.3%
Solubility...................... Soluble in 5 to 10 vol. and more of 90% alcohol

For oils distilled from the cones—the usual procedure—Gildemeister and Hoffmann [11] reported the following values:

Specific Gravity at 15°............ 0.851 to 0.870
Optical Rotation................. −60° 0′ to −84° 0′. Oils from Thuringia occasionally have a lower rotation which is perhaps caused by the presence of oil derived from the cones of spruce trees
Refractive Index at 20°.......... 1.472 to 1.475
Ester Content, Calculated as Bornyl
  Acetate...................... Up to 6%
Solubility...................... Clearly soluble in 5 to 8 vol. of 90% alcohol, on rare occasions with slight turbidity
Boiling Range.................. 11% of the oil distills from 150° to 170°
  37% of the oil distills from 170° to 185°

Four genuine templin oils procured by the author in the Tyrol (I), Yugoslavia (II), Switzerland (III), and in the Black Forest, Germany (IV) had these properties:

[9] *Ber. Schimmel & Co.*, October (1912), 62.
[10] *Ibid.*
[11] "Die Ätherischen Öle," 3d Ed., Vol. II, 177.

	I	II	III	IV
Specific Gravity at 15°	0.858	0.859	0.860	0.860
Optical Rotation	−77° 55′	−76° 35′	−77° 18′	−77° 5′
Refractive Index at 20°	1.4732	1.4733	1.4733	1.4732
Ester Content, Calculated as Bornyl Acetate	2.5%	1.9%	2.5%	1.6%
Total Alcohol Content, Calculated as Borneol	6.7%	4.3%	5.6%	4.6%
Free Alcohol Content, Calculated as Borneol	4.2%	2.9%	3.6%	3.4%
Solubility in 90% Alcohol	Soluble in 8 vol., with turbidity	Soluble in 8 vol., with turbidity	Turbid in 90% alcohol	Turbid in 90% alcohol
Boiling Range:				
Up to 150°	1.1%	0.7%	0.8%	. . .
150° to 155°	6.0%	2.5%	2.5%	5.2%
155° to 160°	5.5%	3.5%	3.5%	2.0%
160° to 165°	12.5%	5.5%	6.5%	4.4%
165° to 170°	12.5%	27.0%	15.3%	12.8%
170° to 175°	27.5%	30.0%	26.7%	41.6%
175° to 180°	14.5%	14.0%	28.7%	17.2%
180° to 185°	8.5%	6.0%	7.0%	6.4%
185° to 190°	0.6%	0.8%	2.6%	1.2%
Above 190° (decomposition products and residue)	11.3%	10.0%	6.4%	9.2%

Shipments of pure templin oil examined by Fritzsche Brothers, Inc., New York, had properties varying within the following limits:

Specific Gravity at 15°/15° .... 0.855 to 0.873
Optical Rotation .... −59° 31′ to −78° 48′
Refractive Index at 20° .... 1.4718 to 1.4758
Ester Content, Calculated as Bornyl
  Acetate .... 0.3 to 3.9%
Solubility .... Soluble in 5 and more vol. of 90% alcohol, to turbid in 10 vol. of 90% alcohol

Chemical Composition.—The earliest investigations of the chemical composition of the volatile oil derived from the cones of *Abies alba* Mill. (templin oil) are those of Flückiger,[12] and Berthelot,[13] which, however, did not give any tangible results. Much more important are the later researches

[12] *Vierteljahresschr. prakt. Pharm.* **5** (1856), 1. *Jahresber. Fortschritte Chem.* (1855), 642.

[13] *J. pharm. chim.* [3], **29** (1856), 38. *Chem. Zentr.* (1856), 139.

of Wallach,[14] Bertram and Walbaum,[15] Schimmel & Co.,[16] and Massera,[17] who reported the presence of the following compounds in the oil:

l-α-Pinene. An important constituent of the oil (Wallach, Bertram and Walbaum, and Massera).

l-Limonene. The oil consists chiefly of *l*-limonene. Identified by the same authors. Tetrabromide m. 104.5°.
    Oil of templin is the most suitable raw material for the technical isolation of laevorotatory limonene.

A Sesquiterpene(?). In an oil derived in Italy from the seed of the European silver fir, Massera noted the presence of a sesquiterpene which was perhaps cadinene. A sesquiterpene of unknown constitution had previously been reported by Schimmel & Co. as a constituent of templin oil.

Borneol. According to Massera, the oil contains small quantities of free borneol. Identified by means of the acid phthalic ester m. 164°.

An Alcohol(?). Years ago Schimmel & Co. found that, aside from borneol, the oil contains another alcohol b. 190°–197°, d_{15} 0.9013, which was not identified.

Bornyl Acetate. Small quantities only. First reported by Schimmel & Co., later confirmed by Massera.

Use.—Because of its suave balsamic odor, oil of templin serves as an adjunct in all kinds of pine needle scents.

OIL OF *ABIES BALSAMEA* (L.) MILL.

Abies balsamea (L.) Mill., syn. *Abies balsamifera* Mich. or *Pinus balsamea* L. (fam. *Pinaceae*), the so-called "American Silver Fir," "Balsam Fir," "Balsam Tree," or "Balm of Gilead Tree," is a graceful tree, up to 40 ft. in height, with a tapering trunk and numerous branches which give to the tree the form of an almost perfect cone. It occurs particularly in Canada (Province of Quebec), Nova Scotia, Maine, and in the mountainous regions further west and south.

[14] *Liebigs Ann.* **227** (1885), 287.
[15] *Arch. Pharm.* **231** (1893), 293.
[16] *Ber. Schimmel & Co.,* April (1909), 47.
[17] *Rivista ital. essenze profumi* **12** (1930), 95.

A. Leaf (*Needle*) Oil

On steam distillation the young branches and adherent leaves of *Abies balsamea* (L.) Mill. yield an essential oil, the odor of which resembles that of hemlock and spruce oils.

Fourteen distillation experiments carried out by Risi and Brule [1] in the Province of Quebec (Canada) gave an average yield of 0.65 per cent of oil. According to the same authors, the yield in commercial production ranges from 1.0 to 1.4 per cent and occasionally even higher. As in the case of hemlock-spruce and thuja oils, the yield depends upon several factors, among them the habitat of the tree, its age, the season, and the packing of the still. Material from a fifteen-year-old tree yielded 70 per cent more oil than that from a one-hundred-and-ten-year-old tree. The yield is highest from January to March, and in September, and lowest from April to August.

The oils distilled by Risi and Brule [2] had properties varying within these limits:

	Extreme Limits	Average
Specific Gravity at 15°........	0.8800 to 0.8890	0.8828
Specific Optical Rotation......	−20° 30′ to −26° 30′	−23° 30′
Refractive Index at 20°.......	1.4727 to 1.4779	1.4754
Acid Number...............	0.45 to 0.85	0.60
Ester Number..............	18.2 to 46.6	29.9
Saponification Number........	18.7 to 47.2	30.5
Boiling Range..............	155° to 163°	161° to 195°
Solubility in 90% Alcohol.....	Soluble in from 4.2 to 7.2 vol.; on the average in 5.4 vol.	

Hunkel [3] found that an oil derived from the twigs and leaves of *Abies balsamea* contained 17.6 per cent of *bornyl acetate* and probably *l-α-pinene*.

According to the author's knowledge, very little oil is produced at present from the leaves of *Abies balsamea*.

B. Turpentine Oil
(Oil of Canada Turpentine—Oil of "Canada Balsam")

Abies balsamea (L.) Mill. separates a liquid oleoresin in special vesicles located beneath the bark; usually the oleoresin penetrates the bark and forms blisters on the surface of the trunk and branches. By breaking these blisters or the vesicles beneath the bark, the oleoresin can be collected. This is usually done from the middle of July to the middle of August,

[1] *Am. Perfumer* **48** (January 1946), 37.   [3] *Am. J. Pharm.* **67** (1895), 9.
[2] *Ibid.*

small metal cans with a pointed, sharp lip being used for the purpose. After the balsam is collected for one season, the tree has to be left to recuperate for one or two years.

The commercial term "Canada Balsam" by which the oleoresin is known in the trade is a misnomer. The product actually represents a true turpentine, because it consists chiefly of resin and volatile oil, and does not contain any benzoic acid or cinnamic acid. Canada turpentine or "Canada Balsam" is used largely as a permanent mounting medium in microscopy and as a cement for glassware. Natives in the producing regions employ it as a popular vulnerary, and as an internal remedy for coughs.

Canada turpentine is a pale yellow or yellowish-green, transparent and viscous mass with a pleasant therebinthinate odor. When exposed to the air, it dries very slowly to a transparent varnish.

On steam distillation, Canada turpentine yields from 15 to 25 per cent of a volatile oil.

Physicochemical Properties.—The volatile oil distilled from "Canada Balsam" is an almost colorless liquid with an odor resembling that of templin oil. Unlike the balsam itself (which exhibits dextrorotation) the oil is laevorotatory.

Schimmel & Co.,[4] (I) and Smith and West [5] (II) reported the following properties of two oils distilled from "Canada Balsam":

	I	II
Specific Gravity at 15°.	0.8614	0.8605
Optical Rotation.	−30° 36′	α_D^{20} −32° 30′
Refractive Index at 20°.	1.47809	1.4758
Acid Number.	0	1.23
Ester Number.	3.7	2.24
Ester Number after Acetylation.	...	15.1

Chemical Composition of the Oil.—About eighty years ago, Flückiger [6] reported that the volatile oil derived from "Canada Balsam" consists chiefly of *l*-α-pinene. A more recent investigation by Smith and West,[7] however, showed that the oil is composed of the following compounds:

l-β-Phellandrene. The oil contains about 20 per cent of *l*-β-phellandrene (cf. **Vol. II** of the present work, p. 48). A solution of the α-nitrosite exhibited slower mutarotation than the α-nitrosite of *l*-α-phellandrene. Confirmed by MacBeth et al.[8]

β-Pinene. Present in smaller quantities.

α-Pinene. In small quantities only.

[4] *Ber. Schimmel & Co.,* April (1914), 38.   [7] *J. Soc. Chem. Ind.* **56** (1937), 300T.
[5] *J. Soc. Chem. Ind.* **56** (1937), 300T.   [8] *J. Chem. Soc.* (1938), 119.
[6] *Jahresber. Pharm.* (1869), 37.

Esters. Small quantities (one of the esters contained in the oil is bornyl acetate—the author).

Alcohols. Also in small quantities. Among the alcohols were probably androl and bupleurol (cf. Vol. II of the present work, pp. 165 and 166, respectively).

Use.—According to the author's knowledge, the volatile oil of Canada turpentine is not produced at present on a commercial scale.

OIL OF ATLAS CEDARWOOD

Cedrus atlantica Manetti (fam. *Pinaceae*), the so-called "Atlas Cedar," is a tall tree attaining a height of about 40 m., with upright leading shoots. As the name implies, it occurs in the Atlas Mountains of Morocco and Algeria. According to Trabut,[1] the Atlas cedar is closely related to the Lebanon cedar. As a matter of fact, it has been classified as *Cedrus libanotica* Lk., subsp. *atlantica* (Manetti) Holmboe, a local subspecies or variety of the Lebanon cedar.

On steam distillation the wood of the Atlas cedar yields from 3 to 5 per cent of an essential oil, which is produced commercially in the Atlas Mountains of Morocco, particularly in Azrou.

Physicochemical Properties.—Oil of Atlas cedarwood is a viscous, light-brown liquid of pleasant balsamic and lasting odor.

Gildemeister and Hoffmann[2] reported the following properties for the oil:

Specific Gravity at 15°..............	0.945 to 0.968
Optical Rotation...................	+43° 0′ to +62° 0′
Refractive Index at 20°.............	1.512 to 1.517
Acid Number......................	Up to 2
Ester Number.....................	3 to 11
Ester Number after Acetylation.......	30 to 46
Total Alcohol Content, Calculated as $C_{15}H_{26}O$..........................	12 to 19%
Solubility........................	Soluble in 1 to 10 vol. of 90% alcohol; the solubility increases with the content of sesquiterpene alcohols

---

[1] "Sur l'huile de Cèdre de l'Atlas," *Bull. sci. pharmacol.* (1900), 262. *Ber. Schimmel & Co.*, April (1901), 61; April (1902), 11; October (1902), 25.

[2] "Die Ätherischen Öle," 3d Ed., Vol. II, 218.

Atlas cedarwood oils distilled in Morocco by Massy [3] had properties varying within these limits:

Specific Gravity.................... 0.9384 to 0.9587
Optical Rotation.................... +35° 16′ to +49° 14′
Refractive Index.................... 1.5061 to 1.5132
Acid Number....................... 0.50 to 2.16
Ester Number...................... 3.75 to 8.86
Ester Number after Acetylation....... 28.26 to 40.01
Solubility.......................... Soluble in 1 to 6 vol. of
                                      90% alcohol

According to a bulletin edited by the Société Marocaine d'Exploitations Forestières,[4] Atlas cedarwood oils of good quality should meet the following requirements:

Specific Gravity at 15°.............. 0.939 to 0.945
Optical Rotation.................... +45° 0′ to +55° 0′
Acid Number....................... Up to 1
Ester Number after Acetylation....... Not less than 20
Solubility at 20°................... Soluble in less than 10
                                      vol. of 90% alcohol

Chemical Composition.—The chemical composition of Atlas cedarwood oil was first investigated by Grimal [5] and about thirty years later by Pfau [6] and Pfau and Plattner,[7] who reported the presence of the following compounds in the oil:

Acetone. Traces in the forerun of the oil.

1-Methyl-4-acetyl-1-cyclohexene (*p*-Methyl-3-tetrahydroacetophenone). First noted by Grimal and later identified by Pfau and Plattner. The oil contains about 1 per cent of this ketone (cf. Vol. II of this work, p. 482). It is not present in the wood of the tree but originates on steam distillation of the wood.

Sesquiterpenes(?). On fractionation of the oil, Pfau and Plattner obtained about 50 per cent of a sesquiterpene mixture which was not thoroughly investigated. Cadinene was one of the sesquiterpenes.

d-Cadinene. First identified in the oil by Grimal, who prepared the dihydrochloride m. 117°–118°, $[\alpha]_D^{20}$ +25° 40′.

Sesquiterpene Alcohols(?). When fractionating their oil, Pfau and Plattner also obtained 30 per cent of a fraction which boiled quite uniformly and exhibited a characteristic sweet odor. The fraction contained several bi- and tricyclic sesquiterpene alcohols which, however, were not identified.

[3] *Bull. Soc. Sci. natur. Maroc, botan. appl.* **16** (1924), No. 1. *Ber. Schimmel & Co.* (1925), 5.
[4] "L'Essence de *Cedrus atlantica*," Paris (1930), 3.
[5] *Compt. rend.* **135** (1902), 582, 1057.   [7] *Ibid.* **17** (1934), 129.
[6] *Helv. Chim. Acta* **15** (1932), 1481.

A Ketone(?). In the same fraction Pfau and Plattner noted the presence of a monocyclic ketone $C_{15}H_{22}O_2$, which appeared to be very unstable. Pfau and Plattner did not succeed in separating this ketone from the atlantones.

α- and γ-Atlantone. The chief constituents of the oil, present in the same fraction as the ketone $C_{15}H_{22}O_2$ and the sesquiterpene alcohols mentioned above. The constitution of the atlantones, i.e., two isomeric monocyclic sesquiterpene ketones $C_{15}H_{22}O$, was elucidated by Pfau and Plattner (cf. Vol. II of this work, p. 448).

Use.—In North Africa, oil of Atlas cedarwood is used externally and internally against all kinds of diseases (bronchitis, tuberculosis, skin diseases, etc.). At one time the oil was employed as a substitute for East Indian sandalwood oil, particularly in the treatment of gonorrhea.[8]

In perfumery and in the scenting of soaps, the oil serves as an excellent odor fixative.

SUGGESTED ADDITIONAL LITERATURE

L. Trabaud, "Pyrogenic Oil of Atlas Cedarwood," *Mfg. Perfumer* **3** (1938), 225.

OIL OF DEODAR CEDARWOOD
(Oil of Himalayan Cedarwood)

The Deodar cedar, a native of the Himalayan Mountain region, is a beautiful and graceful tree of pyramidal outline, growing to a height of 50 m. It has been classified as a distinct species, *Cedrus deodara* (Roxb.) Loud. (fam. *Pinaceae*). Formerly, some taxonomists considered it to be a variety of the "Cedar of Lebanon," *Cedrus libani* Loud.[1]

Distillation of the wood yields about 2.5 per cent of a volatile oil with a pleasant balsamic odor.[2]

Physicochemical Properties.—Roberts,[3] Schimmel & Co.,[4] and Simonsen and Rao[5] reported the following properties for the essential oil derived from the wood of the Deodar or Himalaya cedar tree:

[8] Cf. Gemy, *Perfumery Essential Oil Record* **24** (1933), 127.
[1] Cf. Roberts, *J. Chem. Soc.* **109** (1916), 791.
[2] *Bull. Imp. Inst.* **21** (1923), 501.
[3] *J. Chem. Soc.* **109** (1916), 791.
[4] *Ber. Schimmel & Co.*, April (1915), 54.
[5] *Indian Forest Records* **9** (1922), 111. *J. Soc. Chem. Ind.* **42** (1923), A. 29.

Specific Gravity at 15°............. 0.9530 to 0.9756
Optical Rotation.................. +34° 0' to +53° 8'
Refractive Index at 20°........... 1.515 to 1.523
Acid Number..................... 1.6 to 5.6
Ester Number.................... 4.9 to 20.5
Ester Number after Acetylation..... 30.8 to 39.2
Solubility....................... One of the oils investigated was soluble in all volumes of 90% alcohol. Two other oils were not completely soluble in 90% alcohol

Chemical Composition.—The above-named authors also investigated the chemical composition of the essential oil obtained by steam distillation of the wood of the Deodar cedar, and isolated a number of constituents which are listed below. About ten years later, Pfau,[6] and Pfau and Plattner [7] identified atlantone as the chief constituent of the oil. The presence of the following compounds has been reported in the oil:

1-Methyl-4-acetyl-1-cyclohexene (*p*-Methyl-3-tetrahydroacetophenone). In the fraction b. 258°–265° of the oil; first isolated by Schimmel & Co., later identified by Simonsen and Rao (cf. Vol. II of the present work, p. 482).

A Phenol(?). According to Roberts, the oil contains traces (0.1 per cent) of a phenol, from which he prepared a benzoyl compound m. 70°. Simonsen and Rao could not find any phenols in the oil which they investigated.

A Sesquiterpene(?). The oil consists chiefly of sesquiterpenic compounds. Among them, Roberts isolated a sesquiterpene b. 262°–265°, b_{19} 151°–153°, d_{15}^{15} 0.9276, α_D^{20} +14° 36', n_D^{21} 1.5170. The sesquiterpene did not yield any solid derivatives.

A Sesquiterpene Alcohol(?). Simonsen and Rao isolated from the oil a sesquiterpene alcohol b_{55} 202°–204°, d 0.9578, $[\alpha]_D^{30}$ +38° 25', n_D 1.515.

α- and γ-Atlantone. According to Pfau, and Pfau and Plattner, the chief constituents of the oil are α- and γ-atlantone, i.e., two isomeric monocyclic sesquiterpene ketones $C_{15}H_{22}O$ (cf. Vol. II of the present work, p. 448). These ketones also occur in Atlas cedarwood oil.

Esters of Butyric, Caproic, Enanthic and Stearic Acids. Small quantities of caproic, enanthic, and stearic acids were observed by Roberts. Simonsen and Rao found butyric and caproic acids in the oil, but no enanthic or stearic acids.

Use.—According to the author's knowledge, oil of Deodar cedarwood is not produced on a commercial scale.

[6] *Helv. Chim. Acta* **15** (1932), 1481.
[7] *Ibid.* **17** (1934), 129.

OIL OF LEBANON CEDARWOOD

The "Cedar of Lebanon," *Cedrus libani* Barr. (syn. *C. libanotica* Lk.), fam. *Pinaceae,* a native of Asia Minor and Syria, is a tree growing to a height of 40 m., with upright or spreading leading shoots. Distilling the wood of the Lebanon cedar, Schimmel & Co.[1] obtained about 3.5 per cent of a yellowish oil with a pleasant balsamic odor, slightly reminiscent of methyl heptenone and thujone.

Physicochemical Properties.—The properties of the oils investigated by Schimmel & Co. varied within these limits:

Specific Gravity at 15°.............. 0.940 to 0.947
Optical Rotation.................. +68° 0′ to +86° 0′
Refractive Index at 20°............ 1.5125 to 1.5134
Acid Number..................... 0.5 to 1.5
Ester Number.................... 2.0 to 3.0
Ester Number after Acetylation...... 19.8
Solubility........................ Soluble in 5 to 6 vol.
                               of 95% alcohol

Boiling Range at 754 mm.:
  270° to 275°..................... 30%
  275° to 280°..................... 40%
  280° to 285°..................... 14%
  285° to 290°..................... 6%
  Distillation Residue.............. 10%

Steam-distilling wood shavings of the Lebanon cedar tree, Massy[2] obtained 6 per cent of an oil with the following properties:

Specific Gravity at 15°.............. 0.9570
Optical Rotation.................. +43° 28′
Acid Number..................... 0.7
Saponification Number.............. 4.84
Ester Number after Acetylation...... 33.77
Solubility........................ Soluble in 1 vol. of
                            90% alcohol
Boiling Range at atm. pr........... 270° to 290°

Chemical Composition.—No special investigation of the chemical composition of Lebanon cedarwood oil appears to have been undertaken. Since the Lebanon cedar is related to the Atlas cedar, it may be assumed that

[1] *Ber. Schimmel & Co.,* October (1909), **130.**
[2] *Chimie & industrie* **8** (1922), 464.

the essential oils derived from the wood of the two *Cedrus* species are of similar composition (cf. the monograph on "Oil of Atlas Cedarwood").

Use.—According to the author's knowledge, the oil is not produced on a commercial scale.

OIL OF *PINUS MUGO* TURRA VAR. *PUMILIO*
(Dwarf Pine Needle Oil)

Pinus mugo Turra var. *pumilio*, syn. *Pinus pumilio* Haenke or *Pinus montana* Mill. var. *mugus, pumilio* and *rotundata* (fam. *Pinaceae*), the so-called "Dwarf Pine" or "Swiss Mountain Pine," is a sturdy shrub-like tree growing wild and abundantly on the high mountain slopes of the Alps. It occurs in the form of small patches or large, dense and almost impenetrable stands. In the Tyrol the dwarf pine covers from 5 to 20 per cent of the total forest area. The young branches and adherent leaves contain a volatile oil, 7,000 to 13,000 kg. of which are produced yearly in southern Tyrol (particularly in the high valleys near Bolzano), in northern Tyrol (Inn, Lech and Stubai Valleys), in upper Bavaria (near Garmisch-Partenkirchen), and in northern Italy (Province of Belluno).

The plant material is collected from the beginning of May to the end of October and even later, weather permitting. Farmers and landowners in the mountains consider the dwarf pine a nuisance, which they would like to have eradicated to make room for cattle pastures. Forest officials, on the other hand, see in the dwarf pine an excellent and natural means of preventing soil erosion and are usually hesitant in granting permission to cut the stands. In certain sections of upper Bavaria the government has actually prohibited cutting of the dwarf pine. In Austria, regulations are less strict, but any stands must be cropped in horizontal strips, following the method of contour cultivation practiced in modern soil conservation.

Only the branches of trees growing at an altitude of about 1,300 to 2,100 m. are cut. If the land is owned by the government or a community, the right to crop the stands requires payment of a fee. On privately-owned land, permission of the forest officials must be obtained. Young branches about one-half to three-quarters of an inch thick are hacked off the bushes with small axes and are then tied into bundles. One man can collect up to about 1,000 kg. of plant material per day. The stems and roots are either left in the ground or are extracted for use as fire wood. In the latter case natural regrowth of the tree is prevented, but if the roots are left in the ground they will either rot and die, or produce new growth. The bundled twigs and adherent needles are hooked on to relay cables leading from the mountain slopes to the distillery in the valley—an easy and cheap way of transporting the distillation material (and fire wood). Because the stands of the dwarf pine are so widely scattered, the relay cables must be moved several times in the course of a season; for the same reason most of the distilleries are small, so that they, too, can be moved if the distillation material in any section should become scarce or too far remote to be readily accessible. Quite a number of distilleries have been destroyed by snow avalanches in the spring. According to Kofler,[1] a few large distilleries have been erected in the Lech and Stubai Valleys, and near Lake Piller in the Tyrol.

Prior to distillation the plant material should be reduced to small size in heavy-duty ensilage cutters driven by water power. Comminution increases the yield of oil by about 30 per cent. The stills are constructed of wood or copper and hold from 120 to 1,100 kg. of chopped branches and leaves (needles). Steam is usually generated in a separate steam boiler. Distillation of one charge requires from 2½ to 8 hr., on the average 5 hr. During the height of the season, the distilleries operate day and night.

Yield and Quality of Oil.—Yield and quality of the oil depend upon several factors. According to observations made by the author in the producing regions of the Tyrol, yield of oil averages 0.3 to 0.4 per cent. Kofler[2] reported commercial yields varying from 0.12 to 0.45 per cent. His own experiments showed that the yield is highest in January (0.61 per cent), and lowest in August (0.32 per cent). Kofler also found that young branches contain more oil than the attached needles. With age the content of the oil in the branches diminishes. Distilling young branches, Kofler obtained 0.74 per cent of oil; twenty-year-old branches gave only 0.05 per cent of oil. The bark on the branches, regardless of their age, contains ten times more oil than the wood. In the opinion of Kofler, branches older than twelve years should not be used for distillation. Nevertheless, in actual practice, branches (and adherent needles) fifteen to twenty years old are worked up.

Loesche[3] observed that the odor of the oil depends upon the season during which the branches are cut, the altitude, the condition of the soil, and exposure to the sun. Oils produced in the spring or from sun-exposed plants

[1] *Arch. Pharm.* **275** (1937), 621.
[2] *Ibid.* Cf. *Die Deutsche Heilpflanze* **6** (1940), No. 3.
[3] *Pharm. Ztg.* **79** (1934), 975.

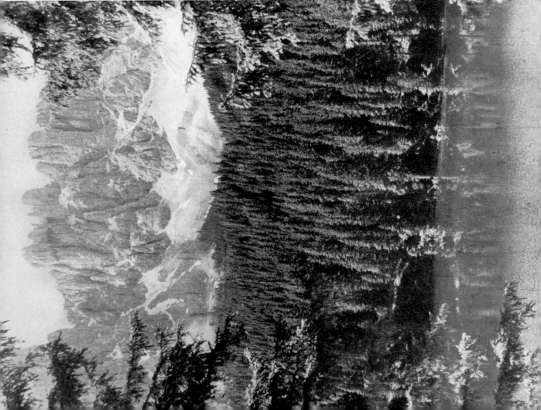

(*Left*) Production of pine needle oils in the Tyrol. Majestic pine forests near Lake Karrer. (*Top*) A pine needle distillery surrounded by extensive pine forests in the Tyrol. (*Bottom*) Discharge of the spent pine needle material from a wooden tilting still. *Photos Fritzsche Brothers, Inc., New York.*

(Above left to right) A branch of Abies alba. A branch of Pinus sylvestris. A branch of Pinus cembra. (Left) A branch of Picea excelsa. (Right) A branch of Pinus mugo Turra var. pumilio. Photos Brüder Unterveger, Thal-Assling, Tyrol, Austria.

have a suave, mellow odor; oils distilled in the fall or from plants growing in shady places exhibit a somewhat harsh and fatty odor.

Physicochemical Properties.—Oil of *Pinus mugo* is a colorless to slightly yellowish liquid with a pleasant, pronounced balsamic odor reminiscent of pine needles, but with a peculiar, somewhat fatty by-note.

Gildemeister and Hoffmann [4] reported the following properties for the oil:

Specific Gravity at 15°...........	0.863 to 0.875; in Tyrolean oils as low as 0.860. Specific gravities higher than 0.871 may be caused by autoxidation (resinification) of the oil
Optical Rotation.................	−4° 0′ to −9° 0′; in Tyrolean oils occasionally as high as −15° 20′
Refractive Index at 20°..........	1.475 to 1.480
Acid Number....................	Up to 1.0
Ester Content, Calculated as Bornyl Acetate......................	3 to 8%
Solubility......................	Soluble in 4.5 to 8 vol. of 90% alcohol, occasionally with slight turbidity

Boiling Range:

Up to 165°....................	...
165°–170°....................	Up to 15%
170°–175°....................	14 to 40%
175°–180°....................	12 to 40%
180°–185°....................	8 to 12%
Above 185°...................	24 to 36%
	About 65% of the oil distilled from 170°–185°

Shipments of genuine dwarf pine oil from the Tyrol examined by Fritzsche Brothers, Inc., New York, had properties varying within these limits:

Specific Gravity at 25°/25°........	0.856 to 0.864
Optical Rotation.................	−7° 0′ to −13° 25′
Refractive Index at 20°..........	1.4750 to 1.4780
Ester Content, Calculated as Bornyl Acetate......................	3.3 to 6.1%
Solubility in 90% Alcohol........	Soluble in 5 vol. and more, to turbid in 10 vol.

As regards the boiling range of the oil, Gildemeister and Hoffmann (see above) claim that no part of the oil distills over below 165°. Similarly, the older editions of the United States Pharmacopoeia (U.S.P. Tenth Revision) specified that less than 1 per cent of the oil should distill below 165°. Most shipments of dwarf pine needle oil received by Fritzsche Brothers, Inc., New York, up to the early thirties conformed with this specification. However, when in 1934 the author undertook a personal

[4] "Die Ätherischen Öle," 3d Ed., Vol. II, 182.

survey of the production of essential oils in the Tyrol, he procured several authentic samples of dwarf pine needle oil which had a boiling range different from that observed formerly. Up to 10 per cent of the oil distilled below 165°. Producers in the Tyrol were unable to give a satisfactory explanation for this obvious deviation. Upon the author's suggestion, Gebrüder Unterweger, in Thal-Assling, the Tyrol, then undertook systematic experiments, distilling branches and adherent leaves of the dwarf pine under varied conditions of plant material, soil and weather. Analyzing 24 oils thus obtained, the author and his collaborators [5] found that the properties varied within these limits:

Specific Gravity at 25°/25°........... 0.854 to 0.871
Optical Rotation at 25°............... −3° 19′ to −15° 16′
Refractive Index at 20°............... 1.4750 to 1.4790
Acid Number........................ 0.2 to 1.3
Ester Content, Calculated as Bornyl Acetate............................. 3.3 to 9.5%
Total Alcohol Content, Calculated as Borneol.......................... 4.2 to 10.3%
Aldehyde Content, Calculated as Caproaldehyde (Hydroxylamine Hydrochloride Method)...................... 0.01 to 0.47%
Solubility in 90% Alcohol............. A few oils were soluble in from 5.5 to 8 vol.; most oils were hazy up to 10 vol.
Boiling Range...................... In the case of 23 oils not more than 10% of the oil distilled below 165°; only in the case of one oil did more than 10% distill below 165°

Grimm, Langenau and Guenther [6] then suggested that the specifications for oil of *Pinus mugo* be modified as follows:

Specific Gravity at 25°/25°........... 0.853 to 0.871
Optical Rotation at 25°............... −3° 0′ to −16° 0′
Refractive Index at 20°............... 1.4750 to 1.4800
Ester Content, Calculated as Bornyl Acetate............................. 3 to 10%
Solubility.......................... Soluble in 4.5 to 10 vol. of 90% alcohol, often with turbidity
Boiling Range...................... Less than 10% of the oil distills below 165°

These values, with slight modifications, were accepted by the United States Pharmacopoeia, and later by the National Formulary.

Investigating the boiling range of dwarf pine needle oil, Fischer [7] on his part also found that in the case of most oils small quantities distill below

[5] Grimm, Langenau and Guenther, *J. Am. Pharm. Assocn., Sci. Ed.*, **30** (1941), 209.
[6] *Ibid.*
[7] *Pharm. Zentralhalle* **82** (1941), 37.

165°. No satisfactory explanation for this obvious change in the boiling range has yet been given.

So far as the seasonal variations in the physicochemical properties of the oil are concerned, Loesche [8] noted that the specific gravity of oils distilled in May was highest (d_{20} 0.8752), that of oils produced in August lowest (d_{20} 0.8700). The optical rotation was highest in June (α_D −14° 9′), and lowest in September/October (α_D −6° 7′). The ester content decreased from 9.24 per cent in oils produced in May to 5.2 per cent in oils distilled from July to August.

Adulteration.—Dwarf pine needle oil is occasionally adulterated with all kinds of low-priced pine oils and fractions thereof, dipentene for example. Fischer [9] found that oils adulterated with more than 10 per cent of dipentene readily yielded a tetrabromide m. 123°–124°. Pure oils did not yield a tetrabromide.

According to the same author,[10] some oils of *Pinus mugo* give a distinctly blue to blue-violet color on addition of an alcoholic solution of guaiac gum and one drop of ferrous chloride solution. This positive test for the presence of peroxides can be explained by autoxidation of dipentene, small quantities of which occur in genuine oil of *Pinus mugo*. On storage and aging of the oil autoxidation may take place, dipentene being very susceptible in this respect.

Chemical Composition.—The chemical composition of the volatile oil derived from the branches and adherent leaves of the dwarf pine has been investigated by Buchner,[11] Atterberg,[12] Bertram and Walbaum,[13] and Böcker and Hahn.[14] The most thorough and recent investigation is that of Wienhaus and Nahme.[15] The presence of the following compounds has been reported in oil of *Pinus mugo:*

l-α-Pinene. First noted in the oil by Atterberg and named "terebentene." Later Bertram and Walbaum identified this compound as *l*-α-pinene. Nitrolbenzylamine m. 122°–123°.

β-Pinene. Characterized by oxidation to nopinic acid m. 125°–126° (Wienhaus and Nahme).

l-Limonene and Dipentene. Identified by the same authors. The mixture of the tetrabromides melted at 116°.

[8] *J. prakt. Chem.* [2], **147** (1937), 75.
[9] *Pharm. Zentralhalle* **82** (1941), 37.
[10] *Ibid.*
[11] *Liebigs Ann.* **116** (1860), 323.
[12] *Ber.* **14** (1881), 2531.
[13] *Arch. Pharm.* **231** (1893), 297.
[14] *J. prakt. Chem.* [2], **83** (1911), 489.
[15] *Ber. Schimmel & Co.,* Jubiläums Ausgabe (1929), 235.

l-Phellandrene. Reported by Bertram and Walbaum who prepared the nitrite m. 102°. Phellandrene is present in the oil probably as α-phellandrene, accompanied by very small quantities of the β-isomer.

Δ^3-Carene (Sylvestrene). Years ago Atterberg expressed the opinion that the oil contains sylvestrene, the dihydrochloride of which melted at 72°. More recently Rao and Simonsen [16] proved that sylvestrene is not a natural constituent of essential oils, but an artifact, originating from Δ^3- and Δ^4-carenes when an oil is treated with hydrochloric acid in order to isolate sylvestrene (cf. Vol. II of this work, p. 32, and the monograph on "Oil of *Pinus sylvestris* L.—Chemical Composition," in the present volume).

Caproaldehyde. Identified by means of its semicarbazone m. 112°, and by oxidation to caproic acid (Wienhaus and Nahme).

Anisaldehyde. Also reported by Wienhaus and Nahme. Semicarbazone m. 203°–204°. Oxidation to anisic acid.

Cuminaldehyde(?). Judging from the odor, cuminaldehyde is a possible constituent of the oil (Wienhaus and Nahme).
　　These aldehydes, although present in traces only, nevertheless exert a considerable influence upon the odor of the oil.

Cryptone (4-Isopropyl-2-cyclohexen-1-one). Identified by means of its semicarbazone m. 85° (Wienhaus and Nahme). This ketone originates in the oil probably by autoxidation of β-phellandrene (cf. Vol. II of the present work, p. 388).

A Terpene Alcohol $C_{10}H_{18}O$(?). Wienhaus and Nahme observed in the oil the presence of a free, secondary, monocyclic terpene alcohol $C_{10}H_{18}O$, containing one double bond. Wienhaus and Nahme temporarily assigned the name "Menthenol P" to this alcohol.

Bornyl Acetate. First reported as constituent of the oil by Bertram and Walbaum; later confirmed by Wienhaus and Nahme.

Bornyl Propionate and Bornyl Caproate. The two last-named authors furthermore found that the oil also contains small quantities of bornyl propionate and bornyl caproate.

Cadinene. Noted in the high boiling fractions by Bertram and Walbaum. Dihydrochloride m. 118°.

Pumiliol(?). An unsaturated sesquiterpene alcohol $C_{15}H_{26}O$, which Wienhaus and Nahme named pumiliol. It contains one double bond.

Tertiary Terpene and Sesquiterpene Alcohols. The same authors also noted that the oil contains appreciable quantities of tertiary terpene alcohols and sesquiterpene alcohols which were not identified. Terpineol and terpinenol were not among them.

A Sesquiterpene Aldehyde(?). Böcker and Hahn reported that the oil contains a sesquiterpene aldehyde $C_{15}H_{26}O$, which was not identified.

[16] *J. Chem. Soc.* **127** (1925), 2494.

A Sesquiterpene Ketone(?). The same authors also noted the presence of a sesquiterpene ketone $C_{15}H_{24}O$ which they could not identify. It appeared to contain two double bonds.

Böcker and Hahn furthermore claimed that the oil contains another ketone, which they named "pumilone." Its semicarbazone melted at 116°–117°. The ketone had the empirical molecular formula $C_8H_{14}O$, and was supposed to have a cyclic configuration. More recently Wienhaus and Nahme showed that the "pumilone" of Böcker and Hahn does not exist in the oil, and that a ketone of the formula $C_8H_{14}O$ could not possibly possess a cyclic structure.

Use.—Oil of *Pinus mugo* is a valuable adjunct in the scenting of soaps and in compositions intended for use as bath salts, deodorants, room sprays, inhalants, etc.

For many years the oil has been employed in pharmaceutical preparations against diseases of the skin and scalp, rheumatism, and ailments of the respiratory organs. Quilico[17] reported his experience in the successful treatment of bladder inflammation, pleurisy, and tuberculosis by the use of dwarf pine oil.

OIL OF *PINUS SYLVESTRIS* L.

A. Leaf (Needle) Oil

The young branches and adherent leaves of *Pinus sylvestris* L., the so-called "Scotch Pine," or "Norway Pine" (fam. *Pinaceae*) contain an essential oil which is produced chiefly in the Tyrol, Yugoslavia, in the Baltic States, in Siberia, and to a small extent in Sweden. Total production per year varies from about 1,000 to 3,000 kg. According to Sandermann,[1] there is only one distillery in Sweden (in Jönköping), cost of production in Scandinavia being too high to permit expansion of the industry.

The physicochemical properties and chemical composition of the oil appear to be greatly influenced by its geographical origin. Oils of best quality come from the Tyrol, particularly from the environments of Thal-Assling, the principle producing region of the oil.

In the Tyrol, oil of *Pinus sylvestris* is produced from spring to the beginning of winter, when snow stops the work. The distillation material is

17 *Rivista ital. essenze profumi* **11** (1929), 7.
1 *Seifensieder-Ztg.* **66** (1939), 803, 833, 863; **67** (1940), 15, 45.

obtained when the forests are thinned out; this must be done at regular intervals by trimming old trees and by felling some of the young ones.

Distillation of one batch requires about 5 hr. The yield of oil ranges from 0.25 to 0.35 per cent.

Physicochemical Properties.—The volatile oil derived from the young branches and adherent leaves of *Pinus sylvestris* is an almost colorless or slightly yellowish liquid of pleasant, balsamic odor, characteristic of pine needles.

Gildemeister and Hoffmann [2] reported these properties for German (including Tyrolean) oils of *Pinus sylvestris:*

Specific Gravity at 15°.............	0.865 to 0.886
Optical Rotation.................	−2° 0′ to +13° 0′
Refractive Index at 20°...........	1.474 to 1.480
Acid Number....................	Up to 2.8
Ester Content, Calculated as Bornyl Acetate......................	1 to 5.6%
Total Alcohol Content, Calculated as Borneol....................	3.9 to 7.3%
Solubility......................	Clearly soluble in 7 to 10 vol. of 90% alcohol
Boiling Range (for Tyrolean oils):	
160° to 165°..................	36% (mostly about 165°)
165° to 170°..................	24%
170° to 175°..................	10%
175° to 180°..................	6%
Above 180°...................	24%

Samples of four genuine oils of *Pinus sylvestris* L. procured by the author in Thal-Assling, eastern Tyrol (I), Chienes, southern Tyrol (II), Oetz Valley, northern Tyrol (III), and in Cerknica, Yugoslavia (IV), had the following properties:

	I	*II*	*III*	*IV*
Specific Gravity at 15°..........	0.874	0.872	0.876	0.871
Optical Rotation..............	+2° 10′	−0° 30′	+2° 12′	−1° 35′
Refractive Index at 20°........	1.4773	1.4743	1.4772	1.4752
Ester Content, Calculated as Bornyl Acetate..............	3.4%	3.6%	3.7%	3.4%
Total Alcohol Content, Calculated as Borneol.................	5.3%	5.8%	5.6%	5.4%
Solubility....................	Soluble in 5 to 6 vol. of 90% alcohol with slight turbidity			

[2] "Die Ätherischen Öle," 3d Ed., Vol. II, 185. Cf. Bertram and Walbaum, *Arch. Pharm.* **231** (1893), 300. *Ber. Schimmel & Co.,* October (1896), 76; (1928), 55.

	I	II	III	IV
Boiling Range:				
Up to 155°.................	15.2%	6.8%	3.0%	1.4%
155° to 160°.................	14.8%	22.9%	17.0%	2.88%
160° to 165°.................	25.6%	28.6%	23.0%	37.0%
165° to 170°.................	8.8%	10.5%	17.5%	19.2%
170° to 175°.................	6.4%	9.7%	7.5%	11.6%
175° to 180°.................	1.7%	4.2%	4.0%	5.6%
Above 180° (decomposition products and residue).......	27.5%	17.3%	28.0%	22.32%

As in the case of the essential oils derived from *Pinus mugo, Pinus cembra, Abies alba* and *Picea abies,* the boiling range of oil of *Pinus sylvestris* observed in recent years differs from that reported more than fifty years ago (see above, Gildemeister and Hoffmann). The reason for this change is still unknown.

Shipments of *Pinus sylvestris* oil from the Tyrol examined by Fritzsche Brothers, Inc., New York, had properties varying within these limits:

Specific Gravity at 15°/15°........	0.865 to 0.872
Optical Rotation.................	$+1° 20'$ to $+4° 25'$
Refractive Index at 20°...........	1.4738 to 1.4769
Ester Content, Calculated as Bornyl Acetate......................	1 to 2.6%
Total Alcohol Content, Calculated as Borneol.....................	3.4 to 5.29%
Solubility.....................	Soluble in 6 vol. of 90% alcohol; occasionally slightly turbid in 10 vol. of 90% alcohol

As regards oil of *Pinus sylvestris* from the Baltic States and the U.S.S.R., the following properties have been observed by Schimmel & Co.[3] on oils from Siberia (I), by Maisit[4] on oils from Latvia (II), and by Muraviev and Ssuvorova[5] on oils from Siberia (III):

	I	II	III
Specific Gravity at 15°..............	0.8658 to 0.8745	0.868 to 0.891	d_{20}^{20} 0.861 to 0.881
Optical Rotation at 20°..............	$+0° 50'$ to $+2° 9'$	$-3° 44'$ to $+3° 15'$	$-4° 21'$ to $+8° 18'$
Refractive Index at 20°..............	1.47488 to 1.47622	1.478 to 1.480	...
Acid Number.......	Up to 0.4	1.08 to 2.70	0.1 to 2.18

[3] *Ber. Schimmel & Co.* (1929), 54.
[4] *Latvijas Univ. Raksti, Chem.* Ser. 2 (1935), 401. *Chem. Zentr.* (1935), II, 3847.
[5] *Pharm. und Pharmakol. Russ.* (1938), No. 2, 22. *Chem. Zentr.* (1938), II, 2658.

	I	II	III
Ester Content, Calculated as Bornyl Acetate	2.0 to 4.3%	2.70 to 10.2%	2.4 to 10.7%
Total Alcohol Content, Calculated as Borneol	...	9.6 to 14.8% (Calculated from Ester Number after Acetylation)	...

An oil from Siberia examined by Schimmel & Co.[6] had this boiling range, at 751 mm. pr.:

	Per Cent
160° to 165°	20
165° to 170°	34
170° to 175°	14
175° to 180°	6
Above 180°	26

The quality of this oil was equal to that of the Tyrolean and German oils.

So far as the oils from Sweden are concerned, Sandermann[7] noted that the yield of oil was 0.22 per cent in December, 0.25 per cent in April, and 0.35 per cent in June. An oil distilled in December from young branches and adherent leaves had the following properties:

Specific Gravity at 20°	0.8688
Specific Optical Rotation	+7° 36'
Acid Number	0.4
Ester Number	3.3

Oils of *Pinus sylvestris* L. distilled experimentally by Umney[8] in Great Britain exhibited pronounced laevorotation ($-7°$ 45' to $-19°$ 0') and had an ester content, calculated as bornyl acetate, ranging from 2.9 to 3.5 per cent. The oils contained laevorotatory α-pinene.

Chemical Composition.—Space does not permit discussing the numerous investigations carried out during the past half century on oils of *Pinus sylvestris* L. from different geographical sources. Bertram and Walbaum,[9] Tröger and Beutin,[10] and Schimmel & Co.[11] examined oils from Germany

---

[6] *Ber. Schimmel & Co.* (1929), 54.

[7] *Seifensieder-Ztg.* **66** (1939), 803, 833, 863; **67** (1940), 15, 45.

[8] *Pharm. J.* **55** (1895), 161, 542.

[9] *Arch. Pharm.* **231** (1893), 300.

[10] *Ibid.* **242** (1904), 521.

[11] *Ber. Schimmel & Co.,* October (1896), 76; April (1910), 61; (1928), 55.

and the Tyrol; Umney [12] oils from Great Britain; Schindelmeiser,[13] Pigulevski,[14] Pigulevski and Riskina,[15] and Maisit [16] oils from Russia and from the Baltic States; Ekecrantz,[17] and Sandermann [18] oils from Sweden.

Early researchers reported that oil of *Pinus sylvestris* L. contains sylvestrene as a natural constituent. More recently, however, it was shown that this terpene is not a natural component of the oil, but an artifact formed from Δ^3-carene when the oil is treated with hydrochloric acid in order to isolate this terpene. By the action of hydrochloric acid Δ^3-carene and Δ^4-carene are converted into a mixture of sylvestrene hydrochloride and dipentene hydrochloride.

Oils from the Tyrol, Germany, Sweden, the Baltic States and the U.S.S.R. appear to contain α-pinene in dextrorotatory form, or as a mixture of *d*- and *l*-α-pinenes in which the former largely predominates. The oils from Great Britain, on the other hand, contain this terpene chiefly in laevorotatory form. Sandermann, who in 1939 undertook a thorough investigation of a Swedish oil, found that its content of terpenes by far exceeded 60 per cent.

Summarizing the findings of the above-named workers, it can be stated that the volatile oil derived from the branches and adherent leaves of *Pinus sylvestris* L. contains the following compounds:

α-Pinene. Mostly in dextrorotatory, but also in laevorotatory form. English oils contain *l*-α-pinene.

β-Pinene. Identified by Sandermann in a Swedish oil.

d- and *l*-Limonene. Schindelmeiser found that a Russian oil contained limonene in laevorotatory form, aside from some *d*-limonene.

Dipentene(?). Presence possible according to several authors.

Δ^3-Carene (Sylvestrene). The sylvestrene reported years ago as a constituent of the oil originates on treatment of the oil with hydrochloric acid (see above). Sylvestrene gives a deep blue color with acetic anhydride and sulfuric acid, whereas the corresponding fraction of the untreated oil does not give this reaction (see Vol. II of the present work, pp. 32 and 49).

Camphene. First identified by Pigulevski in a Russian oil; later confirmed by Maisit in an oil from Latvia.

α- and β-Phellandrene. Reported by Sandermann in a Swedish oil.

[12] *Pharm. J.* **55** (1895), 161, 542.
[13] *Sitzb. Naturforsch. Ges. Univ. Jurjew (Dorpat)* **13**, 2 (1903), 315. *Ber. Schimmel & Co.* (1922), 30.
[14] *J. Russ. Phys. Chem. Soc.* **51** (1919), 66.
[15] *Ibid.* **60** (1928), 1069.
[16] *Latvijas Univ. Raksti, Chem.* Ser. 2 (1935), 401. *Chem. Zentr.* (1935), II, 3847.
[17] *Medd. Vetenskapsakad. Nobelinst.* **5** (1919), 1. *Chem. Zentr.* (1919), III, 380.
[18] *Seifensieder-Ztg.* **66** (1939), 803, 833, 863; **67** (1940), 15, 45.

Caproaldehyde(?). Presence possible (Sandermann).

Cuminaldehyde. Identified by Sandermann.

Anisaldehyde. Also reported by Sandermann.

Cryptone (4-Isopropyl-2-cyclohexen-1-one). Identified by Sandermann (cf. Vol. II of this work, p. 388).

dl-Borneol. Observed by Schindelmeiser in a Russian oil.

Primary and Secondary Alcohols(?). Noted by Sandermann in a Swedish oil.

Tertiary Terpene Alcohols(?). Also observed by Sandermann. One of these alcohols is probably terpineol (Bertram and Walbaum).

Bornyl Acetate. Identified by several workers.

l-Cadinene. Presence in the oil reported by several authors.

Tertiary Sesquiterpene Alcohols(?). Noted by Sandermann in a Swedish oil.

Phenols(?). Reported by the same author.

A Fatty Acid. Sandermann found that the Swedish oil contains a fatty acid $C_{13}H_{25}\cdot COOH$, m. 56°–60°.

The sesquiterpene fraction of the Swedish oil investigated by Sandermann contained a high percentage of a tricyclic sesquiterpene which gave a good yield of cadinene dihydrochloride. Dehydration of the sesquiterpene fraction with palladium-charcoal yielded a compound from which azulene could be isolated.

Use.—Like other pine needle oils, oil of *Pinus sylvestris* L. is used as an adjunct in the scenting of soaps, in bath preparations, room sprays, inhalants, deodorants, and similar products.

B. Turpentine Oil

Distilling the turpentine derived from German *Pinus sylvestris* L., Wienhaus and Sandermann [19] obtained a volatile oil in which they noted the presence of *α-pinene, β-pinene* (small quantities), *Δ³-carene* (large quantities), *camphene* (small quantities), *dipentene* (large quantities), *cadinene*, and primary, secondary and chiefly tertiary *sesquiterpene alcohols*.

Recently Bardyshev [20] identified *β-myrcene* in the turpentine from *Pinus sylvestris*.

[19] Dissertation Wilhelm Sandermann, "Chem. Untersuchung des Deutschen Kiefernterpentins," Leipzig (1936). *Ber. Schimmel & Co.* (1937), 82.
[20] *Doklady Akad. Nauk S.S.S.R.* **71** (1950), **673**. *Chem. Abstracts* **44** (1950), 8315.

C. Root Oil

In an oil obtained by steam distillation of the roots and stumps of *Pinus sylvestris* L., Semmler and von Schiller [21] observed the presence of α- and β-*pinene*, *d*-Δ³-*carene*, *d*-Δ⁴-*carene*, and α-*terpinene*.

An oil of identical origin examined by Schimmel & Co.[22] contained *furfural*, α- and β-*pinene* (35 to 40 per cent), Δ³-*carene* (40 to 50 per cent), and probably terpineol and terpinenol (a few per cent only).

OIL OF *PINUS CEMBRA* L.

A. Leaf (Needle) Oil

Pinus cembra L. (fam. *Pinaceae*), the so-called "Swiss Stone Pine," grows in the Alps at the same altitude as *Pinus mugo* Turra, the "Dwarf Pine," and is often interspersed with the latter. Patches consisting exclusively of *Pinus cembra* are rare. The young branches and adherent leaves [1] contain an essential oil, small quantities of which are occasionally produced in the Tyrol. Distillation material is available only in summer when the forests are thinned out. Trimming of the small trees and collection of the branches go hand in hand with those of the "Dwarf Pine." Production of oil has been irregular, ranging from 100 to 1,000 kg. per year. Prior to distillation the branches should be reduced to small pieces. The yield of oil is high, amounting to about 1 per cent and even more.

Physicochemical Properties.—Oil of *Pinus cembra* L. is an almost colorless liquid with an odor similar to, but finer than, that of dwarf pine oil, *Pinus mugo* Turra.

Ten oils from various parts of the Tyrol examined by Schimmel & Co.[2] (I), and one genuine oil procured by the author in southern Tyrol (II) had these properties:

[21] *Ber.* **60** (1927), 1591. This type of oil had already been investigated in 1918 by Schimmel & Co., but the results were not published until 1928. Cf. *Ber. Schimmel & Co.* (1928), 100.

[22] *Ber. Schimmel & Co.* (1928), 100.

[1] Among all the European species of *Pinus*, *Pinus cembra* is the only one containing five needles (leaves) to each cluster.

[2] Gildemeister and Hoffmann, "Die Ätherischen Öle," 3d Ed., Vol. II, 199.

	I	II
Specific Gravity at 15°..................	0.8616 to 0.8684	0.876
Optical Rotation.......................	−11° 38′ to −15° 12′	−10° 30′
Refractive Index at 20°................	1.475 to 1.478	1.4754
Acid Number..........................	0	0
Ester Number.........................	3.7 to 11.2	18.5
Ester Content, Calculated as Bornyl Acetate................................	1.3 to 3.9%	6.5%
Ester Number after Acetylation (One Determination Only)....................	13.1	27.1
Total Alcohol Content, Calculated as Borneol (One Determination).............	3.6%	7.5%
Solubility in 90% Alcohol..............	Soluble in 5 to 7 vol. and more, occasionally with slight turbidity	Soluble in 9 vol., with turbidity

In this connection it should be mentioned that oils of *Pinus cembra* distilled in Siberia and described in literature [3] have exhibited dextrorotation, whereas the Tyrolean oils are laevorotatory. The explanation is that in the Tyrol needles *and twigs* are used for distillation, while the Siberian oils were distilled exclusively from needles.

Chemical Composition.—Nothing is known about the chemical composition of the Tyrolean oil, but it may be assumed that it resembles that of the Siberian oil. In the latter, Flawitzky,[4] and Pigulevski,[5] reported the presence of *d-α-pinene* and *l-cadinene*.

Use.—As was mentioned above, the odor of the oil derived from the terminal branches of *Pinus cembra* L. is somewhat finer, sweeter and more pleasing than that of *Pinus mugo* Turra. The physicochemical properties of the two oils are similar. Oil of *Pinus cembra* being usually lower priced than oil of *Pinus mugo*, the former is occasionally used as an admixture to the latter.

B. Cone Oil

Schimmel & Co.[6] examined an oil distilled in the Tyrol from the cones of *Pinus cembra* L. and reported these properties:

Specific Gravity at 15°...... 0.8680
Optical Rotation........... −31° 35′

---

[3] Flawitzky, *J. prakt. Chem.* [2], **45** (1892), 115. Pigulevski et al., *J. Russ. Phys. Chem. Soc.* **54** (1922), 259; **55** (1923), 171.
[4] *J. prakt. Chem.* [2], **45** (1892), 115.
[5] *J. Russ. Phys. Chem. Soc.* **54** (1922), 259.
[6] *Ber. Schimmel & Co.* (1932), 74.

Refractive Index at 20°..... 1.47141
Acid Number............. 0
Ester Number............ 9.3
Solubility................ Soluble in 6.5 vol. and more of
                         90% alcohol

Boiling Range at 768 mm.:
    161° to 165°............. 50% of the oil
    165° to 170°............. 22%
    170° to 180°............. 12%
    180° to 190°............. 4%
    Above 190°............. 12%

The oil had a pleasant, balsamic odor which, however, was quite different from that of the oil derived from the cones of *Abies alba*. The aroma of the oil was inferior to that of the oil distilled from the terminal branches and adherent leaves of *Pinus cembra*.

C. Turpentine Oil

According to Mirov, Wang, and Haagen-Smit,[7] the oleoresin of *Pinus cembra* L. consists of 78.6 per cent of rosin and 21.4 per cent of turpentine. The latter contains 85 per cent of d-α-pinene and 9 per cent of l-β-pinene.

AMERICAN TURPENTINES

by

LEO A. GOLDBLATT, PH.D.

Naval Stores Research Division
Bureau of Agricultural and Industrial Chemistry
United States Department of Agriculture
Olustee, Florida

AMERICAN OIL OF TURPENTINE—GUM SPIRITS OF TURPENTINE

Introduction.—Turpentine is the essential oil produced in the largest volume, current annual world production approximating, and probably exceeding, a million barrels of 50 gallons each, or more than 350 million pounds. In 1938–39 world production amounted to 1,270,000 fifty-gallon

---

[7] *J. Am. Pharm. Assocn.* **38** (1949), 404.

barrels.[1] The United States is now, as it has been for over a century, the chief source. Its proportion of the world production during the present century has varied from a high of about 80 per cent in 1908–09 to about 50 per cent in 1949–50. Some turpentine is produced on the American continent outside the United States, chiefly in Mexico.[2] Production in Mexico during the period 1940 to 1948 averaged 34,620 barrels annually.[3] At various times turpentine has been produced, usually for local consumption, in Honduras and in the West Indies, notably Santo Domingo,[4] but such production is negligible in amount.

The U. S. Federal Naval Stores Act enacted in 1923 recognizes four different kinds of turpentine, and classifies them according to methods of production.[5] The four different turpentines may be described as follows:

1. *Gum spirits of turpentine.*—The designation "gum spirits of turpentine" shall refer to the kind of spirits of turpentine obtained by distillation of the oleoresin (gum) from *living* trees, and commonly known prior to the passage of the act as gum spirits, gum turpentine, spirits of turpentine, or oil of turpentine.

2. *Steam-distilled wood turpentine.*—The designation "steam-distilled wood turpentine" shall refer to the kind of spirits of turpentine obtained by steam distillation from the oleoresinous component of wood whether in the presence of the wood or after extraction from the wood, and commonly known prior to the passage of the act as wood turpentine, steam-distilled turpentine, steam-distilled wood turpentine, or S.D. wood turpentine.

3. *Destructively distilled wood turpentine.*—The designation "destructively distilled wood turpentine" shall refer to the kind of spirits of turpentine prepared from the distillate obtained in the destructive distillation (carbonization) of wood, and commonly known prior to the passage of the act as destructively distilled wood turpentine or D.D. wood turpentine.

4. *Sulfate wood turpentine.*—The designation "sulfate wood turpentine" shall refer to the kind of spirits of turpentine prepared from the condensates that are recovered in the sulfate process of cooking wood pulp, and commonly known as sulfate turpentine or sulfate wood turpentine.

In addition, a fifth kind of turpentine, which is not officially recognized, the so-called "sulfite turpentine," is obtained as a by-product from the

---

[1] Hallauer, Progress Report of the Forest Survey, *U. S. Dept. Agr.,* June (1941), 3.
[2] *U. S. Dept. Agr., Misc. Pub.* No. 209, January (1935), 165.
[3] "Naval Stores Review 1949 International Yearbook," H. L. Peace Publications, New Orleans, La. (1949), 27.
[4] *U. S. Dept. Agr., Misc. Pub.* No. 209, January (1935), 165.
[5] *U. S. Dept. Agr., Misc. Circ.* No. 22, March (1924), also Suppl. 5 (1929) to the same. *U. S. Dept. Agr., Misc. Pub.* No. 476, January (1942), 2.

manufacture of wood pulp by the sulfite process. This variety differs materially from the others in composition.

American gum spirits of turpentine are described in this section; the so-called "wood turpentine" will be treated subsequently.

Production of Turpentine in the United States

The annual production of gum spirits of turpentine in the United States in the present century up to 1950 is given in Table 20.1. Production has varied widely; from an all-time high of 750,000 barrels in the 1908–09 season it sank to a low of 340,000 barrels in 1918–19. It then increased

TABLE 20.1. U. S. PRODUCTION OF GUM SPIRITS OF TURPENTINE, IN BARRELS OF 50 GALLONS EACH, BY CROP YEARS (APPROXIMATE) *

1900–01..........	620,000	1926–27..........	510,000
1901–02..........	600,000	1927–28..........	650,000
1902–03..........	581,000	1928–29..........	560,000
1903–04..........	545,000	1929–30..........	625,000
1904–05..........	600,000	1930–31..........	600,000
1905–06..........	590,000	1931–32..........	500,000
1906–07..........	588,000	1932–33..........	450,000
1907–08..........	685,000	1933–34..........	490,000
1908–09..........	750,000	1934–35..........	500,000
1909–10..........	600,000	1935–36..........	497,000
1910–11..........	615,000	1936–37..........	483,000
1911–12..........	660,000	1937–38..........	518,000
1912–13..........	715,000	1938–39..........	534,000
1913–14..........	675,000	1939–40..........	383,000
1914–15..........	560,000	1940–41..........	344,000
1915–16..........	530,000	1941–42..........	285,000
1916–17..........	610,000	1942–43..........	322,000
1917–18..........	520,000	1943–44..........	288,000
1918–19..........	340,000	1944–45..........	245,000
1919–20..........	400,000	1945–46..........	244,000
1920–21..........	525,000	1946–47..........	270,000
1921–22..........	500,000	1947–48..........	294,000
1922–23..........	520,000	1948–49..........	324,000
1923–24..........	565,000	1949–50..........	323,000
1924–25..........	530,000	1950–51..........	272,000
1925–26..........	480,000		

* Data for 1900 to 1930 from "Gamble's International Naval Stores Yearbook" (1930–31), 69; for 1931 to 1939 from "Gamble's International Naval Stores Yearbook" (1939–40), 75; for 1940 to 1949 from *Agricultural Statistics, U. S. Dept. Agr.* (1949), 746; for 1949–51 from *1950–1951 Annual Naval Stores Report, U. S. Dept. Agr., Bur. Agr. Econ.*, May (1951), 3.

again to a high of 650,000 barrels in 1927–28, only to decline to a new low of 244,000 barrels in 1945–46. Recovery of production has been slow. Only 272,000 barrels were prepared in 1950–51. The average yearly production for the entire fifty-one years was 498,000 barrels; for the past ten years, 287,000 barrels.

History and Producing Regions.—American gum spirits of turpentine is obtained almost exclusively by the distillation of the oleoresin obtained from two species of pine, *Pinus palustris* Miller (longleaf pine), and *Pinus caribaea* Morelet (slash pine).[6] In Central America and the West Indies the species is known as Caribbean pitch pine (*Pinus caribaea* Morelet), but botanically is held to be identical with the slash pine of the United States.[7] In Mexico the Mexican white pine (*Pinus ayacahuite*) is used.[8] In the United States certain other pines have been turpentined commercially at various times. During the Civil War, when the supply of naval stores from the south was cut off, an attempt was made to supply the northern states from the ponderosa pines of the Sierra Nevada Range of California. The industry remained active for a few years but declined rapidly when the southern product again became available.[9] Also, the western Jeffrey pine and Digger pine were used in the latter part of the nineteenth century as a source of turpentine, which was used locally, chiefly as a cleaning agent.[10] Interest in this turpentine, which consists chiefly of *n*-heptane, was revived in the 1920's, when a demand arose for this compound, useful as a standard reference fuel for the measurement of detonation in internal combustion engines.[11] This type of turpentine is not produced commercially today.

When longleaf or slash pines are wounded, a gummy fluid (*not* the sap of the tree) exudes freely. This fluid, or oleoresin, is the raw material for the gum naval stores industry—one of the oldest American industries. There are reports that turpentine was obtained from Nova Scotia pines as early as 1606, and that plans were made for the production of turpentine in the Virginia Colony as early as 1610.[12] However, in former times the oleoresin itself was commonly referred to as "turpentine," and the raw oleoresin was shipped abroad for distillation.[13] Very little distilled spirits were produced in the United States before the nineteenth century.[14] Much tar and pitch were produced in Colonial days, at first in the New England

[6] Snow, *Economic Botany* **3** (1949), 377.
[7] *U. S. Dept. Agr., Misc. Pub.* No. 209, January (1935), 166.
[8] Veitch and Grotlisch, *U. S. Dept. Agr., Bull.* No. 898, November (1920), 2.
[9] *U. S. Dept. Agr., Misc. Pub.* No. 209, January (1935), 20.
[10] Kremers, *Pharm. Rev.* **18** (1900), 166.
[11] *U. S. Dept. Agr., Misc. Pub.* No. 209, January (1935), 21.
[12] T. Gamble, "Naval Stores," Savannah (1921), 17.
[13] Schorger and Betts, *U. S. Dept. Agr., Bull.* No. 229, July (1915), 3.
[14] *Ibid.*

States along the Connecticut River, and later in the Carolinas.[15] The term "Naval Stores" is a survival from the days when the tar and pitch obtained from the crude oleoresin were used in quantity in the construction and repair of wooden ships and the preservation of the rigging. Today, where wooden sailing ships have given way to steel steamers, the term "Naval Stores" continues to cling to one group of products—turpentine and rosin—or more broadly, to the resinous, tarry, and oily products of the pine.[16]

The virgin pine forests of New England were soon exhausted, but in the immense forests of North Carolina, where the naval stores industry first became established about 1710 or 1715, the industry developed very rapidly.[17] However, little turpentining, as practiced today, was done before 1820. About that time, the distillation of the oleoresin to produce spirits of turpentine was begun in North Carolina, and the industry spread through the belt of virgin longleaf pine following the new frontiers to the south and thence westward along the Atlantic Coastal Plain and the Gulf Coast through South Carolina, Georgia, Florida, Alabama, Mississippi, Louisiana, and into eastern Texas. Then, as the original stands of timber were depleted, the center of production swung back to the extensive second growth stands which had meanwhile grown up, principally in southern Georgia and northern Florida. This movement of the industry to the southwest and back again is illustrated in Table 20.2. The peak of the turpentine and rosin production from pine gum in Texas occurred between 1908 and 1922 with the greatest annual yield in 1919,[18] when the production of gum turpentine amounted to 18,129 barrels. After 1931 production of gum turpentine in Texas became negligible, and at present none is being produced in that state. The industry is now largely centered near the Georgia-Florida border, as this area provides the best conditions for regrowth of the heavily exploited forests and optimum climatic conditions reduce the hazards of fluctuations in gum flow from year to year. At the northern, southern, and western extremes of the range of the turpentine pines, the climatic and soil conditions, which were only marginal for the virgin timber, are probably submarginal for regrowth.[19]

Reforestation.—Virgin forests of longleaf pine have been practically exhausted. One of the last remaining stands of virgin timber was turpentined in Louisiana in 1945.[20] The second growth stands produced by

[15] Romaine, *Chemical Industries* **45** (1939), 259.
[16] *U. S. Dept. Agr., Misc. Pub.* No. 476, January (1942), 1.
[17] Romaine, *Chemical Industries* **45** (1939), 260.
[18] *Naval Stores Rev.* **41**, No. 12, June 20 (1931), 13.
[19] Ostrom, *Chemurgic Digest* **4**, July 15 (1945), 219.
[20] *J. Am. Turpentine Farmers Assocn.* **7**, August (1945), 9.

TABLE 20.2.   APPROXIMATE PERCENTAGE OF TURPENTINE PRODUCTION BY STATES *

Year	N. Carolina	S. Carolina	Georgia	Florida	Alabama	Miss.-La. and Texas
1850–51..........	87.3	8.3	1.9	1.1	0.6	0.8
1880–81..........	29.9	32.2	24.8	5.0	6.4	1.7
1890–91..........	21.1	18.9	52.5	2.4	1.4	3.7
1900–01..........	5.2	3.9	39.8	31.8	10.0	9.3
1909–10..........	...	4.3 [a]	27.8	47.6	9.8	10.5
1914–15..........	...	1.4 [a]	23.1	45.8	10.1	19.6
1919–20..........	...	0.5 [a]	20.2	37.4	10.4	31.5
1924–25..........	...	1.7 [a]	38.7	35.1	7.0	17.6
1929–30..........	...	4.2 [a]	50.4	31.4	6.4	7.7
1934–35..........	...	3.8 [a]	56.6	27.0	8.7	3.9
1939–40..........	...	2.3 [a]	59.4	27.0	7.5	3.8
1944–45..........	...	0.9 [a]	68.3	23.5	5.7	1.6
1949–50..........	...	...	74.9	18.3	6.1	0.7 [b]
1950–51..........	...	...	76.3	17.3	6.0	0.4 [b]

* Data for 1850 to 1930 from "Gamble's International Naval Stores Yearbook" (1930–31), 65; for 1934 to 1945 from "Naval Stores Review 1948 International Yearbook," H. L. Peace Publications, New Orleans, La. (1948), 37; for 1949–51 from *1950–1951 Annual Naval Stores Report, U. S. Dept. Agr., Bur. Agr. Econ.*, May (1951), 3.

[a] Includes N. Carolina.

[b] Includes N. and S. Carolina.

spontaneous reseeding in southern Georgia and northern Florida, now the chief source of pine used for turpentining, are chiefly slash pine.   With increasing recognition of the need for more conservative forest practices there has come increasing interest in reforestation and orcharding, and improved forest management aimed at providing the maximum income per acre from gum and wood products combined.   Systematic plantings were begun in the 1920's, at first using seedlings lifted from ponds or other low areas where they had come up spontaneously in abundant amounts.[21]   Later nursery seedlings grown from pine cone seed, and supplied by State Agricultural Experiment Stations, were used extensively.   Most pine species are difficult to propagate vegetatively, cuttings of hard or yellow pines being particularly hard to root.[22]   The scope of such reforestation has grown tremendously in recent years.   In 1949–50 more than 44 million seedlings were planted in Georgia and more than 26 million in Florida.   The seedlings

[21] Shirley, *Georgia Agr. Extension Service, Bull.* No. 532 (1947), 36.
[22] Snow, *Economic Botany* **3** (1949), 388.

are mostly slash pine; e.g., in Florida 26,449,106 were slash and only 226,250 longleaf; in Georgia 37,464,750 were slash and only 392,475 longleaf.[23]

Slash pine seedlings are generally recommended, since slash is not only a better producer of oleoresin but also comes into production earlier than does longleaf; moreover it enjoys a better survival ratio, and a much more rapid rate of growth. Seedlings commonly cost about $2.50 per thousand. It is estimated that machine planting costs about $10.00 per acre and hand planting $12.00 to $15.00 per acre.[24]

It would lead beyond the scope of this chapter to discuss comprehensively the methods used to propagate, plant, and cultivate pine trees. Details will be found in numerous State and Federal publications.[25–30] The two species turpentined commercially may be characterized briefly as follows:

Pinus palustris Miller, the longleaf pine, is also known as southern yellow pine, Georgia pine, hard pine, hill pine, heart pine, and longstraw pine. The original virgin pine forests from the Carolinas to Texas comprised largely longleaf pine (*Pinus palustris*), and formerly commercial gum turpentine consisted very largely of the turpentine obtained from the oleoresin of this species. Although large numbers of longleaf pines are still turpentined, this species no longer holds its pre-eminent position.

Longleaf pine grows over a wide area, extending along the coastal region from southeastern Virginia to southern Florida and westward to eastern Texas; to northwestern Georgia, northward to Alabama to the northern part of the state, central Mississippi and western Louisiana. Longleaf pine tends to grow in pure stands, accommodating itself to a wide variety of sites, such as very poor, dry, deep sandy soils or moist poorly drained soils. It can also grow on soil with relatively impenetrable clay only 2 or 3 ft. below the surface. The tree grows best in deep soils underlaid by clay. Its tendency to grow on sandy ridges has earned it the name, hill pine. The tree withstands ordinary fires with relatively small injury. During its early years longleaf pine may grow much more slowly than other common southern species, but it tends to maintain a good rate of growth for many years.

[23] Private communication from Mr. L. C. Hart, Jr., Georgia Forestry Commission, and Mr. C. H. Coulter, State Forester, Florida (1950).
[24] *J. Am. Turpentine Farmers Assocn.* **11**, July (1949), 12.
[25] Merrill, *Georgia Forest Service, Bull.* No. 9 (1929).
[26] Sebring and Thurmond, *ibid., Bull.* No. 16 (1931).
[27] Shirley, *Georgia Agr. Extension Service, Bull.* No. 532 (1947).
[28] Coulter, *Florida Forest Service, Bull.* No. 8 (1931).
[29] Wakeley, *U. S. Dept. Agr., Leaflet* No. 32 (1929).
[30] Downs, *Forest Farmer* **7**, May (1948), 26.

Longleaf pine is characterized by its very long needles, which vary from 8 to 18 in. in length and always occur in bundles of 3. The conspicuous large silvery white buds, and characteristic whitish "candles" that develop from them in the process of new leaf formation, offer an easy means of identifying longleaf pine, especially in the winter and spring. The large size of the cones (6 to 12 in. long and 2 to 3 in. in diameter) also readily distinguishes longleaf from other southern pines. Trees commonly bear from 25 to 50 cones. The seeds are large and heavy and a single cone may contain 50 good seeds. A bushel of cones will yield about one pound of unwinnowed seed. The bark is about one-half inch thick, of orange-brown color, and in mature trees is characterized by broad, smooth scales.

Pinus caribaea Morelet, the slash pine, is also known as yellow slash, swamp pine, hill slash, and Cuban pine. Extensive pure stands of virgin slash pine were rare, except in the lower peninsula and on the Gulf Coast of Florida. In the virgin forest it appears to have been relatively less abundant in proportion to longleaf pine than it is in the young growth and planted stands today. Slash pine may grow in pure stands or mixed with longleaf or other species. Slash pine grows in the coastal region from South Carolina to southern Florida; westward in the coastal region of the Gulf States to Louisiana. It also occurs in the two Honduran states, eastern Guatemala, Nicaragua, Bahamas, Cuba, and Isle of Pines. The tree grows naturally in the moister situations along swamps and ponds, and will tolerate a highly acid condition in the surface soil. It is very sensitive to fire, especially during its early years; and very young slash pines require absolute fire protection if they are to survive. Slash pine is one of the most rapidly growing forest trees in the United States. Growth is particularly rapid during its early life.

Slash pine has needles from 6 to 12 in. in length, averaging about 9 in. long and $\frac{1}{16}$ in. thick. The needles are intermediate in size between those of longleaf and loblolly pine and are a dark glossy green, darker than either longleaf or loblolly. There are usually two but sometimes three leaves, especially in vigorous trees, in a bundle, or fascicle. Buds are smaller than those of longleaf pines. The color of the winter buds is a dark cinnamon brown, often purplish. In the early spring they open to form brownish "candles" which are about $\frac{1}{3}$ in. in diameter. The closed cones, or burrs, average 3 to 5 in. in length and about 1 to 2 in. in diameter. They are egg-shaped and rich chocolate-brown in color. The bark of the slash pine is irregularly divided into thin, dark red-brown scales. Young trees have a thick, deeply furrowed bark. The orange-colored or sometimes silvery bark plates of mature trees are characteristic of slash pine and facilitate its identification.

Turpentine Orchards.—It is well known in the gum naval stores industry that some trees produce far more oleoresin (and some considerably less) than do other trees growing under identical conditions. Careful evaluation of the productive capacity of certain trees in comparison with others in the same stand with similar environment has shown that they do in fact regularly produce more than twice as much oleoresin as their companion trees, which were worked as closely alike as possible.[31] No single or combined external characteristics or environmental factors which might operate, or be used to distinguish between these superior trees, have yet been found.[32]

While yield may be greatly increased through the selection and propagation of the best individuals which occur naturally, further increase in yield through controlled breeding may be feasible, and experiments along this line are now under way by the Forest Service of the U. S. Department of Agriculture.[33] Development of turpentine orchards similar to plantations of the natural rubber industry has been envisioned. Such turpentine orchards would have up to 250 workable trees to the acre, instead of the 25-tree average now being worked. Using "pedigreed" stock of a high-yielding strain, producing twice the average amount of gum per year, the annual per-acre yield would theoretically be about 4,000 lb. instead of the present 200 lb. Although not now a reality, these potentialities do exist and active research in the naval stores industry is pointing the way.[34, 35]

Methods of Obtaining Pine Oleoresin

The early methods of obtaining oleoresins from pines are well exemplified by the following quotation from the *"Instructions for suche things as are to be sente from Virginia"* [36] issued in 1610:

> "Pyne trees, or ffirre trees, are to be wounded within a yarde of the grounde, or boare a hoal with an agar the third pte into the tree, and lett yt runne into anye thinge that may receyve the same, and that wch yssues owte wilbe Turpentyne worth 18£ Tonne. When the tree beginneth to runne softelye yt is to be stopped up agayne for preserveinge the tree."

Boxing.—The early colonists were more prodigal and more destructive of the apparently inexhaustible virgin forest than these relatively conservative directions prescribed. A method which was extensively used for over two centuries, and which at the time seemed well suited to the stands of

[31] Dorman, *Chemurgic Digest* **4,** September 29 (1945), 296.
[32] Snow, *Economic Botany* **3** (1949), 388.
[33] Downs, *Southern Lumberman* **179,** December (1949), 233.
[34] *Ibid.*
[35] Dorman, *Chemurgic Digest* **4,** September 19 (1945), 293.
[36] T. Gamble, "Naval Stores," Savannah (1921), 17.

large virgin timber, was to cut a hole or *box* in the base of the tree to receive the flow of gum which resulted from repeated chipping or wounding.[37] Two to five boxes, individual boxes up to 16 in. in width, were cut in each tree and there were 200 to 250 boxes per acre. The wounding was called chopping and at first extended only to a height of 5 or 6 ft. but later, when the original longleaf pine began to disappear, it was not unusual to see trees wounded to a height of 12 or 15 ft.

The Cup System.—The boxing system was patently destructive and wasteful both of forests and of oleoresin. The obvious need was for a receptacle which could be fastened to the tree. Sporadic attempts were made during the latter part of the nineteenth century to install various cup systems. The extensive experiments of Dr. Charles H. Herty of the U. S. Forest Service in 1901 and 1902 resulted in the publication of his "A New Method for Turpentine Orcharding," [38] and under his aggressive leadership the first extensive use of the cup system was made by the industry in 1904.[39] In the cup system, as it is universally used today, the oleoresin flowing from the wound is guided by one or two pieces of sheet metal called "tins" into the collecting receptacle or cup. The cups may be made of clay or glass and are commonly conical in shape, with a round bottom (somewhat like a flower pot); or they may be made of metal, such as galvanized iron or aluminum, in which case they are generally flat-bottomed and oblong like a long, narrow pan, and flared so that they can be nested for shipping and handling. The capacity of most cups is about 3 pt., although recently there has been a tendency to increase the size of the cup to about 5 pt. More than 32 million new cups have been sold in a single season (1927–28), giving an idea of the magnitude of the industry.[40]

The present approved and generally used working practice for obtaining pine oleoresin may be outlined as follows: trees that are to be worked are selected in advance and marked, bearing in mind the future use of the tree so as best to utilize the forest resources. Trees smaller than 9 or 10 in. in diameter, $4\frac{1}{2}$ ft. from the ground, are not worked (unless they are to be culled). The trees are prepared by smoothing off the rough outside bark where the "face" (the working surface) is to be made for a distance of 15 to 18 in. from the ground level. For this a broad axe is commonly used. After the tree has been faced, the next step is to fasten the "tins" (metal gutters or aprons) to the tree, to guide the flow of oleoresin into the receiver. The tins are installed either in broad axe incisions, without nails or tacks or, when installed higher up the tree, by tacking them on the sur-

[37] Ostrom, *Chemurgic Digest* **4**, July 15 (1945), 219.
[38] *U. S. Dept. Agr., Bur. Forestry Bull.* No. 40 (1903).
[39] Ostrom, *Chemurgic Digest* **4**, July 15 (1945), 220.
[40] *1947–48 Annual Naval Stores Report, U. S. Dept. Agr., Bur. Agr. Econ.* May (1948), 9.

face of the smoothed face. To perform this gutter installation an axeman holds his broadaxe level at the side of the face, leaving only enough distance above the ground for the cup to be seated under the apron. A maul is used by the maulman to strike the axe so that it will penetrate the tree to a depth of ½ in. or less. The apron, a flat rectangular strip of metal about 2½ in. wide, 8 to 12 in. long, is slipped off the axe blade into the incision as the axe handle is tapped with the hand and the axe withdrawn from the tree. The gutter, a flat metal strip, crimped V-shaped lengthwise along the center, is installed in a similar fashion. For this the axe is held above the apron at an angle of about 20 degrees with provision for an overlap of about 2 in. over the apron. The width of the face should be somewhat less than the diameter of the tree at breast height. Thus a tree 10 in. in diameter would have a face 9 in. wide, but in general, faces should not be more than 12 in. wide, irrespective of the size of the tree, and never more than ⅓ its circumference. The width of the face determines the length of the apron and gutter. For average sized faces, a 6-in. apron and an 8-in. gutter are used. A flat bottomed, box-shaped cup is pulled up under the apron and held in place by use of a 20-penny nail. The corners of the apron are turned upward and the outer edge pressed downward to guide the flow of the gum into the cup. Other systems are also used to hang cups—such as two aprons or two gutters, depending upon the size of the tree and shape of the cup.[41, 42]

Cups should be hung during December to February, the dormant season. An advance streak, or "lead streak," is made at that time. It is generally believed that this procedure gives higher yields than if the first streak is cut in March or April, when the regular weekly chipping begins.

Chipping.—After the trees have been selected, the cups hung, and the lead streak cut, the crop is ready for regular working. This consists in periodic chipping with a hack during early years, and with a puller when the faces are 3 to 4 ft. high above the ground. The hack has a U-shaped cutting edge which is held on its side so that the bottom of the U removes a semi-cylindrical chip of wood when drawn across the grain of the tree. A weighted short handle provides a counter balance and momentum to keep the blade moving through the wood. A puller has a similar type of blade mounted on a long handle or pole and is used for chipping high faces out of reach of the hack. The chipper cuts through some of the inner bark of the tree to produce a V-shaped wound known as a "streak," about 8 in. long and about ⅜ to ½ in. high and ½ in. deep.

Wounding the tree causes a gummy fluid to exude freely. Although there has been much speculation, little is known concerning either the origin or

[41] *U. S. Dept. Agr., Misc. Pub.* No. 209, January (1935).
[42] Shirley, *Georgia Agr. Extension Service, Bull.* No. 532 (1947).

function of this fluid.[43,44] Technically, the oleoresin is not the sap of the tree. The sap circulates through the fibrous cells of the sapwood and cells of the soft inner bark. The oleoresin is associated with the excess of materials stored inside the wood and not used up in the production of wood, leaves and bark. Wounding the tree by chipping exposes open vertical resin ducts which are part of an interconnecting network of large vertical ducts and smaller, more numerous, horizontal ducts.[45] The oleoresin or gum continues to exude, drop by drop, from the exposed ends of these ducts, and flows until the ducts are gradually closed. Rechipping is then necessary to renew the flow of oleoresin. It is believed that chipping not only allows the oleoresin to flow from the resin ducts that have been severed, but also actually stimulates oleoresin production by the tree. Chipping frequency is important in obtaining the maximum yields of gum. When a streak is freshly cut, the gum starts to flow immediately and small droplets of exudate may be observed on the freshly cut surface in a few seconds. The rate of gum flow reaches a maximum the first day and continues at this rate for 2 or 3 days before a decline takes place. This is aside from diurnal fluctuations, during which the rate starts to increase in the early morning, reaches a peak about 9:00 A.M., slows up by evening, and is low overnight.[46] After about 5 to 7 days the rate of flow becomes very low, and a fresh streak has to be cut. The first streak is made as low as convenient and each new streak, generally added at weekly intervals, is cut just above the last one. The combined streaks comprise what is known as a face on the tree. A chipper commonly cuts about 32 streaks on each face being worked during the gum flowing season—from early spring to late fall. Thus, about 16 in. are added to the height of the face each year; after five to seven years the working surface becomes too high to be worked conveniently, and the yield of gum does not warrant further working. Another face may then be started on another side of the tree, care being taken to leave a bark bar or space of 4 in. or more between faces. Sometimes two, occasionally even more, faces are worked on the same tree during a single season. Experimentally, as many as 14 faces have been worked simultaneously on a single tree for a few weeks without killing the tree.[47] Only one face is seen on most commercial operations as of today, unless timber is being worked rapidly ahead of a sawmill operation.

The chipper is a skilled workman who may well take pride in the appearance of his "face." The yield of oleoresin to be obtained, as well as the

[43] Gerry and Hall, *Plant. Physiol.* **10** (1935), 537.
[44] Hall, *Chem. Rev.* **13** (1933), 479; **20** (1937), 305.
[45] Snow, *Economic Botany* **3** (1949), 378.
[46] *Ibid.*
[47] Snow, *The Forest Farmer* **6**, February (1947), 14.

health of the stand, depends upon the skill with which the chipper controls the height and depth of his chipping. Formerly a chipper was expected to chip 10,000 faces (the unit or "crop" of the industry) each week, but at present, with trees more widely spaced, a chipper may spend three-fourths of his time walking from tree to tree, so that 5,000 to 7,000 faces now generally constitute a week's work.

Chemical Stimulation.—In the early 1930's it was discovered that the flow of oleoresin from pines could be stimulated by application of solutions of strong acids or bases, or certain salts, to the fresh wound or streak on the face of the turpentine tree immediately after chipping.[48,49,50] Extensive tests were conducted to determine the best chemical agents and mode of application to utilize this technique to best advantage. Today a significant and increasing proportion of pine oleoresin in the United States is obtained by the use of acid stimulation. According to estimates, in 1950 more than 10 per cent of the crop was obtained with the aid of chemical stimulants.

When acid is applied to a fresh streak the rate of gum flow increases more sharply and continues at this accelerated rate for a longer period than it would if the streak were chipped and no acid or other stimulant applied. In conventional untreated chipping the rate of gum flow decreases markedly after 4 or 5 days, whereas if acid is applied the increased rate continues with only slight reduction for about 10 days and is still appreciable even in the third week. In present practice about 1 ml. of 50 per cent sulfuric acid is sprayed on the freshly cut streak by means of a plastic spray gun, with the liquid spray hitting the wound at the junction of the bark and wood in the cambium region clear across the face.

The action of chemical stimulants in accelerating and prolonging the flow of oleoresin is imperfectly known, but is undoubtedly intimately associated with the small resin ducts from which the droplets of oleoresin exude. As described by Ostrom: [51]

"These ducts extend vertically in the wood and horizontally toward the center of the tree in both wood and bark. Where the vertical and horizontal ducts cross, their cavities join, as in the plumbing system of a building. All of these ducts are lined with thin-walled, brick shaped *parenchyma* cells which, in the wood, contrast sharply with the long, thick-walled wood fibers. After treatment with a strong acid the tender cells lining the ducts are collapsed near the site of treatment, and the duct channels are correspondingly enlarged. It is

[48] Nikolaev and Sinelobov, *Forest Chemical Industries U.S.S.R.* **5**, No. 6 (1936), 4. *Chem. Zentr.* (1937), I, 1290.

[49] Hessenland, *Angewandte Chemie* **48** (1935), 636.

[50] Liefeld, *U. S. Forest Service, Southern Forest Expt. Sta., Occasional Paper* No. 97 (1940).

[51] *Chemurgic Digest* **4**, July 15 (1945), 240.

reasonable to suppose that, as a result, the gum can exude more rapidly from the ducts, and that the enlarged ends of the ducts may be less readily closed than normal ducts by the hardening of the gum at the outlets.

"Another effect exerted chiefly by strong acids is the destruction of the tender new cells in the growing region or cambium which lies between the wood and the bark. Over a period of several days the acid works up into this region and causes a splitting away of the bark from the wood, one-fourth to one-half inch above the wound. This process probably serves to tap new horizontal ducts, several hundred of which cross each square inch of the cambium. The solutions applied to the wound may also stimulate the process of gum manufacture in purely chemical ways, but the exact nature and relative importance of such effects are not yet known."

Bark Chipping.—Another advance in chipping technique resulted from the discovery that when an acid spray is used, the removal of the bark only down to the wood ("bark chipping") will result in gum yields comparable to those obtained from conventional chipping where a half-inch strip of wood is cut from the tree.[52] It is possible to obtain oleoresin by removing only the bark without scarring the wood, but the yield is small because the horizontal resin ducts exposed by this method are smaller than the vertical ducts, and are usually closed by parenchyma cells at the junction of the bark and the wood. After acid treatment, however, these radial ducts exposed by removing only the bark effectively drain the resin-duct system. A special bark-chipping hack,[53] its blade a hollow square sharpened at one end, has been devised to facilitate bark chipping. In practice the blade is drawn across the upper end of the face by means of a handle so as to remove a strip of bark ½ in. in height, but not to cut into the wood.

Bark chipping leaves the butt of the tree round and in better condition for use as pulpwood, ties, or lumber. Since no deep incision is made it is probable also that over a period of years of chipping the tree will remain in a better physiological state for gum production. Also, bark chipping requires less physical effort (a chipper using conventional methods would have to cut through about 40 miles of wood in a single year), and less skill, and is therefore easier to teach to unexperienced workmen.

Fungus Stimulation.—Another approach to increasing the efficiency of gum production was the discovery by Hepting[54] that the fungus *Fusarium lateritium* f. *pini* prolongs the flow of gum from infected wounds on several pine species. When spore suspensions of this fungus are sprayed on freshly chipped faces of slash or longleaf pines, gum continues to flow without rechipping or treatment for 2 to 8 weeks. Fungus stimulation, however, is not in commercial use at the present time.

[52] Snow, *Economic Botany* **3** (1949), 385.
[53] Snow and Lanier, U. S. Patent No. 2,434,869, January 20 (1948).
[54] *Science* **105** (1947), 209.

Dipping.—The cups fill up with gum about once a month or after about every 3 or 4 chippings. They are then emptied or "dipped" by means of a metal or wooden dip paddle into dip buckets—containers with a capacity of 4 to 5 gallons—which in turn are emptied into dip barrels holding about 50 gallons or 435 lb. of crude oleoresin. These are transported to a central point in "dip wagons" or "gum buggys"—rubber-tired wagons drawn by a mule—or now commonly by a tractor or a truck, forest roads permitting.

The gum, as it comes from the ends of open resin ducts, is a clear limpid liquid; but as it runs down the face into the cup some of it adheres, thickens, and partially oxidizes and crystallizes, causing an accumulation of comparatively dry resinous material (called "scrape") on the face. Some operators remove the scrape as it forms during the season by having the dippers punch the scrape from the face into the cup at the time of dipping. Other operators remove the scrape separately after the season of free gum flow has ended. The scrape is lower in turpentine content and generally produces a lower grade of rosin. Good practice calls for raising cups and tins each season to reduce the length of face over which the oleoresin has to flow before reaching the cups. Depending on the height of the face the scrape is removed by a "shove down," or "pull down" iron, a dull-bladed tool that pares the scrape from the tree without much adhering wood.

Methods of Processing Pine Oleoresin

Major changes have been made in recent years in methods of processing pine oleoresin to obtain the commercial products, gum turpentine, and gum rosin. When pitch was the principal product made from the crude oleoresin, the gum was heated in an open kettle and boiled down to a thick pitch. Sometimes, in those early days, sheepskins were placed above the kettles and upon them some of the vapors would condense, saturating the wool with oil. The oil (spirits of turpentine) was recovered by wringing out the fleeces. As the demand for turpentine increased it became desirable to obtain higher yields of turpentine. This brought about the use of iron retorts and condensers. The first copper fire still and condenser worm, of the type used in distilling malt, was introduced in North Carolina about 1834.[55] Some modifications in design were made, but for nearly a century it was not materially improved.

Fire Stills.—The fire still consisted of a large copper kettle, of from 500 to 1,000 gallons capacity, supported and partly enclosed by brickwork forming a furnace, and was heated by a wood fire.[56] It was connected by a still head (usually removable) to a condenser or "worm." This was usu-

[55] Snow, *Economic Botany* **3** (1949), 376.
[56] Dunwody, in T. Gamble "Naval Stores," Savannah (1921), 128.

ally of large copper tubing 6 to 8 in. in diameter at the inlet and 2 to 3 in. at the outlet, perhaps 150 ft. long, and formed into a coil about 6 ft. in diameter and 7 ft. high, set in a large wooden tank or tub containing water for condensing the distillate.

The operation of these simple stills has been described in detail by Dunwody.[57] From 7 to 14 barrels of the crude gum, depending on the size of the still and the nature of the gum, were emptied directly from the dip barrels into the still through an opening in the top. The gum as it was placed in the still contained a certain percentage of water, generally from 5 to 10 per cent, which lowered the temperature at which the turpentine would distill. At the beginning of the operation the distillate consisted of about 45 per cent of turpentine and 55 per cent of water. When nearly all the water originally present was distilled over, as shown by the decrease in the amount of water in the distillate to about 30 per cent and by the peculiar frying sound (termed the "call for water") heard on placing the ear close to the tail-pipe of the condenser coil, a small stream of water was allowed to flow into the boiling gum in the still through an opening in the still head. The correct time for concluding the distillation was judged from the emission of other characteristic sounds from the still. The thermometer as an aid in conducting the distillation was first introduced in 1907.[58] Usually the mixture of turpentine and water emerging, still quite warm, from the worm, was received in an open-headed barrel. The turpentine, being lighter than the water, rose to the top and was run off through a pipe into another open receiving barrel, from which it was either pumped to a storage tank or bailed into barrels ready for shipment to market. The water was allowed to flow out of the receiving barrel through an opening at the bottom. When nearly all the turpentine had been distilled out, as judged by certain characteristic sounds emitted by the still, the flow of water was shut off, the still cap or head removed, and the molten rosin remaining in the still (and mixed with bits of bark, pine needles, sand, and chips present in the oleoresin) was drained from the still through a side arm tail-pipe opening at the bottom. To remove the extraneous matter from the rosin the residual contents of the still were passed, while hot, through a series of wire strainers, and finally through layers of cotton batting supported on a wire screen before packaging in wooden barrels or metal drums. The yield of turpentine varied from 16 to 22 per cent of the original weight of the gum, and the yield of rosin amounted to about 60 or 70 per cent. About 3 hr. were required to run a charge of 8 to 10 barrels in a fire still.

These simple fire stills had the advantage of requiring only a small

[57] *Ibid.*   [58] *Ibid.,* 132.

initial investment—a few thousand dollars—and were well suited to the needs of the transient naval stores operator as he moved from one spot to another through the apparently inexhaustible virgin forests; but they possessed inherent disadvantages. For example, the direct heating resulted in numerous fires, the bark and chips present throughout distillation tended to add color or "degrade" the rosin produced, and there was considerable loss of rosin by adherence to the bark, chips, and cotton batting. Moreover, no matter how carefully the straining was done there were always some fine particles present in the rosin which could not be held back by cotton batting. The introduction of a few simple improvements such as improved still settings—which reduced the hazard of fire and gave a more uniform distribution of heat—improved separators, and rock salt dehydrators, enabled skilled or experienced stillers to produce turpentine and rosin of high quality. Detailed designs and working drawings incorporating such improvements have been published by the Naval Stores Research Division of the U. S. Department of Agriculture.[59] This group has also published detailed recommendations for procedures to be used in charging, running, and discharging a fire still.[60, 61, 62]

Steam Stills.—Attempts were made at various times to operate steam stills instead of direct-fire stills. These were quite generally unsuccessful. The rosin from the early steam stills often had a cloudy appearance and particles of wood and bark from the gum lodged on the steam coils where they charred between runs and discolored the rosin from the next charge.

Conversion of the industry from transient exploitation to permanent cropping, and improvements in transportation facilitated the introduction of the modern process for processing pine gum as developed by the U. S. Department of Agriculture in the 1930's.[63] Following this method, the oleoresin, prior to distillation, is cleaned in a process known as "gum cleaning." For this purpose the oleoresin is diluted with turpentine, melted, filtered, washed with warm water, and settled before it is distilled.[64, 65, 66]

Gum Cleaning.—In a typical case, about 12 barrels of the crude oleoresin are drawn from a dump vat into a blow case, charged to a *melter,* which consists of a stainless steel steam-jacketed container with a capacity of

[59] U. S. Dept. Agr., Misc. Pub. No. 387 (1940).

[60] "How to Charge a Turpentine Still," ACE-53, U. S. Dept. Agr., Naval Stores Station, Olustee, Florida (1940).

[61] "Directions for Running Crude Gum on a Turpentine Fire Still," ACE-54, U. S. Dept. Agr., Naval Stores Station, Olustee, Florida (1940).

[62] "How to Discharge a Turpentine Still," ACE-52, U. S. Dept. Agr., Naval Stores Station, Olustee, Florida (1940).

[63] Smith, Reed, Veitch and Shingler, U. S. Patent No. 2,254,785, September 2, 1941.

[64] Smith, Ind. Eng. Chem. 28 (1936), 408.

[65] Reed, Chem. Met. Eng. 48, December (1941), 68.

[66] Patton, Proc. Forest Products Research Soc. 1 (1948), 19.

about 15 barrels, and sufficient turpentine is added to bring the concentration of turpentine up to 35 to 40 per cent. Ordinarily, gum contains 18 per cent of turpentine, and scrape 12 per cent of turpentine. The gum is heated to a temperature of 200° to 220° F. and melts in 20 or 30 min., depending upon the nature of the gum. Scrape requires a higher temperature (220° to 240° F.) and a longer time. A pressure of 15 to 35 lb. is built up to force the melted gum out of the bottom of the melter through a filter. A coarse screen (4-mesh) is generally provided in the bottom of the melter to remove the larger pieces of foreign matter which might otherwise clog the lines or filter. The filter medium consists commonly of cloth or filter paper coated with filter aid, such as diatomaceous earth. In normal operation the filter aid is added with the gum in the blow case or melter, and sometimes a small amount of oxalic acid—from $\frac{1}{4}$ to $\frac{1}{2}$ lb. per barrel of gum—is also added to remove iron rust stain, which would otherwise degrade the rosin. Diluted gum adhering to the coarse material which has been screened out is removed by blowing with live steam, and sometimes subjected to a turpentine wash followed by steaming. The diluted, filtered gum is passed directly from the filter to the wash tank (generally of stainless steel or aluminum) with a capacity of about 100 barrels, jetting it through about 300 to 400 gallons of water. This usually requires from 15 to 30 min. per melter charge. Washing with water removes water-soluble impurities (notably sugars) present in the oleoresin, and also any excess oxalic acid that may have been used. The final temperature of the gum-water mixture ranges from 180° to 200° F. After washing, the gum is settled for 4 to 8 hr., or sometimes overnight, the temperature dropping to about 180° to 160° F. After settling, the wash water is drained from the bottom of the wash tank and discarded.

Central Stills.—Such gum-cleaning plants are centrally located with respect to supplies of pine gum. Processing plants having such facilities have come to be known as "central stills." In these plants the diluted, filtered, washed, and settled gum (which still contains about 0.5 per cent moisture) is pumped into the still. The stills, again usually of stainless steel, are generally cylindrical, from 6 to 10 ft. in height and 4 to 6 ft. in diameter, and have a capacity of 15 to 40 barrels of diluted gum. The gum in the still is heated by steam coils and sparged with live steam. The vapors of water and turpentine are passed through a dephlegmator, a vapor chamber about 4 ft. in diameter and 5 ft. high, to remove entrained rosin acids, and the vapors are condensed by aluminum or stainless steel tubular condensers. The distillate at first contains about equal proportions of water and turpentine, but as the distillation progresses additional sparger steam is used, the temperature rises, and the water-turpentine ratio increases. The distillation is continued until the ratio of water to turpentine issuing from the condenser is about 10 to 1. This requires from 30 to 40 min., and at this time the temperature of the residual rosin is about 330° F. Recording thermometers are generally used to guide the stiller in his operation. The condensed turpentine and water are passed through an automatic separator, and the turpentine, saturated with water, is dehydrated by passing it through a dehydrator before blending in storage tanks with a capacity of 5,000 to 10,000 gallons. The dehydrator usually consists of a barrel or tank of rock salt with a false bottom from which brine is removed periodically. Since the portion of the turpentine which distills over at the end of a charge is relatively rich in acids—both water-soluble acids (chiefly acetic acid) and resin acids—the last portion of the turpentine which distills from each charge and the first portion of the turpentine from the next charge (which washes out the condenser) are commonly collected separately and used to dilute the crude oleoresin; only the "heart cut" is sent to storage and marketed. The melted rosin remaining in the still is run into holding tanks whence it is later emptied into paper bags, galvanized steel drums, or tank cars.

Although such modern gum-cleaning and distillation plants are expensive, costing more than $100,000 each, the increased efficiency, increased yields, and superior quality of turpentine and rosin, have established their worth. Thirty such central gum-cleaning and distillation plants in operation in 1949 produced more than 90 per cent of the American total of gum turpentine and rosin, and the old fire stills (which once numbered about 2,500) have been reduced to less than 100.[67]

"Gum Farming."—Establishment of such central gum-cleaning plants is effecting a major change in the gum naval stores industry, especially in the production of the gum. Thousands of farmers have turned to gum farming as a cash crop. Pine oleoresin can be collected and sold during nine or ten months of the year, and if other farm work is pressing, collection can be postponed without appreciably decreasing the quantity of gum obtainable from the trees. Small-scale gum farmers, who numbered about 300 in 1930, have increased to approximately 40,000 in 1948.[68] Of the approximately 50 million acres of forest lands in the naval stores region of the south, about 30 million produce naval stores, and many owners of land on which there are small stands of pine utilize the pine gum as a new source of cash income. Such gum farmers may work only a few hundred trees or even fewer and at the other extreme, a single operator may work over a million trees.

Yield of Oil.—There are wide variations in the amount of oleoresin that may be obtained from pines, even using similar practices, and in the amount

[67] Patton, *Ind. Eng. Chem.* **40** (1948), 996.
[68] *Ibid.*

TABLE 20.3.* YIELD FOR ONE YEAR OF GUM (DIP AND SCRAPE) AND OF TURPENTINE
FROM SLASH PINES OF DIFFERENT DIAMETERS [a] FOR GOOD AND POOR SITES

Diameter of Tree at 4½ Ft. Above the Ground (Inches)	Better than Average Sites		Poorer than Average Sites	
	Actual Yield of Gum per Tree (Pounds)	Calculated Yield [b] of Turpentine per 10,000 Faces (50-Gal. Bbl.)	Actual Yield of Gum per Tree (Pounds)	Calculated Yield [b] of Turpentine per 10,000 Faces (50-Gal. Bbl.)
6	4.7	25	3.2	17
7	6.1	33	4.4	24
8	7.5	40	5.6	30
9	9.0	48	6.7	36
10	10.4	56	7.9	42
11	11.8	63	9.1	49
12	13.3	71	10.2	55

* Taken from *U. S. Dept. Agr., Misc. Pub.* No. 209 (1935), 77.
[a] The width of face is one-third the circumference of the tree in each case.
[b] Converting factor used here is based on analyses by the Bureau of Chemistry and Soils of dip and scrape from Starke, Florida. Scrape represents 6 per cent of total yield; trash, 6.7 per cent; dip analyses showed 21.5 per cent and scrape showed 9.2 per cent turpentine by weight. One gallon of turpentine weighs 7.2 lb.

of turpentine obtained. Table 20.3 gives typical data for the yield of oleoresin and turpentine from slash pine trees, and Table 20.4 gives similar data for longleaf trees. It will be seen that slash pines produce somewhat more oleoresin than longleaf. Individual trees have been known to produce more than twice the average of oleoresin of similar trees with similar environment, and others little more than half the average. Application of chemical stimulants such as sulfuric acid increases the yield materially.

Slash pine is generally considered to yield a slightly higher percentage of turpentine, on a seasonal basis, than does longleaf pine, as may be inferred from the data in Tables 20.3 and 20.4. Black and Thronson [69] found a seasonal average of 20.0 per cent of turpentine in the oleoresin from slash pine, and 19.1 per cent of turpentine in the oleoresin from longleaf. Veitch and Grotlisch [70] arrived at similar results. Otte,[71] however, obtained con-

[69] *Ibid.*, **26** (1934), 68.
[70] *U. S. Dept. Agr., Bull.* No. 898 (1920), 1.
[71] "A Study of the Composition of the Oleoresin of *Pinus palustris* and *Pinus heterophylla* from High, Medium, and Low Yielding Trees," Master's Thesis, University of Florida (1930).

(*Top Left*) Production of pine oleoresin in the southeastern part of the United States. Collecting and hauling the oleoresin from the forest. (*Top Right*) Pine oleoresin. Spiral gutter and straight apron, with metal cup, on bark-chipped tree. First year work. *Photos U. S. Forest Service.* (*Bottom Left*) Grading of pine oleoresin. The Newton Company, Lake City, Florida. (*Bottom Right*) Emptying barrels of pine oleoresin into dump vats. The Newton Company, Lake City, Florida. *Photos U. S. Dept. of Agriculture.*

(*Top*) Production of turpentine oil in the southeastern part of the United States. Old-fashioned direct fire distillery near Lake City, Florida—now obsolete and rapidly becoming extinct. *Photo Mr. Herbert Smith, Lake City, Florida.* (*Bottom*) Turpentine oil. Modern gum cleaning and central steam distillation plant. Jacksonville Processing Co., Jacksonville, Florida. *Photo U. S. Dept. of Agriculture.*

Table 20.4.* Yield for One Year of Gum (Dip and Scrape) and of Turpentine from Longleaf Pines of Different Diameters [a] for Good and Poor Sites

Diameter of Tree at 4½ Ft. Above the Ground (Inches)	Better than Average Sites		Poorer than Average Sites	
	Actual Yield of Gum per Tree (Pounds)	Calculated Yield [b] of Turpentine per 10,000 Faces (50-Gal. Bbl.)	Actual Yield of Gum per Tree (Pounds)	Calculated Yield [b] of Turpentine per 10,000 Faces (50-Gal. Bbl.)
6	4.7	24	3.4	17
7	5.9	30	4.4	22
8	7.1	36	5.4	27
9	8.3	42	6.4	32
10	9.5	48	7.4	38
11	10.7	54	8.4	43
12	11.9	60	9.4	48

* Taken from *U. S. Dept. Agr., Misc. Pub.* No. 209 (1935), 78.
[a] The width of face is one-third the circumference of the tree in each case.
[b] Converting factor used here is based on analyses by the Bureau of Chemistry and Soils of dip and scrape from Starke, Florida. Scrape represents 25 per cent of total yield; trash, 7.4 per cent; dip analyses showed 22.9 per cent and scrape analyses showed 11.2 per cent of turpentine by weight. One gallon of turpentine weighs 7.2 lb.

trary results, finding that longleaf oleoresin yielded a slightly higher percentage of turpentine than did slash. Results of a large scale test at the Naval Stores Station of the U. S. Department of Agriculture, Olustee, Florida,[72] showed that the oleoresin from 7 crops (70,000 trees) which were 90 per cent longleaf, had an average turpentine content during the entire season of 19.2 per cent; the oleoresin from 10 crops, 90 per cent slash, had an average turpentine content of 18.6 per cent. It appears that the turpentine content of the oleoresin (dip plus scrape) from the two species of pines is almost equal and approximates 20 per cent. Black and Thronson [73] found that the turpentine content of oleoresin tended to decrease with each succeeding season of chipping. Thus, in the first year the average was 20.8 per cent, in the second 20.1 per cent, and in the third year 18.9 per cent.

Physicochemical Properties.—Pine oleoresin as it exudes from a fresh wound is a clear, limpid, colorless fluid. It consists chiefly of a mixture of resinous acids (rosin) and volatile oils (turpentine), but also contains traces of water and water-soluble materials. On standing for a short while

[72] Veitch and Shingler, *U. S. Dept. Agr., Bur. Chem. Soils, Mimeo. Circ.* April 26 (1935).
[73] *Ind. Eng. Chem.* **26** (1934), 68.

it tends to crystallize. The oleoresin from longleaf pine has a much greater tendency to crystallize than does the oleoresin from slash pine, and commonly a considerable amount of crystallized acids with more or less adhering volatile material (scrape) is formed on the face, especially of longleaf pines.

The density [74] of oleoresin containing various percentages of turpentine has been reported by Smith.[75] Oleoresin from longleaf pine appeared to have a slightly higher density than that from slash pine. Typically, longleaf oleoresin containing 22.8 per cent of turpentine (water-free basis) had a density of 1.020 g. per cc. at 20° C., whereas an oleoresin from slash pine containing 22.5 per cent of turpentine had a density of 1.019 g. per cc. at 20° C.

The viscosity of pine gum has been reported by Runckel and Knapp.[76] The viscosity of longleaf oleoresin is distinctly higher than that of slash oleoresin. Typically, longleaf oleoresin containing 21.3 per cent of turpentine (water-free basis) had a viscosity of 952 centipoises at 60° C., and slash oleoresin containing 22.0 per cent of turpentine had a viscosity of only 490 centipoises at 60° C.

The density and refractive index of different samples of commercial gum turpentine differ relatively little, and are usually well within the legal requirements indicated below. Black and Thronson [77] noted that over a whole season turpentine obtained in laboratory distillations from slash oleoresin averaged slightly less as regards specific gravity than did turpentine from longleaf oleoresin (0.8679 and 0.8700, respectively, at 15°/15°). In a second season both averages were somewhat lower—0.8674 and 0.8689, respectively. Mims and Schopmeyer [78] obtained similar results. Black and Thronson reported that for longleaf turpentine the refractive index at 20° averaged 1.4681 during the first season and 1.4705 during the second season; for slash turpentine the averages were 1.4695 and 1.4714. Mims and Schopmeyer reported seasonal averages of 1.4713 and 1.4712 for longleaf turpentine in the first and second season, and 1.4728 and 1.4710 for slash turpentine.

These are also representative values for fresh whole commercial turpentine. Slight deviations from the laboratory-distilled turpentine may well be due to variations in the point at which the distillation processes are terminated, resulting in different percentages of tailings in the turpentine. Turpentine usually increases in density during storage, probably due to

---

[74] The terms density and specific gravity are frequently used interchangeably in the Naval Stores Industry. The author of this chapter has followed the usage of the authorities he quotes. For an explanation of the difference in meaning between the two terms, the reader is referred to Vol. I of the present series, p. 237, fn. 10.

[75] *Ind. Eng. Chem.* **28** (1936), 410.   [77] *Ibid.* **26** (1934), 68.

[76] *Ibid.* **38** (1946), 555.   [78] *Ibid.* **39** (1947), 1504.

oxidation, hydration, and polymerization. It is common commercial practice to "freshen up" a tank of old turpentine with fresh turpentine by continually adding freshly produced turpentine as the old is withdrawn for the market, thus maintaining the available turpentine well within legal tolerances for specific gravity at all times. The changes that occur in turpentine during storage and methods for the preservation of turpentine have been studied.[79, 80]

The optical rotation of the turpentine from longleaf and that from slash oleoresin differ markedly; this property is probably the chief means of distinguishing between the two types of oil. Turpentine from longleaf pine is dextrorotatory, due to the highly dextrorotatory α-pinene present, which more than counterbalances the laevorotation of the β-pinene. On the other hand, the turpentine from slash pine is laevorotatory, owing to the laevorotating β-pinene and the negatively or only very slightly positively rotating α-pinene present. Black and Thronson [81] reported for longleaf turpentine an average optical rotation of $+11°$ $19'$, whereas the average for slash turpentine was $-19°$ $19'$. The turpentine from individual trees varied widely in rotation, ranging from $-3°$ $1'$ to $-27°$ $55'$ for slash pines, and from $+2°$ $0'$ to $+18°$ $12'$ for longleaf. Mims and Schopmeyer [82] obtained similar results, the average rotation for turpentine from slash pine being $-17°$ $33'$ and from longleaf being $+14°$ $17'$.

The specifications of the American Society for Testing Materials and those of the Federal Government, for gum spirits of turpentine,[83] are as follows:

Appearance..................................... Shall be clear and free from
suspended matter and water
Color... Shall be "Standard" or better *

	Maximum	*Minimum*
Specific Gravity at 15.5°/15.5°.....................	0.875	0.860
Refractive Index at 20°...........................	1.478	1.465
Residue after Polymerization with 38 N H_2SO_4 (Volume Per Cent).....................................	2.0	. . .
Initial Boiling Point at 760 mm. pr................	160°	150°
Distilling below 170° C. at 760 mm. pr. (Per Cent).... ...		90

* Color standards (water white, standard, one shade off and two shades off) have been proposed for turpentine [84] but in present commercial practice gum turpentine is considered unmerchantable unless it is water white (Author's note).

[79] Smith and Holman, *ibid.* **26** (1934), 716.
[80] Sumerford, *J. Am. Pharm. Assocn.* **33** (1944), 150.
[81] *Ind. Eng. Chem.* **26** (1934), 68.
[82] *Ibid.* **39** (1947), 1505.
[83] "1949 Book of A.S.T.M. Standards, Part 4," American Society for Testing Materials, Philadelphia (1950), 196.
[84] Veitch and Grotlisch, *U. S. Dept. Agr., Bull.* No. 898 (1920), 10.

The flash point for gum turpentine is 38° C., the aniline point 25° C. and the kauri-butanol solvency value is 50.[85] Turpentine is an excellent solvent for many resins and readily dissolves most varnish resins. The solvent and wetting properties of turpentine are better than those of straight petroleum solvents, but turpentine does not have as high solvent power as aromatic solvents boiling in the range 150° to 200° C. With nitrocellulose, turpentine may be used as a thinner in limited amounts. The iodine number of turpentine varies from 200 to 400, depending on the method of determination used and the time of reaction.[86] For turpentine, hydrogen values are more reliable criteria of unsaturation than iodine numbers.

Many investigators have detected the presence of peroxides in turpentine, and more rapid drying of paint films has been ascribed to their presence.[87] Certain tests indicate that turpentine may contribute to the durability of some paint coatings more than do mineral spirits.[88]

Turpentine is considered safe physiologically in the concentrations usually employed, and much less hazardous than other industrial solvents such as toluene or butanol.[89] It is, however, an irritant, affecting principally the eyes, lungs, and skin. Albaugh[90] states that 3 mg. of turpentine per liter—approximately equivalent to 919 parts per million—causes local symptoms, and that 6 mg. per liter will poison healthy men in 1 to 4 hr. Adequate ventilation should, therefore, be provided where prolonged exposure is necessary.

It is recognized that turpentine has limited therapeutic value. A monograph on turpentine oil, "Spirits of Turpentine," and another on the rectified oil were included in the Twelfth Revision of the "United States Pharmacopoeia."[91]   Karreth[92] has reported that abscesses produced by turpentine have a beneficial effect on persons with sepsis. The turpentine causes a large increase in leucocytes and reticulocytes in the blood, which serve to mobilize a defense action. Turpentine has been demonstrated to have antiseptic action against *Staphyllococcus aureus*,[93] whereas 3 per cent aqueous mercurochrome does not.

[85] Powers, in J. J. Matiello, "Protective and Decorative Coatings," Vol. I, John Wiley (1941), 561.
[86] *Ibid.*, 562.
[87] Krumbhaar, *Oil and Colour Chemists' Assocn. J.* **18** (1935), 294.
[88] Salzberg, Browne and Odell, *Ind. Eng. Chem.* **23** (1931), 1214.
[89] Smyth and Smyth, *J. Ind. Hyg.* **10** (1928), 261.
[90] *Ohio Public Health J.* **6** (1915), 512, through M. B. Jacobs, "Analytical Chemistry of Industrial Poisons, Hazards and Solvents," Interscience Publishers, Inc., New York (1949), 553.
[91] "The Pharmacopoeia of the United States of America," Twelfth Revision (1942), 336, 337.
[92] *Klin. Wochschr.* **15** (1936), 1274. *Chem. Abstracts* **31** (1937), 1098.
[93] Rose, *Am. J. Pharm.* **101** (1929), 52.

Chemical Composition of Commercial Gum Turpentine.—At present, American commercial gum turpentine is derived almost exclusively from the oleoresin of only two species of pine—slash and longleaf. It happens that the chemical composition of the volatile oil from the oleoresin of these two species is quite constant and similar. For this reason the composition of commercial gum turpentines is surprisingly uniform, especially if one considers the differences in mode of processing and storage. It averages close to 64 per cent of *α-pinene,* 33 per cent of *β-pinene* and 3 per cent of tailings.[94, 95] Palkin has reported analyses on five different samples of commercial turpentine varying widely in origin and age. The significant data are given in Table 20.5. These turpentines were all obtained from

TABLE 20.5. ANALYTICAL DATA ON COMMERCIAL TURPENTINES

Sample No.	Refractive Index (n_D^{25})	Density $(d_{15.6})$	Composition (Per Cent)		
			α-Pinene	β-Pinene	Tailings
1	1.4697	0.8707	63.0	31.5	5.6
2	1.4692	0.8662	61.9	32.6	5.3
3	1.4680	0.8664	62.2	28.8	6.1
4	1.4701	0.8692	59.2	36.9	3.9
5	1.4698	0.8667	58.0	35.6	6.4

direct-fire still operations, but analyses of commercial gum turpentine from central stills do not reveal any significant differences in composition. Chadwick and Palkin [96] have reported that the tailings contain major proportions of *dipentene* and *methyl chavicol,* with lesser proportions of *terpinolene, bornyl acetate,* and *pinocarveol,* as well as other unidentified hydrocarbons, alcohols, ethers, and esters. Fenchyl alcohol, one of the predominant alcohols in the tailings of steam-distilled wood turpentine, could not be detected.

Use.—Turpentine is suitable for use as a solvent, thinner, chemical raw material and as a chemical or pharmaceutical. At one time it was extensively used as an illuminant and for the production of lampblack.[97] At present the principal use of the gum is as a solvent, especially for thinning paints and varnishes. According to statistics published by the Department

[94] Palkin, *U. S. Dept. Agr., Tech. Bull.* No. 276, January (1932).
[95] Chadwick and Palkin, *ibid.,* No. 749, February (1941).
[96] *Ibid.*
[97] T. Gamble "Naval Stores," Savannah (1921), 30.

of Agriculture, less than 10 per cent of the total annual production of gum turpentine is utilized for "industrial" consumption.[98] The remainder represents principally unreported distribution of turpentine through retailers, who sell in small quantities to ultimate consumers. The latter use it as a solvent for paints and varnishes for cleaning and softening paint brushes, as well as for numerous household and office purposes—including solvent, cleaning agent, and medicinal purposes as a liniment, antiseptic, and insecticide.

Large quantities of turpentine (upward of 100,000 barrels annually) are employed for diverse industrial purposes in the United States, but the published statistics do not indicate how much gum turpentine and how much wood turpentine are used for each industrial application. The industrial utilization of turpentine has been discussed by Speh,[99] and a list of more than 40 specific industrial uses has been published.[100] Turpentine is a valuable component of numerous paints, varnishes, lacquers, stains, enamels, inks, lubricants, stain removers, wood fillers, waterproofing compounds, various liquid and paste polishes, waxes, crayons, insecticides and pharmaceuticals—including liniments, medicated soaps, and disinfectants. It is also used in the production of a number of chemicals—including camphene, chlorinated camphene, camphor, terpineol and terpin hydrate.

Chemicals from Turpentine.—In general the only constituents isolated in pure form are the pinenes. While the whole turpentine may be employed successfully for some chemical purposes the use of pure α- or β-pinene is generally preferred. These terpene hydrocarbons are generally obtained by fractional distillation of turpentine.

α-Pinene has been employed for many years for the production of camphene, an intermediate in the production of synthetic camphor. Camphene has also been used for the production of isobornyl acetate—an odorant— and isobornyl thiocyanoacetate (*Thanite*)—an insecticide. At the present time large quantities of camphene are being chlorinated, to a chlorine content of approximately 69 per cent, to produce chlorinated camphene (*Toxaphene*) widely employed as an insecticide. α-Pinene is also used for the production of synthetic pine oil, terpin hydrate, and additives for lubricating oils. The largest volume use for β-pinene is in the preparation of synthetic resins. Here β-pinene is polymerized, usually with a Friedel-Crafts type catalyst, to a hard resin which finds application in chewing gum, paint, varnish, paper coatings, and adhesives. β-Pinene has also been reacted with formaldehyde on a semi-commercial scale to produce the inexpensive, bicyclic primary alcohol *Nopol*.

[98] *U. S. Dept. Agr., Bur. Agr. Econ.*, May (1950), 8.
[99] *Ind. Eng. Chem.* **31** (1939), 166.
[100] *U. S. Dept. Agr., Bur. Agr. Chem. and Eng., Mimeo Circ.* No. 40 (1938).

Oleoresins and Turpentines from Individual Pine Species

Some 48 species of the genus *Pinus* are native to the United States,[101] but only two, *Pinus caribaea* (slash pine) and *Pinus palustris* (longleaf pine), are used today to produce American gum turpentine. It is only very rarely that pines of other species (usually loblolly) occurring in a stand of slash or longleaf are chipped along with the other trees in the stand. During and for a short time after the Civil War, when supplies from the South were cut off, turpentine was produced from certain western pines, particularly from *P. ponderosa*,[102] but this tree is not turpentined commercially today. Also, in the 1860's and 1870's, a considerable amount of turpentine was produced on the West Coast from *Pinus sabiniana* Douglas (Digger pine). This turpentine is quite different in composition from other turpentines, as it consists chiefly of *n*-heptane. It achieved a considerable reputation under the names of *Abietene, Erasine, Aurantine*, etc., as a cleaner for the removal of paint and grease from clothing and fabrics;[103] but it could not compete economically with cheaper petroleum solvents. Interest in production of *n*-heptane from pines arose in the 1920's when *n*-heptane was introduced as a standard of reference in the standardization of gasoline as fuel in internal combustion engines.[104] Some was produced for this purpose, but *n*-heptane from pines (*Pinus Jeffreyi*—the Jeffrey pine—was employed chiefly) could not compete successfully with synthetic *n*-heptane, and turpentining of these pines was discontinued.

The turpentines from only 30 of the 48 species of pines native to the United States have been examined, and many of these have been only inadequately analyzed. The turpentines from the two pines used commercially today have, however, been studied intensively and these are discussed in detail below; the significant available data for all thirty turpentines which have been examined even superficially are presented in Table 20.6.

***Pinus Palustris* Miller—Longleaf Pine.**—Numerous analyses of the yields of turpentine and rosin obtained from the oleoresin of longleaf pine have been reported.[105-111] The yield noted differs somewhat, but is generally

101 Mirov, *Ann. Rev. Biochem.* **17** (1948), 521.
102 *U. S. Dept. Agr., Misc. Pub.* No. 209, January (1935), 20.
103 Kremers, *Pharm. Rev.* **18** (1900), 166.
104 *U. S. Dept. Agr., Misc. Pub.* No. 209, January (1935), 21.
105 Herty and Dickson, *Ind. Eng. Chem.* **4** (1912), 495.
106 Black and Thronson, *ibid.* **26** (1934), 66.
107 *U. S. Dept. Agr., Misc. Pub.* No. 209, January (1935), 78.
108 Smith, *Ind. Eng. Chem.* **28** (1936), 410.
109 Runckel and Knapp, *ibid.* **38** (1946), 555.
110 Mims and Schopmeyer, *ibid.* **39** (1947), 1504.
111 Clark and Osborne, *U. S. Dept. Agr.*, AIC-191, December (1948).

TABLE 20.6.   OLEORESINS AND TURPENTINES FROM AMERICAN PINES

Species	Range *	Turpentine Content of Oleoresin (%)	Physicochemical Properties of Turpentine	Chemical Composition of Turpentine	Reference
(1) *Pinus albicaulis* Engelmann (Whitebark pine)	Alberta and Brit. Columbia, south to Montana, Wyoming, Nevada, and California	...	...	Δ^3-Carene (35%) Other Terpenes (10%) A Sesquiterpene (7%) A Diterpene (30%)	1
(2) *Pinus aristata* Engelmann (Bristlecone pine)	High mountains from Colorado to Nevada and California, south to New Mexico and Arizona	Very small	d_4^{25} 0.8649 n_D^{25} 1.4656 $[\alpha]_D^{25}$ +25° 13'	*dl*- and *l*-α-Pinene (96%) A Tricyclic Sesquiterpene (4%)	2
(3) *Pinus attenuata* Lemmon (Knobcone pine)	Oregon and California	24	d_4^{23} 0.8520 n_D^{23} 1.4652 $[\alpha]_D^{23}$ +17° 6'	Over 95% *d*-α-Pinene No β-Pinene or Camphene	3
(4) *Pinus balfouriana* Grev. and Balf. (Foxtail pine)	California	28.3	d_4^{25} 0.8570 n_D^{25} 1.4643 $[\alpha]_D^{25}$ -11° 3'	*dl*- and *l*-α-Pinene (90%) *dl*- and *l*-β-Pinene (2%) *dl*- and *l*-Limonene (2%) A Tricyclic Sesquiterpene (4%)	2

Species	Distribution	Yield	Physical constants	Composition	Ref.
(5) *Pinus banksiana* Lambert (Jack pine)	Nova Scotia and Quebec to Mackenzie south to Massachusetts, New York, Indiana, Wisconsin, Minnesota, and Alberta	20.7	d_4^{20} 0.8595 n_D^{25} 1.4670 $[\alpha]_D^{25}$ +9° 45'	*dl*- and *l*-α-Pinene (85%) *dl*- and *l*-β-Pinene (10%)	4
(6) *Pinus caribaea* Morelet (Slash pine)	South Carolina to Florida and Louisiana. Also in Brit. Honduras, Honduras, Guatemala, and Nicaragua, and in the West Indies	20	d_{15}^{15} 0.867 n_D^{25} 1.470 $[\alpha]_D$ −26° 0'	*l*-α-Pinene (61.5%) *l*-β-Pinene (34%) Tailings (4.5%)	5, 6, 7, 8
(7) *Pinus clausa* (Engelmann) Vasey (Sand pine)	Florida and Alabama	18.93	d_{15}^{15} 0.8723 n_D^{15} 1.4767 α_D^{20} −22° 48'	*l*-α-Pinene (10%) *l*-Camphene (10%) *l*-β-Pinene (75%)	9
(8) *Pinus contorta* var. *latifolia* Engelmann (Lodgepole pine)	Montana, Alberta, Brit. Columbia, and Yukon, south to Colorado, Utah, California and Lower California, Mexico	14.7	d_{15}^{15} 0.8518 n_D^{15} 1.4862 $[\alpha]_D^{20}$ −20° 7'	Almost entirely *l*-β-Phellandrene	10
(9) *Pinus coulteri* D. Don (Coulter pine)	California and Lower California, Mexico	16.92	d_{15}^{15} 0.8505 n_D^{25} 1.4767 $[\alpha]_D$ −15° 13'	*n*-Heptane (5%) *l*-α-Pinene (30–35%) *l*-β-Phellandrene (35–45%) *n*-Undecane (10%) Possibly a small amount of Sesquiterpenes	11

TABLE 20.6.   OLEORESINS AND TURPENTINES FROM AMERICAN PINES (Continued)

Species	Range *	Turpentine Content of Oleoresin (%)	Physicochemical Properties of Turpentine	Chemical Composition of Turpentine	Reference
(10) *Pinus echinata* Miller (Shortleaf pine)	New York to West Virginia, Illinois, Missouri, and Oklahoma south to Florida and Texas	...	...	*d*-α-Pinene (85%) *l*-β-Pinene (11%) Limonene(?)	1, 24
(11) *Pinus edulis* Engelmann (Pinyon, Colorado pinyon pine)	Colorado, Utah, extreme western Oklahoma, Texas, New Mexico, Arizona, and northern Mexico	20.0	d_{15}^{15} 0.8680 n_D^{15} 1.4707 $[\alpha]_D^{20}$ +19° 16'	α-Pinene (70–75%) β-Pinene (5%) α-Cadinene (15–20%)	10
(12) *Pinus flexilis* James (Limber pine)	South Dakota, Montana, southern Alberta, and southern Brit. Columbia, south to Nebraska, Texas, Arizona, Nevada, southern Mexico (Coahuila)	20	d_4^{29} 0.8606 n_D^{28} 1.4707 $[\alpha]_D^{25}$ +41° 12'	*dl*- and *l*-α-Pinene (80%) Albicaulene—A Monocyclic Sesquiterpene (13%) Bicyclic Sesquiterpene (7%)	2
(13) *Pinus glabra* Walter (Spruce pine)	Coastal plain from South Carolina to Florida and Louisiana	...	d_4^{20} 0.862 $[\alpha]_D$ −40° 47'	Probably mainly *l*-Limonene	12

Species	Distribution		Constants	Composition	References
(14) *Pinus Jeffreyi* Grev. and Balf. sometimes designated as *P. ponderosa* var. *Jeffreyi* Vasey (Jeffrey pine)	Oregon, California, and Lower California, Mexico	9.73	$d_{15} = 0.6951\text{--}0.7110$ $n_D^{15} = 1.3927\text{--}1.4060$	n-Heptane (95%) n-Aldehydes—Octylic, Nonylic and Decylic (5%)	13, 14
(15) *Pinus lambertiana* Douglas (Sugar pine)	Coast region, Oregon, California, and Lower California, Mexico	18.4	$d_4^{24} = 0.8669$ $n_D^{27.5} = 1.4753$ $[\alpha]_D^{27.5} = -7°\ 28'$	l-α-Pinene (65%) l-β-Pinene (13%) Bicyclic Sesquiterpene of Cadalene Type (10%) Lambertol (Sesquiterpene Alcohol $C_{15}H_{26}O$) (2%)	10, 15
(16) *Pinus monophylla* Torrey and Fremont (Single-leaf pinyon)	Idaho, Utah, Nevada, California, Arizona, and northern Lower California, Mexico	19.00	$d_{15} = 0.8721\text{--}0.8733$ $n_D^{15} = 1.4732$ $\alpha_D^{25} = +14°\ 25'\text{--}+17°\ 16'$	d-α-Pinene (85%) l-Limonene or Dipentene (4-5%) d-Cadinene (4-6%)	13
(17) *Pinus monticola* Douglas (Western white pine)	Southern Brit. Columbia, Montana, Idaho, Washington, Oregon, and California	18.2	$d_{20}^{20} = 0.8691$ $n_D^{23} = 1.4646$ $\alpha_D^{20} = +20°\ 35'$	d-α-Pinene (60%) β-Pinene (26%) n-Undecane (1-2%) Sesquiterpenes and perhaps Limonene	16
(18) *Pinus muricata* D. Don (Bishop pine)	California and Lower California, Mexico	22.4	$d_{15} = 0.8610$ $n_D^{15} = 1.4693$ $[\alpha]_D^{20} = +11°\ 36'$	d-α-Pinene (98-99%) Camphene (less than 1%)	17
(19) *Pinus palustris* Miller (Longleaf pine)	Coastal Plain from Virginia to Florida, west to eastern Texas	20	$d_{15} = 0.868$ $n_D^{25} = 1.469$ $[\alpha]_D = +15°\ 0'$	d-α-Pinene (65%) l-β-Pinene (31.5%) Tailings (3%)	5, 6, 8, 18

TABLE 20.6. OLEORESINS AND TURPENTINES FROM AMERICAN PINES (*Continued*)

Species	Range *	Turpentine Content of Oleoresin (%)	Physicochemical Properties of Turpentine	Chemical Composition of Turpentine	Reference
(20) *Pinus ponderosa* Lawson (Ponderosa pine)	Southern Brit. Columbia, Washington, and Idaho, south to Nevada, California and Lower California, Mexico	15	d_4^{25} 0.8572 n_D^{20} 1.4765 $[\alpha]_D$ −29° 0′	l-β-Pinene (50%) l-Δ³-Carene (20%) l-Limonene and Dipentene (25%) d-Cadinene (3%) Ponderene—A New Sesquiterpene (less than 1%)	4, 25
(21) *Pinus ponderosa* var. *scopulorum* Engelmann (Rocky Mountain ponderosa pine)	Rocky Mountain region from S. Dakota and Montana, south to extreme western Oklahoma, Texas, New Mexico, Arizona, and Northern Mexico	19.6	d_{15}^{15} 0.8639 n_D^{15} 1.4727	d-α-Pinene (60–70%) β-Pinene (5%) Limonene (20–25%)	10
(22) *Pinus radiata* D. Don (Monterey pine)	California	16.8	d_4^{23} 0.8596 n_D^{22} 1.4727 $[\alpha]_D$ −5° 51′	dl-α-Pinene (75%) l-β-Pinene (22%)	19
(23) *Pinus resinosa* Ait. (Red pine) (Norway pine)	Nova Scotia to Ontario and southeastern Manitoba, south to Pennsylvania, West Virginia, Wisconsin and Minnesota	...	d_{20}^{20} 0.8636 n_D^{20} 1.47127 $[\alpha]_D$ +17° 23′ b. 153°–154°	Mostly α-Pinene	20

	Distribution		Constants		Composition	
(24) *Pinus rigida* var. *serotina* (Michaux) Loudon (Pond pine)	Coastal Plain from New Jersey to Florida and Alabama	About 20	d_{20} n_D^{20} $[\alpha]_D^{20}$	0.8478 1.4734 $-105°\ 36'$	Limonene, almost entirely	21, 26
(25) *Pinus sabiniana* Douglas (Digger pine)	California	11.4	d_{15}^{15} n_D	0.6971 1.3903	n-Heptane (95%) Normal Aldehydes—Octylic, Nonylic, Decylic, Myristic and perhaps Lauric (5%)	10, 22
(26) *Pinus strobus* Linnaeus (Eastern white pine)	Newfoundland and Quebec to southeastern Manitoba, south in mountains to Georgia, and Illinois and Iowa	25	d_4^{21} $n_D^{20.5}$ $[\alpha]_D^{21}$	0.8611 1.4714 $-0°\ 45'$	dl-α-Pinene (75%) l-β-Pinene (15%) Terpene Alcohols and Ketones (4%) A Tricyclic Sesquiterpene (0.3%)	19
(27) *Pinus taeda* Linnaeus (Loblolly pine)	Coastal Plain from New Jersey to Florida and Texas, north in Mississippi Valley to Tennessee, Arkansas and Oklahoma	18.6	d_4^{22} $n_D^{27.5}$ $[\alpha]_D$	0.8570 1.4675 $+20°\ 10'$	d-α-Pinene (85%) l-β-Pinene (12%)	19
(28) *Pinus torreyana* Parry (Torrey pine)	Southern California	17.1	$d_4^{23.5}$ n_D^{25} $[\alpha]_D^{25}$	0.8360 1.4656 $-118°\ 7'$	l-Limonene (75%) n-Decylaldehyde (10%) n-Undecane (5%) Longifolene (4%) Laurylaldehyde (0.2%) Heptane and Nonane (less than 0.1% of each)	23

TABLE 20.6. OLEORESINS AND TURPENTINES FROM AMERICAN PINES (*Continued*)

Species	Range *	Turpentine Content of Oleoresin (%)	Physicochemical Properties of Turpentine	Chemical Composition of Turpentine	Reference
(29) *Pinus virginiana* Miller (Virginia pine)	New York and Pennsylvania to Indiana, south to Georgia and Mississippi	23	d_4^{26} 0.8563 $n_D^{27.5}$ 1.4657 $[\alpha]_D^{25}$ −3° 50'	*dl*-α-Pinene (90%) *l*-α-Pinene (8%)	19
(30) *Pinus washoensis* Mason and Stockwell	Western Nevada	19.4	d_4^{23} 0.8522–0.8613 $n_D^{21.5}$ 1.4744–1.4777 $[\alpha]_D^{25}$ −9° 45' to +8° 24'	*d*-Δ³-Carene (chiefly), α-Pinene, Dipentene, A Cyclic Sesquiterpene, *l*-β-Pinene (if Δ³-Carene content is low)	4

(References to Table 20.6)

* U. S. Forest Service, "Check List of the Native and Naturalized Trees of the United States including Alaska," Washington, D. C. (1944), 325 p., *processed.*

1. Cf. *Ann. Rev. Biochem.* **17** (1948), 521. More recently, see Haagen-Smit, Wang and Mirov, *J. Am. Pharm. Assocn., Sci. Ed.* **40** (1951), 557.
2. Haagen-Smit, Wang and Mirov, *J. Am. Pharm. Assocn., Sci. Ed.* **39** (1950), 254.
3. Mirov and Haagen-Smit, *J. Forestry* **47** (1949), 721.
4. Haagen-Smit, Redemann, Wang and Mirov, *J. Am. Pharm. Assocn., Sci. Ed.* **39** (1950), 260.
5. Palkin, *U. S. Dept. Agr., Tech. Bull.* No. 276, January (1932).
6. Dupont and Barraud, *Bull. Inst. du Pin* No. 60, May (1929), 155.
7. Hall, *Ind. Eng. Chem.* **29** (1937), 637.
8. Mims and Schopmeyer, *ibid.* **39** (1947), 1504.
9. Schorger, *ibid.* **7** (1915), 321.

10. Schorger, *U. S. Dept. Agr., Forest Service Bull.* No. 119 (1913).
11. Mirov, *Ind. Eng. Chem.* **38** (1946), 405.
12. Long, *J. Am. Chem. Soc.* **16** (1894), 844.
13. Schorger, *Ind. Eng. Chem.* **5** (1913), 971.
14. Foote, *J. Am. Pharm. Assocn.* **18** (1929), 350.
15. Mirov, Haagen-Smit and Thurlow, *ibid., Sci. Ed.* **38** (1949), 407.
16. Foote and Mirov, *J. Am. Pharm. Assocn.* **22** (1933), 828.
17. Mirov, *J. Forestry* **45** (1947), 659.
18. Black and Thronson, *Ind. Eng. Chem.* **26** (1934), 66.
19. Mirov, Wang and Haagen-Smit, *J. Am. Pharm. Assocn., Sci. Ed.* **38** (1949), 403.
20. Frankforter, *J. Am. Chem. Soc.* **28** (1906), 1467.
21. Herty and Dickson, *ibid.* **30** (1908), 872.
22. Uhl, *J. Am. Pharm. Assocn.* **24** (1935), 380.
23. Haagen-Smit, Redemann and Mirov, *J. Am. Chem. Soc.* **69** (1947), 2014.
24. Mirov, *J. Am. Pharm. Assocn.* **40** (1951), 410.
25. Recently, Mirov (*ibid.,* 412) found that the turpentine of *Pinus ponderosa* from southwestern Utah contains *dl-* and *d-α-*pinene (45%), *dl-* and *d-α-Δ³-*carene (40%), *l-*limonene (2-3%) and the sesquiterpene *l-*longifolene (10%).
26. Recently, Mirov (*ibid.,* 411) investigated the turpentine of the closely related *Pinus rigida* Mill. and found that it contains *l-α-*pinene (65%), *l-β-*pinene (20%), and *l-*limonene (10%).

quite close to 20 per cent of turpentine. The effect of numerous variables on the yield of the oleoresin, as well as its composition, has been studied.[112-115] These variables include weather, season of the year, size of tree, size of tree crown; frequency, height, and depth of chipping, and the year of chipping (i.e., whether first, second, or third year, and so on). The oleoresin from longleaf pines has a strong tendency to crystallize, with the formation of significant proportions of scrape; the dip and scrape have been analyzed separately.

Wyman [116] has reported in detail on the yield of scrape and dip from longleaf pines. He concluded that it averages about 24 per cent of the total yield of oleoresin obtained during the season, but depends upon the frequency of raising tins and the height of chipping as well as other variables. On the basis of a large number of analyses, it was concluded [117] that, for longleaf pines, scrape represents 25 per cent of the total yield, and that the turpentine content of longleaf scrape averages 11.2 per cent and of longleaf dip 22.9 per cent.

Dupont and Barraud [118] found a sample of longleaf turpentine to be composed of 64.3 per cent of α-pinene, 31.8 per cent of β-pinene and 4.6 per cent of tailings. The characteristics and composition of longleaf turpentine have been carefully determined by Palkin,[119] and Chadwick and Palkin.[120] Palkin's analytical data on turpentine samples from authentic sources are tabulated below:

	Optical Rotation		Refractive		Composition		
Source	$\alpha_J =$ *578 mμ*	$\alpha_V =$ *546 mμ*	*Index* (n_D^{25})	*Density* $(d_{15.6})$	α- *Pinene*	β- *Pinene*	*Tailings*
Longleaf 1, Fresh........	+14° 2′	+16° 16′	1.4691	0.8680	68.4	28.6	3.0
Longleaf 2, Fresh........	+12° 17′	+14° 20′	1.4692	0.8694	62.5	33.3	4.2
Longleaf, Gum Dip........	+11° 0′	+12° 52′	1.4690	0.8667	62.5	34.4	3.1
Longleaf, Scrape	+7° 21′	+8° 51′	1.4681	0.8675	67.0	29.2	3.8

Palkin [121] also reported on the composition of the tailings, which he found to have the following gross composition: about two-fifths was monocyclic

[112] Wyman, *U. S. Dept. Agr., Tech. Bull.* No. 298, April (1932).
[113] *U. S. Dept. Agr., Misc. Pub.* No. 209, January (1935).
[114] Harper and Wyman, *U. S. Dept. Agr., Tech. Bull.* No. 510, April (1936).
[115] Liefeld, *J. Agr. Research* **64** (1942), 81.
[116] *Naval Stores Rev.* **41**, January 9 (1932), 16.
[117] *U. S. Dept. Agr., Misc. Pub.* No. 209, January (1935), 78.
[118] *Bull. Inst. du Pin*, No. 60, May (1929), 156.
[119] *U. S. Dept. Agr., Tech. Bull.* No. 276, January (1932).
[120] *Ibid.*, No. 749, February (1941).
[121] *Ibid.*

hydrocarbons, chiefly *dipentene* and *terpinolene;* about one-fifth was terpene alcohols (probably *pinocarveol*) and phenols; and the remainder was a mixture, consisting principally of ethers and esters (chiefly *methyl chavicol* and optically inactive *bornyl acetate*). It is noteworthy that fenchyl alcohol, one of the predominant alcohols in the tailings of steam-distilled wood turpentine, could not be detected. Palkin [122] also found that not more than 0.07 per cent of the turpentine distills below the boiling point of α-pinene; consequently any low-boiling components are present only in extremely small proportions.

Pinus Caribaea **Morelet—Slash Pine.**—Numerous analyses of the yield of turpentine and rosin obtainable from the oleoresin from slash pines, which produces a significant and increasing portion of American commercial gum turpentine, have been reported.[123-130] The proportion noted differs somewhat, but is generally quite close to 20 per cent of turpentine.

The oleoresin from slash pine has less tendency to crystallize than does the oleoresin from longleaf pines. Wyman [131] has reported in detail on the yield of scrape and dip from slash pine. He found that the scrape from slash pine averages about 8 per cent. On the basis of a large number of analyses it was concluded [132] that for slash pine, scrape represents about 6 per cent of the total yield; slash dip analyses about 21.5 per cent, and slash scrape 9.2 per cent of turpentine by weight.

Dupont and Barraud [133] found the turpentine of slash pine to consist of 75.6 per cent of α-pinene, 21.2 per cent of β-pinene and 3.2 per cent of tailings. The characteristics and composition of slash turpentine have been carefully determined by Palkin.[134] His analytical data on turpentine samples from authentic sources are tabulated below:

Source	Optical Rotation		Refractive Index (n_D^{25})	Density $(d_{15.6})$	Composition		
	$\alpha_J =$ 578 mμ	$\alpha_V =$ 546 mμ			α-Pinene	β-Pinene	Tailings
Slash, Old.....	−20° 30′	−22° 34′	1.4698	0.8667	58.0	35.0	6.4
Slash, Gum Dip	−22° 35′	−24° 54′	1.4694	0.8657	61.0	33.7	5.3
Slash, Scrape...	−25° 3′	−27° 48′	1.4700	0.8704	58.8	33.6	7.6

[122] *Ibid.,* 5.
[123] Herty, *U. S. Dept. Agr., Forest Service Bull.* No. 90, August (1911), 15.
[124] Wyman, *U. S. Dept. Agr., Tech. Bull.* No. 298, April (1932), 22.
[125] Black and Thronson, *Ind. Eng. Chem.* **26** (1934), 66.
[126] *U. S. Dept. Agr., Misc. Pub.* No. 209, January (1935), 77.
[127] Smith, *Ind. Eng. Chem.* **28** (1936), 410.
[128] Hall, *ibid.* **29** (1937), 637.
[129] Runckel and Knapp, *ibid.* **38** (1946), 555.
[130] Mims and Schopmeyer, *ibid.* **39** (1947), 1504.
[131] *Naval Stores Rev.* **41**, January 9 (1932), 16.
[132] *U. S. Dept. Agr., Misc. Pub.* No. 209, January (1935), 77.
[133] *Bull. Inst. du Pin* No. 60, May (1929), 155.
[134] *U. S. Dept. Agr., Tech. Bull.* No. 276, January (1932).

AMERICAN WOOD TURPENTINES

Introduction.—The *wood* turpentines comprise a group of turpentines obtained as by-products of the pine pulp and paper industry or by the solvent extraction or destructive distillation of *dead* pine wood, "lightwood." Three classes of wood turpentine are officially recognized:

I. Steam-distilled wood (S.D.W.) turpentine
II. Sulfate wood turpentine
III. Destructively distilled (D.D.) wood turpentine.

These have been defined on p. 254.
To these should be added:

IV. Sulfite turpentine (sometimes also called spruce turpentine) which, though *not* officially recognized, has attracted much attention and will be considered here along with the wood turpentines.

I. Steam-Distilled Wood (S.D.W.) Turpentine

History.—Steam-distilled wood (S.D.W.) turpentine is a product of the steam-solvent wood naval stores industry. This industry was developed largely on the premise, commonly held at the turn of the twentieth century but since proved erroneous, that with the depletion of the virgin pine forest the living tree would shortly cease to be a commercial source of turpentine and that the gum naval stores industry in the United States would become extinct. As late as 1920, it was generally thought, and officially predicted, that within another ten years gum production in this country would practically cease.[135,136] However, as a result of planned reforestation and the natural or self-seeding of the rapidly growing slash pine (a good source of pine oleoresin) on the cut-over pine lands of the south, as well as of improved methods for procuring pine gum, the gum naval stores industry is still a healthy survivor. It is now expected to continue indefinitely. In turn, at mid-century some experts are predicting the decline of the southern wood naval stores industry, which may be considered a mining operation based upon the utilization of the stumps remaining from the same virgin forests. In 1934, the Forest Survey estimated the total supply of wood naval stores stumps in the entire lower south as 140 million tons.[137] Annual

[135] Schantz and Marvin, *Ind. Eng. Chem.* **31** (1939), 587.
[136] Ward, "Naval Stores: The Industry," in *U. S. Dept. Agr.*, "Trees; The Yearbook of Agriculture" (1949), 287.
[137] *Naval Stores Rev.* **59**, February 25 (1950), 25.

consumption was then about 700,000 tons, but it has since risen to nearly 2 million tons, and involves the clearing of stumps from about 400,000 acres of land each year. It is roughly estimated that in the past fifteen years wood naval stores operations have reduced the stump supply by about 25 million tons; and that other causes, such as rot, fire, local use of lightwood and land clearing have made an additional reduction in the supply. Stover [138] estimated that Mississippi, which produces one-third of the United States wood naval stores and consumes over 500,000 tons of wood annually, had left in 1948 only about 6,500,000 tons of stumpwood—enough for ten to fifteen years more operation at the present rate. However, technological developments resulting in increased efficiency of operation may permit use of material such as "catfaces" from gum naval stores operations and other saw mill wastes which contain a smaller proportion of resin than do the stumps. The tremendous reserves of stumps of virgin western pines are now being investigated, and pilot-plant scale operations using residues from these pines are under way at Klamath Falls, Oregon.[139]

The first successful commercial plant for the recovery of naval stores from logging residues was built at Gulfport, Mississippi, by Homer T. Yaryan about 1909; in the first year of operation (1910–11) it produced 14,000 barrels of rosin, 1,700 barrels of turpentine and 700 barrels of pine oil.[140] In the early years of its existence, growth of the steam and solvent wood naval stores industry was limited; but later, and especially after about 1920, it grew and expanded rapidly. At present its products exceed the value of the gum segment of the industry both in volume and in value. Data for the production of steam-distilled wood turpentine and other volatile products of the steam-solvent wood naval stores industry for representative years are given in Table 20.7.

Production of Steam-Distilled Wood Turpentine.—The raw material is the "lightwood" of the millions of acres of cut-over pinelands of the south, especially longleaf yellow pine stumps, including the roots. "Lightwood" is a local term commonly applied to very resinous or "fat" pieces of wood, such as pine knots or faces of turpentined trees (catfaces); but in general it applies to the residue of dead wood left on the ground or in stumps, which residue contains a very large proportion of resinous material.[141] There is a sharp contrast between the complexity and technology of the steam-solvent wood naval stores industry and the simple methods required by the gum naval stores industry.

The oleoresin content of a stump depends both upon the age of the stump

[138] *Ibid.*, 24.
[139] *Chemical Industries* **65** (1949), 700.
[140] Garvie, *ibid.* **44** (1939), 263.
[141] Hawley, in T. Gamble "Naval Stores," Savannah (1921), 237.

TABLE 20.7.   PRODUCTION OF STEAM-DISTILLED WOOD TURPENTINE AND OTHER
VOLATILE OILS *

(Barrels of 50 Gal. Each)

Year	Turpentine	Pine Oil	"Dipentene"	Other Mono-cyclic Hydrocarbons
1910–11	1,700	700	...	...
1914–15	6,461	2,503	...	...
1919–20	20,838	10,358	...	...
1924–25	57,025	32,615	...	...
1929–30	85,736	56,678	...	...
1934–35	77,494	73,440	...	...
1944–45	117,265	103,487	18,636	33,716
1948–49	207,160	148,670	26,170	39,470
1949–50	199,630	141,260	29,710	44,030
1950–51	237,080	173,170	44,630	50,530

* Data for 1910–1940 from "Gamble's International Naval Stores Yearbook" (1939–40), 78; for subsequent years from the *Annual Naval Stores Report* issued by the United States Department of Agriculture.

and the age of the tree from which the stump is derived. Green wood is difficult to grind or shred and produces much lower yields of resin. The wood naval stores industry uses only those stumps that have remained in the ground at least eight to ten years, preferably longer. During this time the bark and sapwood slough off, leaving the rich heartwood, in which the resinous material is concentrated. As the age of a longleaf or slash pine increases, the proportion of heartwood and its oleoresin content increase. Demmon [142] concluded that the formation of heartwood in southern pines does not begin until the trees are fifteen to twenty years of age. Shortleaf and loblolly pines, as a rule, contain much smaller proportions of heartwood, for equally aged trees, than do longleaf and slash pines. Demmon [143] found that the heartwood content of unturpentined longleaf pines ninety years old was somewhat more than 20 per cent (by volume), compared to less than 5 per cent of heartwood for those thirty years old. A stump from a young tree contains little oleoresin, and in a short time (two to five years) it has rotted and completely disintegrated. Since practically all second growth pines are cut before reaching an age at which they would have a sufficient amount of heartwood, only a small

[142] *J. Forestry* **34** (1936), 776.
[143] *Ibid.*, 775.

percentage of the stumps from second growth pines now being cut in the south are of use to the steam-solvent industry.

Methods of removing the stumps from the ground vary with the terrain. Formerly most of the stumps were removed by blasting with explosives. Today the stumps are generally unearthed by various types of tractors, stump pullers, or "push-dozers," and then worked into suitable handling size by dynamite, axes, and saws. The stumps constitute the major portion of the total wood waste used, but other rich resinous material—such as "top" wood—may also be employed. This includes limbs which may usually be handled without any mechanical treatment, and large trunks of dead wood which may be reduced to handling size with an ax or saw. When reduced to convenient handling size the wood is shipped to the processing plant, sometimes more than 200 miles distant.

A flow sheet [144] and rather detailed descriptions of the processes used at the plants have been published.[145-148]

There is wide variation in details of the processes used in different plants, but the general principles are the same. Conveyors carry the wood under a spray of water where most of the dirt is washed off, then to a mechanical "hog" provided with a rotary disk chipper, and next into shredders where the wood is reduced to small chip-size.[149] This produces splinter-type chips, the largest of which are about 0.25 in. in diameter and 1.5 in. long. The shredded wood is then conveyed to the extractors. These are tanks or pressure vessels of various shapes and sizes provided with steam coils and a false perforated bottom to retain the wood and to permit the injection of solvents or live steam. Each extractor may hold 10 to 15 tons of chips. Formerly the wood in the extractors was steamed to remove the bulk of the volatile oils and then countercurrently solvent-extracted by flooding with a close-cut petroleum naphtha solvent. In a newer modification of the process the initial steaming step is omitted, and the turpentine, pine oil, and rosin are extracted from the wood by the solvent, and the spent chips steamed to remove solvent.[150] The solvent may suitably be a petroleum naphtha with an initial boiling point of 95° and a dry point of 115° C., or a low boiling aromatic solvent.

The extract is then distilled to separate the volatile material from the residual rosin (FF wood rosin). Turpentine, "dipentene," other mono-

[144] *Chem. Met. Eng.* **49**, March (1942), 112.
[145] Palmer, *Ind. Eng. Chem.* **26** (1934), 703.
[146] Garvie, *Chemical Industries* **44** (1939), 263.
[147] Harper, in "Rogers' Manual of Industrial Chemistry," D. Van Nostrand Co., Inc., New York, Sixth Ed., Vol. I (1942), 667.
[148] Humphrey, *Ind. Eng. Chem.* **35** (1943), 1062.
[149] *Ibid.,* 1063.
[150] *Ibid.*

cyclic hydrocarbons, and pine oil are separated from each other and from the solvent by vacuum fractional distillation. The volatile oils are commonly washed with caustic soda or soda ash to remove acidic materials before fractionation.

Yield.—The resinous wood used typically contains from about 22 to 27 per cent of material extractable by petroleum solvents, but of this only about 20 to 24 per cent is actually recovered in commercial practice. About 10 to 12 gal. of volatile oils and 300 to 350 lb. of FF grade wood rosin are obtained per ton of air-seasoned "fat" wood when petroleum naphtha is used. If an aromatic solvent is employed, an additional 50 to 75 lb. of nonvolatile extractives, chiefly oxygenated products, may be obtained.

The liquids obtained from the steam-solvent process are conveniently grouped, according to their distillation temperature, into four classes:

1. Steam-distilled wood turpentine.
2. "Dipentene."
3. Other monocyclic hydrocarbons.
4. Pine oil.

This is the classification used by the Department of Agriculture in collecting statistics on the production of wood naval stores.

It should be noted that the ratio of rosin produced to liquids obtained is substantially the same whether they are obtained by the steam solvent processing of aged stumps or by the distillation of oleoresin drawn from the living tree. The traditional "unit" of the gum naval stores industry is a 50-gal. barrel of turpentine and 2⅔ drums (1,400 lb.) of rosin. In 1949–50 there were produced 199,630 barrels of S.D.W. turpentine, 29,710 barrels of "dipentene," 44,030 barrels of "other monocyclic hydrocarbons," and 141,260 barrels of pine oil—a total of 414,630 barrels of liquids, as against 1,098,610 drums of rosin for a ratio of 2.64 to 1.[151] In 1950–51 the industry produced 505,410 barrels of oils and 1,339,410 drums of rosin [152] for a ratio of 2.65 to 1.

Physicochemical Properties.—Steam-distilled wood turpentine is a distilled fraction of the volatile oils obtained in the steam-solvent process, the fraction being cut so as to conform to Federal, as well as American Society for Testing Materials, specifications for steam-distilled wood turpentine. These specifications, except as to origin of the oil, are identical with those previously given for gum spiritis of turpentine (p. 275), and the

[151] *1949–1950 Annual Naval Stores Report, U. S. Dept. Agr., Bur. Agr. Econ.,* May (1950), 3.
[152] *1950–1951 Annual Naval Stores Report, U. S. Dept. Agr., Bur. Agr. Econ.,* May (1951), 3.

physical properties of the two types of turpentine correspond quite closely. Naturally the product from different processors, or even from the same processor at different times, may vary somewhat within the limits of the specifications. A typical sample examined by Palkin et al.[153] had the following physical characteristics:

Specific Gravity at 15.5°/15.5°..... 0.859
Optical Rotation at 20°........... +22° 12′
Refractive Index at 25°........... 1.4668
Boiling Range.................... 92% distills below
170°

Other properties, such as flash point, aniline point and kauri-butanol solvency value, are substantially the same as for gum spirits and sulfate wood turpentine. The aniline point for eleven samples of S.D.W. turpentine was reported by Snider and Burstein [154] to range from 19° to 25.5° C.

Chemical Composition.—Palkin et al.[155] have reported the results of a comprehensive examination of 15 kg. of a representative sample of steam-distilled wood turpentine. The turpentine was shown to consist of the following:

Bicyclic Hydrocarbons:
α-Pinene (about 80 per cent of the turpentine)
β-Pinene ⎱ very small quantities
Camphene ⎰

Monocyclic Hydrocarbons (constituting most of the remainder of the turpentine):
Dipentene
Limonene
Terpinene
Terpinolene
p-Menthane

Terpene Alcohols (present in small quantities):
Fenchyl Alcohol
Borneol
α-Terpineol

Other Compounds (present only in traces):
Paraffin Hydrocarbons, Low Boiling
Benzaldehyde
Furfural
Cineole
Sobrerol
Methyl Chavicol
Phenols

[153] *U. S. Dept. Agr., Tech. Bull.* No. 596, December (1937), 9.
[154] *Ind. Eng. Chem., Anal. Ed.* **16** (1944), 603.
[155] *U. S. Dept. Agr., Tech. Bull.* No. 596, December (1937), 26.

The nonhydrocarbon portion probably did not, in the aggregate, exceed 2 per cent of the turpentine. Although benzaldehyde is present only in a very small proportion (22 to 60 parts per million), it is completely absent from all other commercial turpentines. Its presence has been proposed by Snider [156] as a means of detecting and estimating steam-distilled wood turpentine in gum spirits of turpentine.

Use.—Steam-distilled wood turpentine is employed for the same general purposes as gum spirits of turpentine, except that it is not recognized by the United States Pharmacopoeia. Inasmuch as it contains only a very small proportion of β-pinene, it is not fractionated to produce that compound. A very large proportion is used industrially. According to the annual reports on naval stores issued by the United States Department of Agriculture, approximately 35 per cent of all wood turpentine is utilized for "industrial consumption," mostly in the production of "chemicals and pharmaceuticals." No breakdown is available, however, as to what proportion of this is steam-distilled wood turpentine.[157] α-Pinene derived from wood turpentine is used in the production of lubricating oil additives, terpene ethers, synthetic pine oil and camphene, which in turn serves as starting material for the production of synthetic camphor and synthetic insecticides.

Other Volatile Compounds from the Steam-Solvent Process

The major volatile products obtained from the steam-solvent process for extraction of wood wastes are turpentine and pine oil, but other hydrocarbons, such as *dipentene, terpinene,* and *terpinolene,* are also recovered. These hydrocarbons have a boiling range intermediate between that of α-pinene, which is the principal component of the turpentine, and that of the pine oil; they may be fractionated out as intermediate cuts in the refining of the crude turpentine and pine oil. In recent years these intermediate oils have become standard products in the industry, as they are valuable solvents for a wide variety of special purposes and are widely marketed under numerous proprietary trade names.

The average recovery is about 5.5 gallons of turpentine, 1.5 gallons of intermediate oils, and 4 gallons of pine oil together with about 325 lb. of FF grade rosin per ton of wood. Data concerning the production of these volatile oils are included in Table 20.7.

Dipentene.—Commercial dipentene, or "dipentine," is not pure dipentene, although dipentene is generally the major component. Dipentenes mar-

[156] *Ind. Eng. Chem., Anal. Ed.,* **17** (1945), 107.
[157] *1949–1950 Annual Naval Stores Report, U. S. Dept. Agr., Bur. Agr. Econ.,* May (1950).

keted by different producers may vary somewhat in composition depending on the fractions present. Federal specifications for dipentene [158] include the following requirements:

	Minimum	Maximum
Specific Gravity at 15.5°/15.5°	0.845	0.860
Refractive Index at 20°	1.473	1.480
Flash Point	110° F.	...
Aniline Point	...	0° C.
Boiling Range:		
Initial Boiling Point	168° C.	...
Distillate below 173° C., per cent by volume	...	5
Distillate below 188° C., per cent by volume	95	...
Residue after Polymerization with 38 N H_2SO_4, per cent by volume	...	3.0

Such a product typically contains only about 50 per cent of the chemical compound *dipentene*. About half of the rest is *p-cymene* and *p-menthane*. The remainder is composed of relatively small proportions of *pinenes*, *α-terpinene, terpinolene* and other *p-menthadienes* and oxygenated terpenes (alcohols, ethers and ketones).

Commercial dipentene evaporates readily, but not quite so readily as turpentine. As indicated by its low aniline point, it is a good solvent. It has found extensive use as a solvent and antiskinning agent, particularly in enamels and primers containing the more difficultly soluble phenolic-base resins. Dipentene is employed as a rubber-reclaiming solvent and processing aid, and as a solvent in numerous proprietary compositions. Also, it serves as the raw material for the manufacture of *p*-cymene by dehydrogenation, or *p*-cymene and *p*-menthane by disproportionation. Dipentene was used extensively as the commercial source of isoprene for several types of synthetic rubber at the start of World War II, but was replaced by the more abundant hydrocarbons as a raw material.

Other Monocyclic Hydrocarbons.—The quantitative composition of the different commercial products—generally balanced mixtures for use as special purpose solvents, but which may be included in this category—varies considerably. Qualitatively, such mixtures probably contain the same compounds found in commercial dipentene. In addition to finding uses as special solvents they serve also as bases for the manufacture of terpene ethers.[159]

Pine Oil.—The pine oils comprise a major group of products of the steam-solvent industry. Pine oil consists principally of a mixture of tertiary and secondary terpene alcohols, together with smaller amounts of terpene

---

[158] "Dipentene," Federal Specifications, TT-D-376, December 18 (1947).
[159] Palmer, *Ind. Eng. Chem.* **35** (1943), 1025.

oxides, ketones, and a phenol ether (methyl chavicol). The pine oil, which has no counterpart in the gum naval stores industry, was at first almost entirely a waste product and producers had considerable difficulty disposing of it. Intensive research to develop markets met with such success, however, that production by the extraction of pine wood fell behind the demand, and considerable quantities of synthetic pine oil have been produced at various times (by hydration of pinenes) to overcome shortages. Pine oil is marketed in several grades for specific purposes. Pine oil derived by steam distillation normally has a characteristic light straw color. Water white pine oil is made by a redistillation of the oil with steam over alkali or by dry fractional distillation under reduced pressure. Federal specifications [160] provide that steam-distilled pine oil shall not be darker than a light lemon color, shall have a mild and piney or aromatic odor, and shall meet the following requirements:

	Maximum	*Minimum*
Water Content (per cent by weight)	1.0	...
Terpene Alcohol (per cent by weight)	...	65
Specific Gravity at 15.5°/15.5°	0.945	0.930
Polymerization Residue (per cent by volume)	2.5	...
Boiling Range:		
Distillate below 185° C. (per cent by volume)	5	...
Distillate below 200° C. (per cent by volume)	30	...
Distillate below 225° C. (per cent by volume)	...	90

An approximate quantitative analysis of steam-distilled pine oil has been reported by Pickett and Schantz [161] as follows:

	Per Cent
Terpene Hydrocarbons	5 to 10
Borneol	5 to 10
Fenchyl Alcohol	5 to 10
α-Terpineol	50 to 60
Other Terpineols	15 to 25
Terpene Ethers	5 to 10
Ketones and Phenols	1 to 2

This represents the probable average composition of pine oil. A "High Grade" pine oil has been reported by Garvie [162] to have the following approximate composition:

	Per Cent
α-Terpineol	68.5
Menthanols	4.2

[160] "Pine Oil," Federal Specifications, LLL-O-358, July 13 (1945).
[161] *Ind. Eng. Chem.* **26** (1934), 709.
[162] *Chemical Industries* **44** (1939), 384.

	Per Cent
Fenchyl Alcohol	8.0
Borneol	9.0
Methyl Chavicol / Phenol Ethers	10.0
Moisture	0.3

Pine oil is a powerful germicide; soon after its introduction on the market the oil found application in disinfectants, and in cleaning and scouring soaps. One of the earliest major uses developed for pine oil was as a frothing agent in the flotation process for reclaiming low-grade copper-, lead-, and zinc-bearing ores. The mining industry is still probably the largest single consumer of pine oils, but very large quantities are now also used as solvents and wetting agents in a variety of textile and synthetic fiber manufacturing operations. Pine oil is also widely employed as an ingredient of many liquid soaps, disinfectants, preservatives, insecticides, deodorants, polishes, sweeping oils, and cattle sprays.[163] The components of the oil cannot conveniently be separated by fractional distillation, but certain individual compounds are recovered by chemical separation; in fact, considerable quantities of pine oil are processed for this purpose. Palmer[164] has described the production in this way of the "β-terpineol" of commerce (used as a perfume base, principally for soaps), of anethole from the methyl chavicol, and of fenchone and camphor from the fenchyl alcohol and borneol present in pine oil. The camphor thus produced is optically active, having a dextrorotation, whereas synthetic camphor from pinene is optically inactive.

II. Sulfate Wood Turpentine

History.—Crude sulfate wood turpentine is obtained as a by-product of the manufacture of paper pulp by the alkaline sulfate process. The recovery of the crude sulfate turpentine is a relatively simple procedure, consisting merely of condensing the vapors relieved from the digesters during the cooking of the wood, and separation of the oily layer from the aqueous layer in the condensate.[165] Romaine[166] states that, although sulfate wood turpentine was obtained in Norway and Sweden as early as 1910, it was not produced in quantity in the United States before 1918; and that for several years before 1930 the output averaged from 4,000 to 5,000 barrels (50 gallons each) annually. Since 1930 the United States Department of

163 Palmer, *Ind. Eng. Chem.* **35** (1943), 1025.
164 *Ibid.* **34** (1942), 1030.
165 Lawrence, *Paper Trade J.* **124,** No. 9 (1947), 128.
166 *Chemical Industries* **45** (1939), 408.

Agriculture has included data on the production of sulfate wood turpentine in its annual reports on naval stores. The data in Table 20.8 showing the rapid increase in production of sulfate wood turpentine are taken from these reports. Although the sulfate wood naval stores division is, therefore, the youngest of the American naval stores family, it has grown to be an important member, so that currently about half as much sulfate turpentine as gum turpentine is produced. Sulfate turpentine, when refined, closely resembles gum turpentine in composition. A comprehensive review of the literature on sulfate turpentine containing 87 references has been published by Collins and Schmitt.[167]

TABLE 20.8.   PRODUCTION OF SULFATE WOOD TURPENTINE *

Year	Barrels of 50 Gallons Each
1929–30	2,906
1934–35	9,832
1939–40	56,631
1944–45	104,307
1948–49	124,870
1949–50	147,500
1950–51	194,180

* Data for 1929–1940 from *Agricultural Statistics, U. S. Dept. Agr.* (1941), 688; for subsequent years from the *Annual Naval Stores Report* issued by the U. S. Department of Agriculture.

Collection of Sulfate Wood Turpentine.—A review of the various methods and equipment used by twenty-four American pulp mills for the collection of sulfate wood turpentine has been published by Lawrence.[168] He states:

"The procedure for collecting sulfate turpentine is fairly well standardized. Vapors relieved during the cooking of pine wood are passed through separators to remove entrained liquor and fiber. The separators are usually of the cyclone type and some mills employ more than one. Where two or more separators are used they are operated in series or parallel. From the separator, the vapors then pass to a condenser, generally of straight tube construction. The condensed water and turpentine are passed to a decanter, and the separated turpentine is withdrawn to storage. In some mills, the storage tank also serves as a decanter."

[167] *Paper Ind. and Paper World* **26** (1944), 1136; (1945), 1573.
[168] *Paper Trade J.* **124**, No. 9 (1947), 128.

Yield of Oil.—The yield of crude sulfate wood turpentine is highly variable, depending primarily upon the species of wood cooked, but also upon the locality and type of soil in which the trees have grown, the proportion of heartwood, the cutting season and the yard age of the wood, the procedure and efficiency of the equipment used to recover the turpentine, variations in the pulping process, and possibly other factors. Yields reported have ranged from as little as 0.5 gallon to as much as 10 gallons of turpentine per ton of pulp.[169] Lawrence [170] reported that:

"In terms of gallons of crude sulfate turpentine per ton of air-dry pine pulp, slash and longleaf pine yield 2.8 to 4.3 gal.; loblolly, shortleaf, and Virginia pine yield 1.5 to 2.7 gal.; jack and white pine yield 1.5 to 3.1 gal."

Romaine [171] estimated the average yield obtained by the pulp mills in the south at approximately 1.65 gallons per ton of pulp.

Purification of Crude Sulfate Wood Turpentine.—Crude sulfate wood turpentine recovered from the relief gases is an amber-colored, nauseating liquid containing 10 to 15 per cent of sulfur-bearing compounds. Of these, dimethyl sulfide is the chief component, with lesser proportions of dimethyl disulfide and methyl mercaptan.[172] The sulfur-containing compounds are relatively low boiling, and the major portion may be removed by fractional distillation; but even traces of sulfur compounds remaining in the refined turpentine will impart a characteristic and highly offensive odor. Accordingly, chemical treatment is commonly resorted to. Numerous chemical methods have been proposed; these have been reviewed by Collins and Schmitt.[173] Generally the crude sulfate turpentine is refined by a combination of one or two fractional distillations and chemical treatment. Thus the crude turpentine may be "topped" to remove the major portion of the sulfur compounds, treated with an oxidizing agent such as alkaline hypochlorite, and then again distilled. A study of the corrosion caused by crude sulfate turpentine has been reported by Norton et al.[174]

Chemical Composition.—Crude sulfate wood turpentine varies widely in composition depending upon the locality, type of soil, age, and species of pine trees, and variations in the pulp-making process. The composition of a crude sulfate turpentine has been reported by Collins: [175]

169 Collins and Schmitt, *Paper Ind. and Paper World* **26** (1944), 1137.
170 *Paper Trade J.* **124**, No. 9 (1947), 128.
171 *Chemical Industries* **45** (1939), 408.
172 Collins and Schmitt, *Paper Ind. and Paper World* **26** (1944), 1138.
173 *Ibid.*, 1139.
174 *Paper Trade J.* **124**, No. 18 (1947), 34.
175 U. S. Patent No. 2,409,614, October 22 (1946).

	Per Cent
Boiling at 35° to 40° C.	1.5
Pinene Fraction (90% of α- form, 10% of β- form)	82.0
Monocyclic Hydrocarbons	11.5
Pine Oil	1.5
Estragole (Methyl Chavicol)	0.2
Other High Boiling Oils Distilling from 180° to 212°	1.3
Nondistillable Constituents	2.0

Klason [176] has reported the presence of a small amount of *trimethylamine.*

Norton [177] states that as an aid toward uniformity crudes from various sources are frequently blended before processing, and that averaged analyses would be about as follows:

	Per Cent
α-Pinene	50 to 60
β-Pinene	15 to 20
Monocyclic Terpene Hydrocarbons	10 to 15
Sulfur compounds and impurities	10 to 15

Such a crude sulfate wood turpentine would produce a refined turpentine containing approximately 65 per cent of α-pinene, 25 per cent of β-pinene, and 10 per cent of tailings (chiefly monocyclic hydrocarbons, including *dipentene* and *terpinolene*). This composition is quite similar to that of some commercial gum spirits of turpentine reported by Palkin.[178]

After refining, the sulfate wood turpentine may contain traces of sulfur or chlorine or both. Tests for these elements may serve to characterize sulfate turpentine. Thus Smith [179] found no chlorine or sulfur in gum spirits of turpentine, steam-distilled wood turpentine, or destructively distilled turpentine; but found from 0.011 to 0.016 per cent of sulfur in six samples of American sulfate wood turpentine, and from 0.16 to 0.28 per cent of chlorine in three of the samples. The chlorine in these samples apparently arose from hypochlorites used in refining them.

Physicochemical Properties.—Crude sulfate wood turpentine is an amber-colored liquid characterized by a vile, sickening odor. The methyl sulfide present has a narcotic effect and is poisonous.[180] The following physical properties of crude sulfate wood turpentine were reported by Collins: [181]

Specific Gravity at 15.6°/15.6°	0.8654
Specific Optical Rotation	+2° 43′
Refractive Index	1.4709

[176] *Papier Ztg.* **33** (1908), 3779.
[177] *Paper Trade J.* **120**, No. 7 (1945), 36.
[178] *U. S. Dept. Agr., Tech. Bull.* No. 276, January (1932).
[179] *Ind. Eng. Chem., Anal. Ed.* 3 (1931), 354.
[180] Collins and Schmitt, *Paper Ind. and Paper World* **26** (1944), 1139.
[181] U. S. Patent No. 2,409,614, October 22 (1946).

The refined turpentine is a water white liquid. It meets the specifications for gum spirits of turpentine, except as to odor, which, in all but perhaps the most highly refined grades, is distinct, and characteristic of sulfate wood turpentine.

Use.—Refined sulfate wood turpentine is used for the same general purposes as gum spirits of turpentine; a large proportion is employed industrially. Large quantities are fractionated to produce α- and β-pinene. The α-pinene is used for the same purposes as the α-pinene from steam-distilled wood turpentine. The β-pinene serves to produce resinous polymers, terpene phenol resins, and chemicals such as myrcene and the primary bicyclic alcohol *Nopol* $C_{11}H_{17}OH$.

III. Destructively Distilled (D.D.) Wood Turpentine

History.—Early wood distillation, formerly called "tar burning," was a very crude operation. The wood was distilled in sod pits or brick kilns and only the tar and pitch were recovered. Later, iron retorts and iron and concrete kilns were developed. Patents relating to the process were granted as early as 1841. Romaine [182] states that the first plant to employ the basic principles of the present destructive distillation process, using waste pine wood as its raw material, was erected by James Stanley at Wilmington, N. C., in 1872. By 1900 the industry had become quite well established as a supplier of raw materials, and it assumed considerable importance in the period between 1900 and 1930. In more recent years production has declined. Data for the production of D.D. turpentine for representative years are given in Table 20.9.

Production of D.D. Wood Turpentine.—The raw material is substantially the same as that used by the steam-solvent industry, i.e., the "lightwood" of the cut-over pinelands of the south. In outline, the process consists of cutting selected stump and top wood in proper lengths, generally 20 to 36 in., placing them in suitable retorts equipped with condensers, and there heating the wood to charring point. The condensable vapors and tars obtained are processed to meet consumer requirements. Operating procedures vary widely, and descriptions of various operations have been reported.[183-187]

[182] *Chemical Industries* **45** (1939), 403.
[183] Veitch and Donk, *U. S. Dept. Agr., Bur. Chem., Bull.* No. 144, December (1911).
[184] Hawley, in T. Gamble, "Naval Stores," Savannah (1921), 251.
[185] Smith, *ibid.*, 253.
[186] Clendenon, in "Gamble's International Naval Stores Yearbook" (1930–31), 164.
[187] Harper, in "Rogers' Manual of Industrial Chemistry," Sixth Ed., D. Van Nostrand Co., New York, Vol. I (1942), 667.

TABLE 20.9. PRODUCTION OF DESTRUCTIVELY DISTILLED WOOD TURPENTINE *

Year	Barrels of 50 Gallons Each
1919–20	4,575
1924–25	8,200
1929–30	9,624
1934–35	5,767
1939–40	6,791
1944–45	4,477
1948–49	2,780
1949–50	3,150
1950–51	5,410

* Data for 1919–1940 from *Agricultural Statistics, U. S. Dept. Agr.* (1941), 688; for subsequent years from the *Annual Naval Stores Report* issued by the U. S. Department of Agriculture.

The retorts now employed are of different types and sizes. Small cylindrical retorts, which are charged and discharged by hand, may hold from one to three cords. Large oven retorts, each of which may hold ten cords or more, are charged by running in cars loaded with wood. After the distillation is completed the cars are pushed into iron coolers, where they are sealed up and allowed to cool away from contact with air. The normal cycle for charging, distillation, cooling, and discharging may require 24 hr. or more. Mims [188] reports that one large concern has a continuous retort in operation. The retorts may be heated by direct fire or by hot gases. The temperature inside the retorts reaches about 700° F. The vapors produced as the temperature is raised are passed through condensers; and the distillate, consisting of oil and pyroligneous acid, is collected. In addition to the distillate drawn from the condensers, some processors obtain more or less pitch or tar drawn from the bottom of the retorts.

The oils and tars are subsequently distilled and fractionated to prepare merchantable products. The distillation is often run through two or three stages. Thus the first stage may be carried out in a simple iron still (heated with steam and operated at atmospheric pressure) to produce a light oil as the distillate, with a light, medium, or heavy tar as residue. The light oil may then be fractionated to produce fractions of different specific gravities, depending upon subsequent uses, specifications of the consumer, and sales outlets; these fractions are sold as solvent oils under

[188] "Naval Stores Review 1948 International Yearbook," H. L. Peace Publications, New Orleans, La. (1948), 120.

various trade names. Sometimes the light oils are redistilled several times. They are then known as XX or XXX oil, according to the number of times they have been distilled. Phenolic compounds are sometimes separated by extraction with alkali and acidification. The products of the destructive distillation of pine wood include, besides D.D. turpentine and charcoal, solvent oils, pine tar oils, pine oils, creosote oils, and pine tars.

Since the resin content of the wood employed varies widely, and different producers use different conditions, widely different yields of the various products may be obtained. Clendenon [189] states that the yield of crude products (exclusive of charcoal, pyroligneous acid and charcoal) should total 30 to 35 per cent of the weight of the wood. This compares with about 22 per cent obtained by the steam-solvent process. The charcoal resulting amounts to 15 to 20 per cent of the weight of the wood used. Hawley [190] estimates the ordinary yields obtained in practice per cord (4,000 lb.) of "lightwood" as follows:

Total Oils (including tar)......... 65 to 100 gallons
Refined Turpentine.............. 8 to 15 gallons
Tar............................ 40 to 60 gallons
Charcoal...................... 25 to 35 bushels

The annual Naval Stores Reports of the United States Department of Agriculture indicate that in the past five years the ratio of pine tar to D.D. turpentine produced has ranged from 18 to 1 in 1945–46 to as high as 39 to 1 in 1948–49. Such variations in the ratio of pine tar to turpentine are undoubtedly in part a reflection of the demand for turpentine, as the proportion of light oil distillate (which can be included in the D.D. turpentine cut and still remain within the limits prescribed by specifications for D.D. turpentine) may be varied considerably.

Physicochemical Properties.—D.D. wood turpentine is a distilled fraction cut so as to conform to recognized specifications for destructively distilled wood turpentine. Federal specifications,[191] which differ from those of the other recognized classes of turpentine, include the following:

	Maximum	*Minimum*
Specific Gravity at 15.5°/15.5°.....................	0.865	0.850
Refractive Index at 20°...........................	1.483	1.463
Residue after Polymerization with 38 N H_2SO_4 (per cent by volume).....................................	2.0	...
Initial Boiling Point at 760 mm. pr.................	157° C.	150° C.
Distilling below 170° C. at 760 mm. pr. (per cent).....	...	60
Distilling below 180° C. at 760 mm. pr. (per cent).....	...	90

[189] "Gamble's International Naval Stores Yearbook" (1930–31), 166.
[190] In T. Gamble, "Naval Stores," Savannah (1921), 252.
[191] "Destructively Distilled Wood Turpentine," Federal Specification, TT-T-806, May 27 (1948).

A.S.T.M. specifications [192] differ from Federal specifications in that the A.S.T.M. prescribes a minimum specific gravity of 0.860 and a maximum of 0.875. However, the A.S.T.M. is presently (1950) giving consideration to changing its specifications to conform with Federal specifications as regards specific gravity. Destructively distilled wood turpentine has a characteristic odor. It is a more powerful solvent than the other classes of turpentine, a fact reflected in its lower aniline point and higher kauri-butanol solvency value. Snider and Burstein [193] found that the value for the aniline point of three samples of D.D. wood turpentine ranged from $-20.8°$ to $-20.0°$ C. They proposed that the aniline point be used to identify D.D. turpentine and to detect its presence as an adulterant in other classes of turpentine. Colledge [194] reported the kauri-butanol solvency value of D.D. turpentine to be 82.1 by comparison with 56 for gum turpentine and 58 for S.D.W. turpentine. Other solvents from the D.D. process were reported by Colledge [195] to have kauri-butanol values of 114.8 (Laksol) and 105.0 (D.D. dipentene).

Chemical Composition.—D.D. wood turpentine is produced in several types of retorts and under quite diversified operating conditions. Therefore, the composition varies. Only fragmentary analyses of various D.D. wood turpentine may be found in the literature.[196, 197] No comprehensive analysis of D.D. wood turpentine has been reported. According to Bain,[198] the various D.D. wood turpentines differ quantitatively with respect to composition, but are all very similar qualitatively. Analysis of a sample carefully fractionated by Bain in a six-foot Stedman column demonstrated that D.D. wood turpentine is an extremely complex mixture, containing more than a dozen compounds, indicated by breaks in boiling point, refractive index, specific gravity and kauri-butanol solvency test curves. *Dipentene* and *p-cymene* were major components. No β-pinene was present and not more than 10 per cent (probably much less) of α-*pinene*. α- and β-*Pyronene*, which are found on pyrolysis of turpentine, were doubtless present.

Use.—D.D. wood turpentine, which usually brings a lower price than the other classes of turpentine, finds use as an industrial solvent. D.D. dipentine is employed as an anti-skinning agent, as a pigment-dispersing agent,

[192] "1949 Book of A.S.T.M. Standards, Part 4," American Society for Testing Materials, Philadelphia (1950), 196.
[193] *Ind. Eng. Chem., Anal. Ed.* **16** (1944), 603.
[194] *Paint Oil Chem. Rev.* **95,** No. 10 (1933), 13.
[195] *Ibid.*
[196] Veitch and Donk, *U. S. Dept. Agr., Bur. Chem., Bull.* No. 144, December (1911).
[197] Hawley, *U. S. Dept. Agr., Forest Service Bull.* No. 105, January (1913).
[198] Private communication from Dr. J. P. Bain, Technical Director, Naval Stores Division, The Glidden Co., Jacksonville, Fla. (1950).

and for reclaiming rubber. D.D. pine oil serves in ore flotation, in wetting pigments for grinding and for promoting proper flow of enamels, and in disinfectant compositions. The chief use for pine tar is as a rubber-compounding ingredient. It is also employed to impregnate oakum and paper bags for garment storage, and in medicinal and disinfectant preparations such as soaps and salves.[199]

A monograph on D.D. pine tar and another on rectified oil of tar are included in the twelfth revision of the United States Pharmacopoeia.[200] The U.S.P. requires that the tar be heavier than water and that the rectified oil of tar have a specific gravity not less than 0.960 and not more than 0.990 at 25° C. Rectified tar oil is produced by steam distillation of pine tar. The more volatile fractions are separated; then a fraction of the distillate meeting specifications for rectified tar oil is collected. This fraction represents only about 5 per cent of the crude pine tar. It contains about 25 per cent of phenols and 40 per cent of hydrocarbons; the remainder consists of terpene alcohols corresponding to those found in pine oil. Federal specifications for pine tar [201] require that not more than 2 per cent (by volume) shall distill below 170° C. and not less than 70 per cent below 365° C., and that the viscosity shall be not less than 1,400 centipoises nor more than 2,300 centipoises at 30° C.

IV. Sulfite Turpentine

This turpentine (sometimes called spruce turpentine, and not an officially recognized turpentine), is not produced commercially in the United States today; it differs in composition from all other turpentines. It has attracted a great deal of interest at various times; for example, Collins [202] in a review of the literature on sulfite turpentine lists 103 references. Sulfite turpentine is a by-product in the production of wood pulp by the acid-sulfite pulping process. The chief component is *p-cymene*. Although some *p*-cymene was recovered from this source on a commercial scale in Germany during World War I, it appears never to have been recovered on other than an experimental scale in the United States.

The yields of sulfite turpentine reported by various investigators differ enormously but appear to be consistently small. In a tabulation of findings by sixteen investigators, Collins [203] lists six of these as reporting less than

[199] Bain, "Naval Stores Review 1949 International Yearbook," H. L. Peace Publications, New Orleans, La. (1949), 101.
[200] "The Pharmacopoeia of the United States of America," Twelfth Revision, Mack Printing Co., Easton, Pa. (1942), 366, 333.
[201] "Tar; Pine, Technical Grade," Federal Specification, JJJ-T-121, April 1 (1942).
[202] *Paper Ind. and Paper World* **27** (1945), 537, 719.
[203] *Ibid.*, 538.

1 lb. per ton of pulp (one reports 0.2); four from 1 to 3 lb., five from 3 to 8 lb., and one reporting 10 to 30 lb.   Although *p*-cymene is the principal component of sulfite turpentine, the proportion observed ranging from about 70 to 90 per cent, this turpentine also contains *dipentene, borneol,* and *sesquiterpenes.*[204]

[204] Wise, *ibid.* **24** (1943), 1223.

CHAPTER XXI

ESSENTIAL OILS OF THE PLANT FAMILY *TAXODIACEAE*

OIL OF *SCIADOPITYS VERTICILLATA* (THUNB.) SIEB. ET ZUCC.

("Oil of Kinsho"—"Oil of Koyamaki")

The trunk and roots of *Sciadopitys verticillata* (Thunb.) Sieb. et Zucc. (fam. *Taxodiaceae*), the "Umbrella Pine"—"Koyamaki" in Japanese—contain an essential oil which can be obtained by steam distillation under pressure. About 20 tons of the oil are distilled yearly in Japan; the chief area of production, since the end of World War II, has been the section around Mount Kaya, in the Prefecture of Wakayama.

A commercial sample of kinsho oil examined by Fritzsche Brothers, Inc., New York, exhibited these properties:

Specific Gravity at 15°/15°.......... 0.938
Optical Rotation.................. −5° 30′
Refractive Index at 20°............. 1.5047
Acid Number..................... 1.3
Ester Number.................... 3.0
Ester Number after Acetylation...... 31.9
Cedrol Content................... 12.9%
Solubility at 20°................. Soluble in 4.5 to 5 vol. and
more of 95% alcohol

The odor of the oil was "woody," similar to that of American cedarwood oil, but more terpene-like (due to the much lower content of cedrol).

According to Kawamura,[1] the chief constituent of kinsho wood oil is *cedrol*—whence the use of the oil as an odor fixative in perfumes and in the scenting of soaps. *Cedrene* is also present, but no diterpene hydrocarbons.

In the *leaf* oil (which is not produced commercially), the following compounds have been identified:

d-α-Pinene. Observed by Kawamura, and by Nishida and Uota.[2]

A Diterpene, Podocarprene. (Kawamura, and Nishida and Uota.)

A Diterpene, $C_{20}H_{32}$. Noted by Kawamura.

Sciadopitene, $C_{20}H_{32}$. Reported by Nishida and Uota.

[1] *Bull. Imp. Forestry Expt. Sta. Tokyo* No. 31 (1931), 93. *Chem. Abstracts* **26** (1932), 4679.
[2] *J. Agr. Chem. Soc. Japan* **11** (1935), 489; **12** (1936), 308. *Chem. Abstracts* **29** (1935), 6590; **30** (1936), 6356.

In the *twig* oil, Kawamura reported the presence of:

α-Pinene, Cedrene, and Cedrol.

An oil distilled from *leaves* and *twigs* by Nishida and Uota contained a crystalline diterpene, *sciadopitene* (*phyllocladene*).

For details of the diterpenes above, see the Diterpene Table, opposite page 126, Vol. II of the present work.

OIL OF *CRYPTOMERIA JAPONICA* (L.f.) D. DON
("Oil of Sugi")

Cryptomeria japonica (L.f.) D. Don (fam. *Taxodiaceae*), called "Sugi" in Japanese, grows wild and abundantly in the mountainous regions of Japan; it has also been planted extensively. The term "Japanese Cypress" or "Japanese Cedar" by which this tree is occasionally designated in occidental literature, originates from the former botanical classification *Cupressus japonica* L.

The wood of *Cryptomeria japonica* (L.f.) D. Don is one of the most important Japanese building and construction materials. Since ancient times it has also been employed for the making of barrels for "Sake," a kind of beer or wine made from rice. Sugi wood is said to impart its characteristic aroma to this popular beverage. For the same reason tinctures of the wood, or solutions of its essential oil, are used for the flavoring of sake.

Commercial sugi oil consists almost exclusively of *root oil;* this is distilled from old roots and stumps dug up thirty to fifty years after the trees have been felled.

A. Root Oil

According to Hiraizumi,[1] the stumps and roots are reduced to chips and charged into wooden barrel stills ("Koshiki") of the same type as those used in Japan for the production of camphor and camphor oil (cf. Vol. IV of the present work, p. 266). Distillation of sugi wood closely resembles that of camphor wood, except that spiral condensers are used. The cumbersome box condensers required for the separation of camphor from camphor

---

[1] The author is greatly obliged to Dr. Teikichi Hiraizumi, Tokyo, for much of the information contained in this monograph.

oil are unnecessary in the case of sugi oil. After 3 hr. of distillation of sugi wood the flow of the condensate diminishes gradually; distillation is then interrupted, the charge removed from the still, dried, and returned to the still for further distillation. If the material is not taken out and dried, the heavier and higher-boiling portions of the oil do not pass over, for the simple reason that during the first hours of distillation excessive wetting of the chips under the influence of low pressure steam takes place. As a matter of fact, native distillers have learned from experience that moist wood (wetted by rain for example) never yields its full amount of essential oil. Even with dry chips the yield of oil in the old-fashioned barrel stills ("Koshiki") seldom exceeds 1.5 per cent. Recently a progressive producer installed modern steam stills, operating with direct steam of 7.5 atm. pr. With this equipment he has been able to obtain yields of oil as high as 5.5 per cent; moreover, the exhausted chips can be utilized in the pulp industry. However, practically all producers still use the old "Koshiki" system.

Centers of sugi oil production lie in the Prefectures of Ko-shi and Tokushima on Shikoku Island. Although large quantities of wood from roots and stumps are available, total production of sugi oil amounts to only 15 to 20 metric tons per year.

Physicochemical Properties.—The volatile oil derived from the roots of *Cryptomeria japonica* (L.f.) D. Don is a viscous colorless to yellow or light green liquid, with a "woody" odor. According to Gildemeister and Hoffmann,[2] the oil has the following properties:

Specific Gravity at 15°.............. 0.9325 to 0.9453
Optical Rotation................... −8° 20′ to −23° 0′
Refractive Index at 20°............ 1.50910 to 1.51075
Acid Number..................... Up to 0.3
Ester Number.................... 0.9 to 9.3
Ester Number after Acetylation...... 36.4 to 57.9
Solubility........................ Usually not clearly soluble in 90% alcohol, not even in 10 vol. Usually miscible in 95% alcohol, in every proportion
Boiling Range at atm. pr............ 270° to 300°

Steam-distilling sugi roots, S. Kimura and Mizoshita[3] obtained an oil exhibiting these values:

Specific Gravity at 25°/4°........ 0.936
Specific Optical Rotation......... −16° 42′
Refractive Index at 25°.......... 1.508
Acid Number.................. 0.9
Ester Number.................. 8.9
Boiling Range at 754 mm........ 255° to 285°

[2] "Die Ätherischen Öle," 3d Ed., Vol. II, 222.
[3] *Mem. Coll. Sci. Kyoto Imp. Univ.* Ser. A., **14** (1931), 273.

Sugii and Sengoku [4] submitted sugi root oil to fractional distillation and reported the following boiling range (at 1 mm. pressure):

	Per Cent
89°–94°	19
94°–96°	28
96°–99°	17
99°–105°	16
105°–112°	8
112°–118°	10
118°–130°	1.4

A commercial sample of sugi oil analyzed in the laboratories of Fritzsche Brothers, Inc., New York, had these properties:

Specific Gravity at 15°/15°	0.943
Optical Rotation	−28° 54′
Refractive Index at 20°	1.5088
Acid Number	0
Ester Number	11.4
Ester Number after Acetylation	69.4
Solubility at 20°	Soluble in 8 vol. and more of 90% alcohol

The odor of the oil was somewhat "woody" and slightly reminiscent of the ionones.

Chemical Composition.—The volatile oil obtained by steam distillation of the roots of *Cryptomeria japonica* has been the subject of several investigations carried out over a period of about thirty years. Results of the earlier research, however, were none too conclusive, because various workers assigned different terms to compounds probably identical. It was only in 1932 that S. Kimura and Mizoshita [5] succeeded in bringing some order into the confused picture. These authors found that an oil investigated by them consisted of:

54% of sesquiterpenes b_{17} 140°–155°
38% of sesquiterpene alcohols b_9 145°–150°
6% of residue and tar

Almost thirty years previously, Keimatsu [6] had isolated a sesquiterpene b. 267°, $[\alpha]_D$ +18° 55′, apparently related to cadinene; this he named *cryptene*. A few years later, H. Kimura [7] investigated a sugi root oil boiling chiefly between 150° and 160° at 17 mm. pr. In this oil H. Kimura

[4] *J. Pharm. Soc. Japan* **51** (1931), 197.
[5] *Mem. Coll. Sci. Kyoto Imp. Univ.* Ser. A., **14** (1931), 273.
[6] *J. Pharm. Soc. Japan* (1905), 189.
[7] *Ber. deut. pharm. Ges.* **19** (1909), 372. *Chem. Zentr.* (1910), I, 274.

identified *cadinene* by means of its dihydrochloride m. 117°–118°. Another sesquiterpene, which he isolated from the oil (b_{17} 150°–160°), H. Kimura named *suginene*, $[\alpha]_D$ −10° 34′; this yielded only a liquid hydrochloride addition compound. H. Kimura [8] also noted the presence of a sesquiterpene alcohol b_{10} 162°–163°, $[\alpha]_D$ −37° 5′, to which he assigned the name *cryptomeriol*. On purification by means of its xanthogenate, cryptomeriol appears to undergo molecular rearrangement, with the formation of iso-cryptomeriol m. 135°–136°.

In 1929, Wienhaus and Scholz [9] isolated from sugi root oil a new sesquiterpene alcohol m. 79°–80°, which they named "cryptomeradol." Shortly afterward, Sugii and Sengoku [10] noted the presence of "machilol" in sugi root oil. This bicyclic tertiary sesquiterpene alcohol (m. 84°, dihydroxy compound m. 110°, anhydrous form m. 106°–107°, monobenzoate m. 144°–145°) had already been noted in other essential oils (cf. Vol. II of the present work, p. 758). Sugii and Sengoku claimed that "cryptomeradol" and "machilol" are identical, and suggested that the former term be abandoned. In 1931, however, Ruzicka, Wind and Koolhaas [11] proved that both "cryptomeradol" and "machilol" are actually *eudesmol*, the β-isomer of this last compound predominating (cf. Vol. II of the present work, p. 274).

The most recent investigation of sugi root oil is that of S. Kimura and Mizoshita [12] (see above), who isolated from it a sesquiterpene $C_{15}H_{24}$, $b_{4.5}$ 108°–114°, d_4^{25} 0.9150, $[\alpha]_D$ −22° 24′, which they named *kiganene* (cf. Vol. II of the present work, p. 748). The results obtained by hydrogenation and oxidative degradation of this substance led S. Kimura and Mizoshita to the conclusion that kiganene possesses one of the following structural formulas:

Aside from the sesquiterpene kiganene, S. Kimura and Mizoshita,[13] also isolated from the oil a sesquiterpene alcohol $C_{15}H_{26}O$, b_9 145°–150°, d_4^{25} 0.9657, $[\alpha]_D$ −6° 20′, which they named *kiganol* (cf. Vol. II of the pres-

[8] *Ibid.*
[9] *Ber. Schimmel & Co., Jubiläums Ausgabe* (1929), 275.
[10] *J. Pharm. Soc. Japan* **51** (1931), 196.
[11] *Helv. Chim. Acta* **14** (1931), 1178.
[12] *Mem. Coll. Sci. Kyoto Imp. Univ.* Ser. A., **14** (1931), 273.
[13] *Ibid.*

ent work, p. 757). In the opinion of S. Kimura and Mizoshita this sesquiterpene alcohol has one of the following configurations:

Use.—In Japan the oil derived from the root of *Cryptomeria japonica* is
used as an odor fixative in perfumery, as a substitute for cedarwood oil,
and occasionally as an adulterant of ionone. In Europe and America the
oil is comparatively little known, despite occasional offers from Japan.

B. Leaf Oil

The leaves of *Cryptomeria japonica* (L.f.) D. Don, the Japanese "Sugi,"
contain a volatile oil of some interest to the essential oil chemist. For this
reason it has been investigated quite thoroughly by Japanese researchers.
The oil is not produced commercially, however.

Physicochemical Properties.—The oil derived by steam distillation of
sugi leaves is a mobile, yellow-brown liquid of strong and aromatic odor.
It boils between 155° and 350° at atmospheric pressure. Distilling fresh
sugi leaves, Uchida [14] obtained 0.7 per cent of an oil with these properties:

Specific Gravity at 15.5°/15.5°..........	0.9217
Specific Optical Rotation (in 10% Chloro-	
form Solution) at 15°................	+19° 18′
Refractive Index at 20°................	1.4895
Acid Number........................	1.0
Ester Number........................	6.56
Ester Number after Acetylation.........	14.35
Boiling Range at atm. pr.:	
155°–190°........................	33%
190°–230°........................	4%
230°–270°........................	4%
270°–310°........................	28%
310°–350°........................	23%

Chemical Composition.—The chemical composition of sugi leaf oil has
been investigated quite thoroughly by Uchida,[15] and Uchida and Murata,[16]
who reported the presence of the following compounds:

[14] *J. Am. Chem. Soc.* **38** (1916), 694.
[15] *Ibid.*
[16] *J. Soc. Chem. Ind. Japan* **40** (1937), Supplementary Binding, 159.

Terpenes $C_{10}H_{16}$ (34%). Dipentene, chiefly; d-α-Pinene, smaller amount.

Terpene Alcohol $C_{10}H_{18}O$ (4.5%). Odor reminiscent of camphor and peppermint. B. 212°–214°, d_{18}^{18} 0.9414, $[\alpha]_D$ +56° 4′ (in 8.98% $CHCl_3$ solution), n_D^{18} 1.4832. The alcohol could not be acetylized completely.

Sesquiterpenes $C_{15}H_{24}$ (30%). Chief fraction b. 266°–268°, $d_{15.5}^{15.5}$ 0.9335, $[\alpha]_D$ +15° 11′ (in 6.08% $CHCl_3$ solution), $n_D^{22.8}$ 1.5041; dihydrochloride liquid.
  Cadinene, small amount in the fraction b. 272°–275°.

Sesquiterpene Alcohols $C_{15}H_{26}O$ (12%). Sesquicryptol (cf. Vol. II of the present work, p. 759) m. 49°–51°, b_{20} 172°–174°, $[\alpha]_D^{22}$ +22° 43′.

Diterpenes $C_{20}H_{32}$ (18%). Chiefly α-cryptomerene m. 61° (cf. Vol. II of the present work, p. 126, Table).

Another investigation of sugi leaf oil was carried out by Noda,[17] who noted that his oil (d_{15}^{15} 0.8785, α_D^{20} +8° 43′, n_D^{15} 1.4765, ester number 9.01, ester number after acetylation 31.15) contained these compounds:

d-α-Pinene (50%).

d-Camphene (15%).

A Sesquiterpene (10%).

d-α-Terpineol (small quantities).

Sesquiterpene Alcohols (small quantities).

A Compound $C_{10}H_{16}O_2$.

Caprylates (2 to 3%).

Free Acids (0.09%).

A Phenol (0.09%).

Use.—Oil of sugi leaves has not found any practical use; it is not produced commercially.

---

[17] *Waseda Applied Chem. Soc. Bull.* **18** (1932), 6 (English Abstracts 5A). *Chem. Abstracts* **27** (1933), 565. *Waseda Applied Chem. Soc. Bull.* **20** (1933), 18. *British Chem. Abstracts* B (1934), 301.

CHAPTER XXII

ESSENTIAL OILS OF THE PLANT FAMILY *CUPRESSACEAE*

OIL OF *CALLITROPSIS ARAUCARIOIDES* COMPT.
(Oil of Araucaria)

The essential oil produced and offered by a firm in Western Australia under the name of "Oil of Araucaria" was formerly thought to be derived from a plant species similar to *Araucaria cookii* R. Br.;[1] hence the commercial term "Oil of Araucaria" which is still in use. In 1927 Welch[2] reported that the oil is actually distilled from the wood of *Callitropsis araucarioides* (fam. *Cupressaceae*), a species first described by Compton[3] in 1922. The plant resembles the trees of species belonging to the genus *Callitris*, native to Australia. In fact, the genera *Callitropsis* and *Callitris* exhibit certain affinities, but are undoubtedly distinct.

Callitropsis araucarioides Compt. appears to be confined to a single limited locality in New Caledonia, where it grows on serpentine rock at an elevation of about 800 ft., near the Rivière de Carénage. It attains a height of approximately 30 ft.

On steam distillation, the wood of the tree yields from 6 to 7 per cent of essential oil. Distilling samples of imported fresh and weathered wood, Schimmel & Co.[4] obtained 10.5 and 11.7 per cent, respectively, of oil.

Physicochemical Properties.—The oil derived from the wood of *Callitropsis araucarioides* Compt. is a dark yellow-green to reddish, very viscous liquid, or a semisolid, grainy mass resembling semicrystalline honey. The odor of the oil is pleasant, balsamic, and slightly rose-like, somewhat reminiscent of guaiac wood oil.

The two oils distilled from fresh wood (I), and from weathered wood (II)—see above—had these properties:

	I	*II*
Specific Gravity at 15°............	0.9756	0.9742
Optical Rotation.................	+4° 10′	+8° 5′
Refractive Index at 20°..........	1.51139	1.51520
Acid Number....................	10.2	8.4
Ester Number...................	24.3	46.7
Ester Number after Acetylation....	177.3	186.7
Total Alcohol Content, Calculated as $C_{15}H_{26}O$....................	81.1%	86.0%
Solubility......................	Soluble in 1.1 vol. and more of 80% alcohol	

[1] *Ber. Schimmel & Co.* (1926), 5; (1927), 4.
[2] *Perfumery Essential Oil Record* **18** (1927), 335.
[3] *J. Linnaean Soc.* **14** (1922), 432.
[4] Gildemeister and Hoffmann, "Die Ätherischen Öle," 3d Ed., Vol. II, 236.

Two commercial oils from Western Australia examined by Schimmel & Co.[5] exhibited the following values:

	I	II
Specific Gravity at 15°..............	0.9812	0.9776
Optical Rotation...................	+26° 0′	+16° 2′
Refractive Index at 20°............	1.51048	1.50882
Acid Number......................	2.6	2.2
Ester Number.....................	5.6	15.9
Ester Number after Acetylation....	164.3	175.5
Total Alcohol Content, Calculated as $C_{15}H_{26}O$....................	74.3%	80.1%
Solubility in 70% Alcohol.........	Soluble in 3.2 vol. and more	Soluble in 4 vol. and more

Penfold and Morrison,[6] who were the first to distill the oil experimentally, noted properties varying within these limits:

Specific Gravity at 15°/15°.........	0.9606 to 0.9684
Optical Rotation...................	+6° 54′ to too dark for determination
Refractive Index at 20°............	1.5131 to 1.5181
Ester Number.....................	64.5 to 92.15
Ester Number after Acetylation......	171.54 to 207.28
Solubility........................	Soluble in 1.4 to 1.6 vol. of 70% alcohol

Boiling Range at 10 mm. pr.:

105° to 130°.....................	5%
130° to 140°	8%
140° to 150°.....................	23%
150° to 165°.....................	60%

Chemical Composition.—The chemical composition of oil of *Callitropsis araucarioides* Compt. has been investigated by Penfold and Morrison,[7] and Cahn, Penfold and Simonsen,[8] who reported the presence of the following compounds:

Eudesmol. The chief constituent, the oil containing from 50 to 70 per cent of eudesmol m. 79°–80°, $[\alpha]_D^{20}$ +37° 48′. (Cf. Vol. II of the present work, p. 274.)

Eudesmene(?). The sesquiterpene observed in the oil by Penfold and Morrison was probably eudesmene (cf. Vol. II of this work, p. 109).

Phenols(?). According to the same authors, the oil contains about 1 per cent of phenols, which were not identified, however.

[5] *Ber. Schimmel & Co.* (1929), 4.
[6] *Perfumery Essential Oil Record* **16** (1925), 3, 41, 78.
[7] *Ibid.*
[8] *J. Chem. Soc.* (1931), 3134.

Geranyl Dehydrogeranate. Cahn, Penfold and Simonsen found that the acid $C_{10}H_{14}O_2$, m. 183°–184°, first observed in the oil by Penfold and Morrison, is dehydrogeranic acid. (Cf. Vol. II, p. 589.) It occurs in the oil esterified with geraniol.

Use.—Oil of *Callitropsis araucarioides* Compt. is used as an excellent odor fixative, particularly in the scenting of cosmetics and soaps. In this respect it resembles oil of guaiac wood.

OIL OF *THUJOPSIS DOLABRATA* (L.f.) SIEB. ET ZUCC. VAR. *HONDAI* MAK.

("Oil of Hiba")

Thujopsis dolabrata (L.f.) Sieb. et Zucc. var. *hondai* Mak. (fam. *Cupressaceae*), a tree particularly abundant in the Prefecture of Aomori in Japan, supplies a lumber highly esteemed for its resistance to the attacks of certain fungi, *Merulius lacrymans* (Wulf.) Schum. and *Polyporus gilvus* Schw. among them. This property makes the wood of *Thujopsis dolabrata* (also known as "False Arborvitae," or "Hiba" in Japanese) very durable in the ground or under water, hence most useful in general construction work for the building of bridges, houses, docks and ships. The wood owes its fungicidal action to the presence of an essential oil [1] that can be isolated by steam distillation.

A. Oil of Hiba Wood

The oil is produced commercially in Japan, chiefly in the Prefecture of Aomori. Total production per year varies from 3 to 5 metric tons. According to Hiraizumi [2] the oil is obtained by steam distillation of trunk wood shavings and of sawdust, the yield of oil ranging from 1.0 to 1.5 per cent.

A sample of commercial hiba oil examined by Fritzsche Brothers, Inc., New York, exhibited the following properties:

Specific Gravity at 15°/15°..........	0.944
Optical Rotation...................	−44° 48′
Refractive Index at 20°.............	1.5059
Acid Number......................	0

[1] S. Uchida, *J. Soc. Chem. Ind. Japan* **31** (1928), 501. *Chem. Abstracts* **22** (1928), 3732.
[2] Private communication from Dr. Teikichi Hiraizumi, Tokyo.

Ester Number...................... 3.9
Ester Number after Acetylation...... 30.9
Solubility at 20°.................... Slightly hazy in 10 vol. of
95% alcohol

The odor of the oil was "woody," slightly reminiscent of cedarwood oil.
S. Uchida[3] reported these properties for a sample of hiba oil distilled
from wood shavings (yield 1.08 per cent):

Specific Gravity at 22°/15°..................... 0.9574
Specific Optical Rotation (in 17.23% chloroform
solution).................................... −26° 43′
Refractive Index at 22.7°...................... 1.5110
Acid Number................................. 5.62
Ester Number................................ 11.97
Boiling Range............................... 256° to 295°

In the oil he investigated, S. Uchida[4] observed the presence of an (unidentified) optically inactive, tricyclic sesquiterpene $C_{15}H_{24}$ (b. 261°–262°,
$d_{22.8}$ 0.9458, $n_D^{22.8}$ 1.5055).

In 1930 Kawamura[5] isolated from hiba wood oil a substance $C_{10}H_{12}O_2$,
called *hinokitiol*. This isopropyl cycloheptatrienolone occurs also in hinoki
root oil (cf. the monograph on "Oil of *Chamaecyparis obtusa* [Sieb. et
Zucc.] Endl. p. 346), and is the active principle responsible for the bactericidal and bacteriostatic action of these two oils (Katsura[6]).

The acidic portions of hiba wood oil are now used in Japan for the commercial isolation of hinokitiol; the neutral portions serve for the scenting
of soaps.

B. Oil of Hiba Leaves

Like the wood, the leaves of the hiba tree contain a volatile oil that can
be isolated by steam distillation. However, this oil is not produced commercially.

Steam-distilling hiba leaves, S. Uchida[7] obtained 0.83 per cent of an oil
with these properties:

Specific Gravity at 26°/15.5°........ 0.8857
Specific Optical Rotation............ +27° 40′
Refractive Index at 27°............. 1.4729
Acid Number..................... 3.76
Ester Number..................... 29.12
Ester Number after Acetylation...... 113.2

[3] *J. Soc. Chem. Ind. Japan* **31** (1928), 501. *Chem. Abstracts* **22** (1928), 3732.
[4] *Ibid.*
[5] *J. Bull. Imp. Forest Expt. Sta.* (Japan) **30** (1930), 59.
[6] *Medical Time* (Tokyo) **3**, No. 10 (August 1948), 29.
[7] *J. Soc. Chem. Ind. Japan* **31** (1928), 491. *Chem. Abstracts* **22** (1928), 3732.

The oil had the following composition:

Terpenes (about 50%). Sabinene and some dipentene.

Terpene Alcohols (22%). Sabinol and some borneol.

Esters (10%). Sabinyl acetate and some bornyl acetate.

A Diterpene $C_{20}H_{32}$ (13%). Tetracyclic, b. 336° (cf. Vol. II of the present work, p. 126, Table).

A Sesquiterpene $C_{15}H_{24}$ (2%). Bicyclic, b. 270°–280°.

A Sesquiterpene Alcohol (3%). Monocyclic, b. 290°–300°.

Undecylenic Acid (0.1%).

OIL OF THUJA
("Cedar Leaf Oil"—White Cedar Leaf Oil)

Essence de Thuja   *Aceite Esencial Thuja*   *Thujaöl*   *Oleum Thujae*

Thuja occidentalis L. (fam. *Cupressaceae*), the Eastern Arborvitae, commonly called "Eastern White Cedar," or "Northern White Cedar," or "Swamp Cedar," occurs widely in the northeastern part of the United States and in eastern Canada.[1] The ends of the branches and adherent leaves contain an essential oil which can be extracted by steam distillation. The principal producing centers of thuja oil are in the northern parts of New York State, with Vermont following next in importance. New Hampshire, Maine and the Province of Quebec (Canada) supply only small quantities.

Oil of thuja, or as it is often loosely called "Cedar Leaf Oil," must not be confused with cedarwood oil, i.e., the oil distilled from the wood of the *red* cedar, *Juniperus virginiana* L. (The *leaves* of the latter tree are not exploited industrially. The commercial term "Cedar Leaf Oil," therefore, always refers to the oil derived from the leaves of the *white* cedar, *Thuja occidentalis* L.).

Distillation.—Oil of thuja is produced chiefly by farmers during their spare time. Since this work is not allowed to interfere with their more vital tasks of farming, the amount of oil to be produced in a given year can never be predicted. Supplies also depend to a great extent upon the price which the oil fetches on the New York market. The producing season

---

[1] Note, however, that the tree called the "White Cedar" in the New Jersey pine barrens is actually *Chamaecyparis thyoides*.

lasts from March or April to November and even December, until snowfall stops the work. In general the weather plays an important role in the production of thuja oil. Prices are usually at the lowest from April to June, because most producers start distilling the oil before their fields are in condition to be plowed for the planting of regular crops.

In actual practice two or three farmers form a team, cutting and distilling the brush that grows on a certain tract of land. In most cases a whole tree is felled, and the ends of the branches with adherent leaves are trimmed off by means of long heavy knives. Nothing is wasted; the wood serves as fuel, and even the distilled (exhausted) material is dried and then used as fuel.

After one section has been cleaned of white cedar trees, the still and steam boiler are moved to another location. Thus it may often be necessary to move the equipment several times in the course of one season.

According to Thiele,[2] distillation takes place in rather crude stills, the boiler or engine being the only modern piece of equipment. The still box is usually constructed of spruce planking, tongued and grooved, the planks being fitted tightly together. Any crevices are calked with oakum or other packing material so as to prevent the escape of steam. The still box is closed with a cover that can be raised or lowered with the aid of ropes and pulleys attached to a long pole. A steam-connecting pipe leads to the condenser, the latter usually made from piping and resembling an ordinary wall radiator. The condenser is enclosed in a box with an open top into which water is allowed to flow, if possible by gravity, or with the aid of either steam or hand pumps. The steam necessary in the distillation is generated by old boilers which have seen service as hoisting engines or, in some cases, even as locomotives. Instead of regular oil separators, large cans are occasionally employed to catch the distillate, and as the oil separates from the water it is scooped from the top.

The oil thus produced is often sold in local country stores. The storekeepers may have to accumulate small lots from as many as ten individual producers before being able to ship a single drum of oil. Local dealers, as well as the few producers who have large quantities to offer, sell their oil to essential oil houses in New York where the crude product must be treated (elimination of traces of water by decantation and filtration) before the oil can be offered on the market.

Yield of Oil.—According to Ayer,[3] and Risi and Brule[4] the yield of oil in commercial production varies between 0.6 and 1.0 per cent. Nineteen experimental distillations carried out in the Province of Quebec by Risi

---

[2] *Drug Markets* **26** (1930), 354.
[3] *Oil Paint Drug Reptr.* (June 25, 1906), 17.
[4] *Am. Perfumer* **48** (January 1946), 39.

and Brule with cedar branches and attached leaves showed an average yield of only 0.45 per cent. The yield of oil depends upon several factors, viz., the season, the age of the trees, their exposure to sunlight, and the packing of the distillation material in the still. It is highest in February and March and lowest from the middle of June to September. Risi and Brule found that cedar branches from a fifteen-year-old tree yielded 50 per cent more oil than those of a thirty-year-old tree. Comparative distillations of branches from isolated sun-exposed trees and from trees grown in dense bush revealed a higher oil content of the former. Hashed branches yielded 30 per cent more oil than whole branches. This clearly indicates that better compactness of the charge prevents the steam from escaping along some channels of lower resistance, thus assuring a more intimate contact of the steam with the material. With a large charge of hashed branches a steam pressure of about 40 lb. per sq. in. appears to give best results.

Studying industrial production of cedar leaf oil near Canton, New York, Brown [5] observed that the small trees are permitted to obtain a height of 4 to 5 ft., when they are considered to be in prime condition to give the highest yield and best quality of oil. Older trees are not cut for oil recovery. Distillation of one charge requires 8 hr.; each batch of 2,000 lb. of leaf material yields about 30 lb. of oil.

Physicochemical Properties.—Oil of thuja is a colorless to yellow or yellowish-green mobile liquid with a characteristic strong and camphoraceous odor, reminiscent of sage (*Salvia officinalis*). According to Gildemeister and Hoffmann,[6] oil of thuja has these properties:

Specific Gravity at 15°...............	0.915 to 0.935
Optical Rotation...................	$-10°\,0'$ to $-14°\,0'$
Refractive Index at 20°.............	1.456 to 1.459
Acid Number......................	Up to 1
Ester Number.....................	16.8 to 31.7
Ester Number after Acetylation......	32 to 48
Boiling Range.....................	160° to 250°, the principal fraction distilling between 180° and 205°
Solubility.........................	Clearly soluble in 3 to 4 vol. of 70% alcohol

Numerous commercial lots of pure thuja oil received directly from the producing regions and examined by Fritzsche Brothers, Inc., New York, had properties varying within the following limits:

Specific Gravity at 25°/25°..........	0.905 to 0.919, seldom below 0.910
Optical Rotation...................	$-8°\,39'$ to $-14°\,5'$, usually between $-10°\,0'$ and $-13°\,0'$

[5] *Drug Cosmetic Ind.* **37** (1935), 587.
[6] "Die Ätherischen Öle," 3d Ed., Vol. II, 239.

Refractive Index at 20°............. 1.4559 to 1.4590
Ketone Content, Calculated as Thu-
  jone (Hydroxylamine Hydrochloride
  Method)....................... 55.0 to 64.3%, seldom below 60.0%
Solubility........................ Soluble in 2.5 to 4 vol. of 70% alcohol. Some-
                                    times cloudy in 10 vol. Usually soluble in
                                    3 vol. and more of 70% alcohol

According to Brown,[7] the optical rotation of cedar leaf oil (from *Thuja occidentalis*) ranges from −5° to −14°. At 70° to 80° F. 1 vol. of oil is clearly soluble in 3 to 4 vol. of 70 per cent alcohol. Temperatures much below this range may cause turbidity; this, however, should clear on warming to 80° F.

Nineteen lots of thuja oil produced experimentally by Risi and Brule[8] in the Province of Quebec exhibited these properties:

	Extreme Limits	*Average*
Specific Gravity at 15°..........	0.9102 to 0.9232	0.9192
Specific Optical Rotation........	−5° 6′ to −16° 18′	−12° 9′
Refractive Index at 20°.........	1.4540 to 1.4687	1.4595
Acid Number.................	0.71 to 1.43	0.96
Ester Number................	14.0 to 69.5	30.2
Saponification Number.........	15.4 to 70.3	31.2
Boiling Range.................	170° to 215°	177° to 207°
Solubility in 90% Alcohol.......	Soluble in from 0.2 to 0.6 vol.; on the average in 0.4 vol.	

Adulteration.—According to Brown,[9] adulteration of cedar leaf oil is not commonly practiced, analytical data revealing a quite remarkable uniformity of quality and composition. However, when sophisticated, the most commonly used adulterants are turpentine oil, pine oil, and kerosene or other petroleum products.

Chemical Composition.—The volatile oil derived from the branches and adherent leaves of *Thuja occidentalis* L. has been investigated by Jahns,[10] Rutovski and Gusseva,[11] and particularly by Wallach,[12] who reported the presence of the following compounds:

d-α-Pinene. In the lowest boiling fraction b. ∼160° (Wallach).

d-α-Thujone. The chief constituent of the oil, identified by Wallach (cf. Vol. II of the present work, p. 423). On prolonged boiling (distillation at atmospheric pressure) thujone is isomerized to carvotanacetone $C_{10}H_{16}O$.

[7] *Drug Cosmetic Ind.* **37** (1935), 587.
[8] *Am. Perfumer* **48** (January 1946), 39.
[9] *Drug Cosmetic Ind.* **37** (1935), 587.
[10] *Arch. Pharm.* **221** (1883), 749, footnote.
[11] *Riechstoff Ind.* (1927), 185. Cf. *Perfumery Essential Oil Record* **19** (1928), 391.
[12] *Liebigs Ann.* **272** (1893), 99; **275** (1893), 182; **279** (1894), 384; **353** (1907), 213.

l-Fenchone. In the fraction b. 190°–200° of the oil; also identified by Wallach (cf. Vol. II of this work, p. 418).

l-Borneol, Free or as Ester. In his work on *l*-fenchone isolated from thuja oil, Wallach first noted the presence of *l*-camphor. A renewed investigation of the oil, however, convinced Wallach that the oil contains no *l*-camphor but *l*-borneol, either in free or in esterified form. (The *l*-camphor earlier observed was not a natural constituent of the oil but an artifact, obtained by oxidation of *l*-borneol in the course of the usual isolation of *l*-fenchone through oxidative means.)

Acids. More recently Rutovski and Gusseva found *acetic acid* and *isovaleric acid* in the saponification products of a thuja oil.

The first runs of the oil contain *formic acid* and acetic acid.

Use.—Oil of thuja is no longer used in any official medicinal preparation. Formerly it was employed externally as a mild counterirritant and internally as a heart stimulant. Because of its content of thujone and fenchone, the action of thuja oil is similar to that of camphor.

At present the oil is used chiefly as a constituent in pine and cedar blends for the scenting of technical preparations, room sprays, and deodorants of the wick type.

OIL OF THUJA WOOD
("White Cedarwood Oil")

The volatile oil derived from the wood of *Thuja occidentalis* L., the "Eastern White Cedar," or "Northern White Cedar" (see above), is not a commercial product. A sample of "White Cedar Oil" examined by Schimmel & Co.[13] closely resembled the oil distilled from the wood of the *red* cedar, *Juniperus virginiana* L., large quantities of which are produced in the southeastern part of the United States (cf. monograph on "Oil of Cedarwood"). The oil described by Schimmel & Co. had a slightly balsamic odor and exhibited these properties:

Specific Gravity at 15°..............	0.9500
Optical Rotation...................	−22° 6'
Refractive Index at 20°.............	1.50790
Acid Number.....................	0.9
Ester Number....................	4.1
Ester Number after Acetylation......	29.9
Solubility.......................	Soluble in about 9 to 10 vol. of 90% alcohol. Clearly miscible in 0.5 vol. of 95% alcohol; turbid and separation of oil on addition of more alcohol; again clearly and permanently soluble in 3.5 vol. and more of 95% alcohol

On distillation at atmospheric pressure the following fractions were obtained:

[13] Gildemeister and Hoffmann, "Die Ätherischen Öle," 3d Ed., Vol. II, 241.

Per Cent

265° to 270°.........	24
270° to 275°.........	42
275° to 280°.........	12
280° to 290°.........	14
Residue.............	8

Some years ago, a firm in Norfolk, Virginia, started to produce oil from the wood of *Thuja occidentalis* L. on a commercial scale, but soon afterward was forced to cease operation, owing to a dearth of wood and to high prices. With the outbreak of World War II, however, a great number of white cedar trees were employed in the construction of ships for the United States Navy. Large quantities of wood shavings and sawdust became available and distillation of oil from the wood was resumed in Norfolk.

Two types of oil were offered on the market, viz., the so-called "Oil of White Cedarwood, Single Distilled," and "Oil of White Cedarwood, Redistilled." Two samples examined in the laboratories of Fritzsche Brothers, Inc., New York, had these properties:

	Single Distilled Oil	*Redistilled Oil*
Specific Gravity at 15°/15°........	0.966	0.961
Optical Rotation.................	−7° 22′	−9° 42′
Refractive Index at 20°...........	1.5085	1.5068
Saponification Number............	9.5	6.9
Cedrol Content..................	37.2%	31.2%
Solubility in 90% Alcohol at 20°...	Soluble in 1 vol., cloudy in 1.5 vol., again soluble in 4.5 to 5 vol. and more	Faintly opalescent in 7 vol. Soluble in 0.5 vol. and more of 95% alcohol

These values differ considerably from those of the oil derived from *red* cedarwood, *Juniperus virginiana* L. The odor of the oils distilled from the white cedarwood was quite pleasant.

In late years the oil seems to have disappeared from the market, or is produced in small quantities only.

OIL OF *THUJA PLICATA* D. DON

On steam distillation of the heartwood of *Thuja plicata* D. Don (fam. *Cupressaceae*), the so-called "Western Red Cedar," Erdtman and Gripenberg [1] obtained a volatile oil, from which they isolated dehydroperillic acid $C_{10}H_{12}O_2$, and a highly poisonous ketone $C_{10}H_{12}O_2$, viz., γ-thujaplicin m. 82°.

Dehydroperillic acid has the following formula:

The structure of γ-thujaplicin is perhaps

According to Gripenberg,[2] α-, β-, and γ-thujaplicin are unsaturated ketones occurring in the heartwood of various coniferous trees, and perhaps responsible for the resistance of the wood of these trees against rot.

α-Thujaplicin m. 34° occurs only in trees grown in Sweden, the β-isomer m. 52°–52.5° only in trees grown in the United States, and the γ-isomer m. 82° in trees grown in both countries. α-Thujaplicin has been synthesized by

[1] *Nature* **161** (1948), 719. *Chem. Abstracts* **42** (1948), 6772.
[2] *Acta Chem. Scand.* **2** (1948), 625, 639, 644. Cf. *Angewandte Chemie* **62** (1950), 158.

Nozoe, Kitahara, and Ito.[3]   All three isomers were synthesized in 1951 by Cook, Raphael and Scott.[4]

Dehydroperillic acid was first isolated (and named) from the heartwood of the American "Western Red Cedar" by Anderson and Sherrard.[5]   Recently, Kurth [6] noted the presence of the methyl ester of dehydroperillic acid in the heartwood of the American tree.   The ester forms clear, water-white crystals, m. 34.5°–35°, and is highly fragrant.

OIL OF CYPRESS

Essence de Cyprès   *Aceite Esencial Cipres*   *Cypressenöl*
Oleum Cupressi

Of all *Cupressus* species the most important one is *Cupressus semper-virens* L. var. *stricta* Ait. (fam. *Cupressaceae*), the well-known columnar, so-called "Italian" cypress.   It has been known in Mediterranean countries since antiquity.   The Greeks and Romans planted it on temple and burial grounds, and even today the tree is associated with parks and cemeteries in temperate countries.   It is a tree of serene beauty, blending well into the Mediterranean landscape; its dark foliage contrasts with the lucid sky, and etches delicate silhouettes against the blue sea.

Formerly this cypress was classified as *Cupressus sempervirens* var. *pyra-midalis* Nymann, *C.s.* var. *fastigiata* Hansen, *C. fastigiata* DC., or simply as *C. sempervirens* L.   It must not be confused with the more broadly pyramidal variety, viz., *Cupressus sempervirens* var. *horizontalis* (Mill.) Gord.   The latter is also frequently grown in Mediterranean and other warm countries, often side by side with the var. *stricta,* but it yields an essential oil quite inferior to that of the var. *stricta* (see below).

Large stands of *Cupressus sempervirens* var. *stricta* Ait. are found in Algeria (North Africa), and in a section called "La Crau," between Salon and Arles, in Provence (Southern France).   Here the trees have been planted for a long time to protect fields against the *mistral,* a strong and cold north wind which descends the Rhône Valley occasionally, and may do great damage to crops.   However, var. *horizontalis* is a quicker growing tree than var. *stricta,* for which reason the farmers now prefer to plant the

[3] *Proc. Japan. Acad.* **26**, No. 7 (1950), 47.   Cf. *Science of Drugs* (Japan) **3** (1949), 172. *Chem. Abstracts* **45** (1951), 7099.

[4] *J. Chem. Soc.* (1951), 695.   [6] *Ibid.* **72** (1950), 5778.

[5] *J. Am. Chem. Soc.* **55** (1933), 3813.

former variety, and the number of the latter is gradually diminishing. The trees of the variety *stricta* still existing in "La Crau"—and there are many left—have now attained an age of fifty or sixty, and even one hundred, years. Every four or five years their tops must be pruned to prevent them from growing too high, which would expose the trees to the danger of uprooting under the heavy blows of the *mistral*. The pruning is usually done from mid-October to April. The terminal branches and leaves thus obtained are sold to distillers. There is a distillery in Noves (between Avignon and Salon) specializing in the local production of cypress oil; the plant material has also been trucked to Grasse (A.M.) for distillation, obviously a costly procedure. When purchasing terminal branches and leaves, the distillers have to guard against admixed material from the var. *horizontalis*, which is pruned by the farmers at the same time, and which yields a poor quality of oil.

Distillation, Yield, and Quality of Oil.—The yield, quality, and physicochemical properties of the oil depend upon the condition of the plant material, and the method and length of distillation. Only terminal (young) branches and adherent leaves of var. *stricta* should be used. All species of *Cupressus* other than *sempervirens,* and all varieties of the latter species other than *stricta* yield essential oils, the odor, physicochemical properties and chemical composition of which differ widely from those of *C. sempervirens* var. *stricta.* Several attempts have been made to produce so-called cypress oils in other parts of the world, in Central America for example, but none of these oils can be compared with the true cypress oil, derived from the leaves of the "Italian Cypress."

Woody branches should be eliminated from the distillation material. Distilling the wood of *Cupressus sempervirens* L., Chiris[1] obtained an oil with physicochemical properties (d_{15} 0.9538, α_D + 5° 32', n_D 1.4995, acid number 1.4, ester number 23.15, ester number after acetylation 40.68, soluble in 2 vol. of 85 per cent alcohol) which differed substantially from those of the leaf oil.

Pigulevski and Fichtenholz[2] found that the age of the branches influences the properties and composition of the oil. Young branches yield an oil with a lower specific gravity and higher optical rotation than those of the oil from old branches.

The yield of oil from fresh terminal branches and leaves averages 0.2 per cent; it may be higher from dried material.

The quality of the oil depends to a great extent upon the length of distillation or steam pressure used. To obtain a high grade oil, a charge of 600 kg. should be distilled, with direct steam of low pressure, for not less than 17 hr. With steam of higher pressure, the time may be shortened.

[1] *Parfums France* **14** (1936), 103.   [2] *J. Russ. Phys. Chem. Soc.* **51** (1919), 87.

but then care must be exercised not to impair the odor of the oil. Oil of cypress owes its merits (medicinal properties, ambergris-like odor of the evaporation residue, and fixative value) primarily to the high boiling constituents, but these are not easily volatile and can be recovered only by very long distillation. With a charge of 600 kg. of plant material in the still, about one-half of the oil will distill over within the first 3 hr. Then the rate of distillation decreases, and toward the end only about 30 g. of high boiling fractions will distill over per hour. These fractions, however, contain the most valuable components. The specific gravity of the fractions increases as distillation proceeds; for example:

Hours of Distillation	Specific Gravity at 15°
1 to 3	0.870
3 to 10	0.876
10 to 13	0.880
13 to 15	0.885
15 to 17	0.890

The complete oil obtained in this case had a specific gravity of 0.877 at 15°.

The specific gravity of the oils produced in spring is usually lower than that of the late fall or winter oils, because in spring the branches contain many new shoots and leaves.

Physicochemical Properties.—The volatile oil derived from the young branches and adherent leaves of *Cupressus sempervirens* var. *stricta* Ait. is a yellowish liquid with an odor characteristic of the leaves themselves. On evaporation on a test paper, the originally terpene-like odor of the oil changes to a most pleasant, lasting ambergris- and labdanum-like note.

According to Gildemeister and Hoffmann [3] the oils formerly (but no longer) produced in Germany exhibited a higher specific gravity and a lower optical rotation than the French and Algerian oils.

Gildemeister and Hoffmann [4] reported the following properties for cypress oils from Germany (I), France (II), and Algeria (III):

	I	II	III
Specific Gravity at 15°	0.88 to 0.90	0.868 to 0.884	0.8696 to 0.8835
Optical Rotation	+4° 0′ to +18° 0′	+7° 30′ to +31° 0′	+22° 18′ to +31° 0′
Refractive Index at 20°	1.474 to 1.480	1.471 to 1.476	1.46974 to 1.47593
Acid Number	1.5 to 4.0	Up to 2	Up to 0.8
Ester Number	13 to 22	3 to 17	11 to 32

[3] "Die Ätherischen Öle," 3d Ed., Vol. II, 246.
[4] *Ibid.*

	I	II	III
Ester Number after Acetylation.	27 to 51	9 to 32	16.8 to 35.5
Solubility in 90% Alcohol	Soluble in 2 to 7 vol. and more, occasionally with slight turbidity	Soluble in 4 to 7 vol., occasionally with slight turbidity	Soluble in 6 to 8 vol., eventually with slight turbidity. Not clearly soluble in 10 vol.

Genuine oils of cypress produced in Southern France, and examined by Fritzsche Brothers, Inc., New York, had properties varying within these limits:

Specific Gravity at 15°/15°...... 0.870 to 0.891, old oils as high as 0.907
Optical Rotation............... +4° 32' to +29° 20'
Refractive Index............... 1.4740 to 1.4821
Saponification Number.......... 5.1 to 19.6
Solubility..................... Soluble in 5.5 to 10 vol. of 90% alcohol.
Sometimes turbid in 10 vol.

Chemical Composition.—The chemical composition of the volatile oil derived from the young branches and adherent leaves of *Cupressus sempervirens* var. *stricta* Ait. has been investigated by Schimmel & Co.[5] who reported the presence of the compounds listed below. The oil examined contained 8.8 per cent of esters, calculated as $C_{10}H_{17}OCOCH_3$, and 14.8 per cent of alcohols, calculated as $C_{10}H_{18}O$.

Furfural. In the very first portions of the distillate.

d-α-Pinene. Identified by means of the nitrosochloride m. 102°–103°, and the nitrolbenzylamine compound m. 122°–123°, and m. 124°.

d-Camphene. In the fraction b. 160°–170°, which is the principal fraction of the oil. Conversion to isoborneol m. 206°–207°.

Fenchene(?). Schimmel & Co. concluded from the moldy odor of the isoborneol obtained from *d*-camphene that the original oil also contains fenchene.

d-Sylvestrene(?) and Carene. The hydrocarbon isolated by means of its dihydrochloride m. 72° and bromide m. 134°–135° was most probably not sylvestrene, but Δ³- or Δ⁴-carene (cf. Vol. II of this work, pp. 32, 49 and 51).

p-Cymene. Small quantities only. Oxidation to *p*-hydroxypropylbenzoic acid m. 155°–156°. Propenylbenzoic acid m. 160°–161°.

A Ketone(?). The fraction b_{3-4} 80°–90° contained a ketone which yielded a semicarbazone m. 177°–178°, but which was not identified. The odor of the ketone in question resembled that of menthone or thujone.

[5] *Ber. Schimmel & Co.*, October (1894), 71; April (1903), 23; April (1904), 32; October (1904), 19; April (1910), 36; April (1913), 44.

Sabinol(?). In one of their earlier investigations Schimmel & Co.[6] arrived at the conclusion that the oil contains sabinol. Later research,[7] however, did not confirm this.

1-Terpinen-4-ol. Identified in the course of the last-mentioned investigation.

An Alcohol $C_{10}H_{18}O$(?). After purification through its benzoate and phthalate, the alcohol in question had these properties: b. 210°–212°, b_{4-5} 76°–77°, d_{15} 0.9422, α_D +43° 38′, n_D^{20} 1.46678. The odor was pleasant, reminiscent of rose and borneol.

Esters of *d-α-Terpineol*. The *d-α*-terpineol b. 35°, α_D +36° 32′ was identified by preparation of its phenylurethane m. 112°. The fraction of the oil b_4 96°–98° contained 66.85 per cent of esters, calculated as $C_{10}H_{17}OCOCH_3$. The acids forming the terpinyl esters were *acetic acid, valeric acid*, and an acid b. 210°–260°, m. 129°. The oil did not contain any terpineol in free form.

l-Cadinene. Identified in the high boiling fractions; dihydrochloride m. 117°–118°.

Cedrol ("Cypress Camphor"). The fractions b_5 above 135° contained cedrol, which was isolated in pure and odorless form by repeated recrystallization from dilute alcohol and petroleum ether.

Prior to its identification as cedrol, the substance, which can be isolated by freezing of the high boiling fractions, was called "Cypress Camphor."

A Sesquiterpene Alcohol(?). In addition to cadinene and cedrol, the high boiling fractions contain a liquid sesquiterpene alcohol $C_{15}H_{26}O$; b_{4-5} 136°–138°. It is probably the carrier of the characteristic ambergris- and labdanum-like odor of the evaporation residue of the oil. The alcohol has not yet been identified. Schimmel & Co. did not obtain any characteristic derivatives.

In the distillation waters of the oil, Schimmel & Co. noted the presence of *methyl alcohol, diacetyl* and *furfural*.

Use.—Oil of cypress is a valuable perfumery material, useful particularly in compositions of the chypre type. By removal of most of the terpenes a concentrated oil can be obtained in which the ambergris- and labdanum-like odor of the high boiling fractions becomes predominant.

For years the oil has been employed to alleviate the temporary distressing effects of whooping cough on children.[8] For this purpose a 25 per cent alcoholic solution of the oil should be dropped four times daily on the bed linen, pillowcases, and underwear of children afflicted with this disease. The number, length, and intensity of the cough paroxysms are thereby greatly diminished.

SUGGESTED ADDITIONAL LITERATURE

M. Fesneau, "Etude du Cyprès Sempervirens Espagnol," *Ind. parfum.* **6** (1951), 60.

[6] *Ibid.*, April (1904), 34.

[7] *Ibid.*, April (1913), 44.

[8] Soltmann, "Keuchhusten und Cypressenöl," *Therapie der Gegenwart*, March (1904). Cf. Winterseel, "Das Cypressenöl," Inaug.-Dissert. med. Fakultät., Bonn (1908).

(*Left*) Naval Stores Industry in the United States. Stump-pulling machine (Yoke, U. S. Patent) removing a pine stump from the ground. (*Right*) Aerial view of Hercules Powder Company Naval Stores Plant, Brunswick, Georgia. Note reserve wood in lower right corner. From left to right: extractor house, power house, millroom, and reserve supply of stump wood. *Photos Hercules Powder Company, Wilmington, Delaware.*

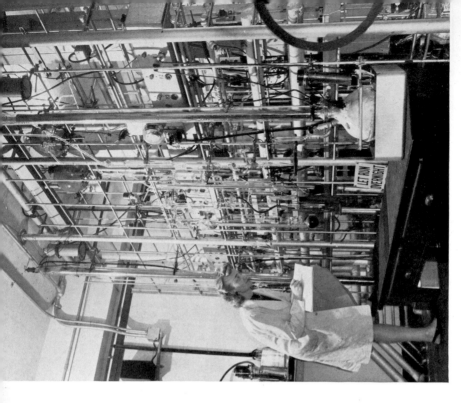

(*Left*) Production of turpentine oil. Continuous still for distillation of pine oleoresin, designed and developed by the Naval Stores Research Division, U. S. Dept. of Agriculture. Picture shows the condenser, heat exchanger, continuous still, turpentine separator, rosin drums and gum washing tanks. (*Right*) Distillation laboratory of the Naval Stores Research Division. Used for

OIL OF *CUPRESSUS LUSITANICA* MILL.

Cupressus lusitanica Mill. (syn. *C. glauca* Lamb., *C. pendula* l'Hérit., or *C. sinensis* hort.), fam. *Cupressaceae,* the so-called "Portuguese Cypress," is grown in gardens and parks of the Iberian Peninsula, Italy and Southern France. Some years ago the tree was introduced to Kenya Colony in East Africa for the purpose of reforestation. In 1937, when the author visited Kenya Colony, about 12,000 acres near N'joro, on the slopes of the great Rift Valley, had been planted with *Cupressus lusitanica* Mill. At that time the acreage was being increased every year by about 300 acres. The young trees have to be trimmed annually until they are about fifteen years old, when they have grown so tall that the branches can no longer be reached easily.

At the time of the author's visit there was a distillery near N'joro specializing in the production of essential oil from the terminal branches and leaves (trimmings) of *Cupressus lusitanica.* Distillation of one charge required about 5 hr. The yield of oil averaged 0.1 per cent.

Physicochemical Properties.—Oil of *Cupressus lusitanica* Mill. is a light colored liquid with an odor somewhat reminiscent of oil of *Pinus mugo* Turra, but sharper.

An oil procured by the author in N'joro (I), and another oil from Kenya examined by Sfiras [1] (II) had these properties:

	I	II
Specific Gravity at 15°..............	0.878	0.8750
Optical Rotation....................	+24° 10′	+22° 40′
Refractive Index at 20°.............	1.4762	1.4788
Acid Number......................	0	0.5
Ester Number.....................	22.9	20.9
Ester Number after Acetylation.....	48.8	50.9
Solubility in 90% Alcohol..........	Hazy in	Soluble in
	10 vol.	4.5 vol.

Chemical Composition.—Sfiras [2] investigated his oil for its chemical composition, and reported the presence of the following compounds:

Terpenes and Aromatic
Hydrocarbons (ca. 70%) α-Pinene (chiefly)
Δ³-Carene
d-Limonene
Myrcene (small quantities)

[1] *Roure-Bertrand Fils, Recherches* **2** (1938), 17, 111; **3** (1939), 115.
[2] *Ibid.*

p-Cymene
Camphene
α-Terpinene
α- or β-Phellandrene
Sabinene
Terpenes with two double bonds (not identified)

Sesquiterpenes (ca. 10%).. Two dextrorotatory sesquiterpenes(?), one of them containing one double bond
A laevorotatory sesquiterpene(?)

Alcohols (ca. 12%)........ Borneol
Citronellol
1-Terpinen-4-ol
An unidentified alcohol which amounts to 80 per cent of the alcohol fraction
(About 50 per cent of the above-listed alcohols occur in the oil in free form; the balance esterified with formic, acetic, propionic(?), and caproic acids)
3-Octanol, present as formate or acetate
α-Terpineol, in free form
An unidentified secondary alcohol b_{10} 90°–93°, d_{15}^{15} 0.8849, n_D^{20} 1.4647
A secondary sesquiterpene alcohol(?)
A tertiary sesquiterpene alcohol(?)

Ketones (ca. 5%)......... Umbellulone (chiefly)
Two sesquiterpene ketones(?)

Use.—Oil of *Cupressus lusitanica* Mill. has been recommended as an adjunct in the scenting of soaps, room sprays, deodorants, and many technical preparations.

OIL OF CYPRESS FROM GUATEMALA

About 1940 Guatemala (C.A.) started to produce cypress oil, and limited quantities have occasionally been offered on the North American market. However, it is not known from which species of *Cupressus* these oils are obtained. Several samples of so-called Guatemala cypress oil have been examined in the laboratories of Fritzsche Brothers, Inc., New York. The properties of these oils varied within the following limits:

Specific Gravity at 15°/15°...... 0.875 to 0.886
Optical Rotation............... +10° 43′ to +14° 50′

Refractive Index at 20°......... 1.4764 to 1.4786
Saponification Number........... 15.1 to 36.4
Solubility...................... Hazy to turbid in 10 vol.
                              of 90% alcohol

The odor of these oils was very different from that of the true French cypress distillates, the Guatemalan samples showing a distinct umbellulone by-note. In one sample the ketone content, calculated as umbellulone, determined by the hydroxylamine hydrochloride method was found to be 2 per cent.

A sample of cypress oil produced in California, also from an undefined botanical species, was found to be of the same abnormal type. The umbellulone content in this case was found to be 6.1 per cent.

OIL OF *CUPRESSUS MACROCARPA* GORD.

The so-called "Monterey Cypress," *Cupressus macrocarpa* Gord. (syn. *C. lambertiana* Carr.), fam. *Cupressaceae,* has probably the most restricted range of any conifer; it grows naturally as an endemic plant only around Monterey Bay (Cypress Point) and on the island of Guadeloupe. At Monterey the main grove occupies an area only two miles long and two hundred yards wide. The cypress occurring in Guadeloupe has been classified as var. *guadalupensis* (Watkins) Masters.

The tree has been introduced into many parts of the world, including the Riviera and New Zealand, where it is grown extensively as an ornamental plant.

The leaves and terminal branchlets contain an essential oil which has been produced experimentally by Schimmel & Co.[1] (I), and more recently by Briggs and Sutherland[2] (II). The yield of oil was 0.1 and 0.2 per cent, respectively. The oils had the following properties:

	I	II
Specific Gravity....................	d_{15} 0.8656	d_4^{25} 0.8607
Optical Rotation....................	α_D +31° 53′	$[\alpha]_D^{25}$ +11° 19′
Refractive Index at 25°..............	...	1.4718
Acid Number.......................	1.5	1.0
Ester Number......................	13.9	0.4
Ester Number after Acetylation.......	50.82	33.7

[1] *Ber. Schimmel & Co.,* April (1905), 84.
[2] *J. Org. Chem.* **7** (1942), 397.

Briggs and Sutherland reported these compounds as constituents of the oil:

Terpenes............ α-Pinene (40%)
Sabinene (15%)
Myrcene (3%)
α-Phellandrene (4%)
α-Terpinene(?)
γ-Terpinene and Terpinolene (6%)
Unidentified Terpenes (12%)

Alcohols............ *d*-Terpinen-4-ol (8.8%)
Unidentified Alcohol b_{10} ~100° (0.8%)
Macrocarpol (0.1%)

Ester............... Unidentified Ester b_{10} ~110° (0.5%)

Acids, Aldehydes,
Ketones........... (Traces)

Sesquiterpenes....... Unidentified
(a) b_{10} 115°–117°
(b) b_{10} 120°–121°
(c) b_{10} 124°–127° (0.7%)

Diterpenes.......... Isophyllocladene (3.5%)
Cupressene (0.1%)

Other Compounds,
including Residue.. (5.5%)

(Regarding macrocarpol, cupressene, and isophyllocladene, see Vol. II of this work, p. 761, and the Table of Diterpenes, opposite p. 126.)

The oil is not produced on a commercial scale.

OIL OF *CUPRESSUS TORULOSA* D. DON

Steam-distilling the leaves of *Cupressus torulosa* D. Don (fam. *Cupressaceae*), the so-called "Himalaya Cypress," Simonsen [1] obtained from 0.5 to 0.8 per cent of a light brown oil with a pleasant odor and these properties:

Specific Gravity at 30°/30°.................. 0.87
Specific Optical Rotation at 30°.............. +41° 43′
Refractive Index at 30°..................... 1.479

[1] *Indian Forest Records* **10** (1923), 1.

Acid Number............................. 0.68
Saponification Number.................... 10.71
Saponification Number after Acetylation...... 41.4

Simonsen [2] identified the following compounds as constituents of the oil:

α-Pinene

d-Sabinene

Dipentene

Terpinene

γ-Terpineol........................ Presence probable, in small quantities

1-Terpinen-4-ol (1-*p*-Menthen-4-ol)...... Presence probable, in small quantities

A Sesquiterpene(?).................... $C_{15}H_{24}$, b_{100} 195°–200°, d_{30}^{30} 0.9162, $[\alpha]_D^{30}$ −15° 54', n_D^{30} 1.507

A Sesquiterpene Alcohol(?)............. $C_{15}H_{26}O$, b_{100} 205°–220°, d_{30}^{30} 0.9419, $[\alpha]_D^{30}$ −19° 12', n_D^{30} 1.506

Propionic, Caproic, and Lauric Acids.... Free and in esterified form

Use.—According to the author's knowledge the oil is not produced on a commercial scale.

OIL OF *CHAMAECYPARIS OBTUSA* (SIEB. ET ZUCC.) ENDL.
("Oil of Hinoki")

Occurrence, Botany, and Production.—The Japanese "Hinoki" tree supplies a white wood which, like that of certain pines, and of "Sugi" (*Cryptomeria japonica* [L.f.] D. Don, fam. *Taxodiaceae*), ranks high in general utility. Hinoki wood, in particular, has been valued since antiquity for the building of temples, and the making of lacquered furniture and ornaments.

The hinoki tree grows wild and abundantly in Japan and Formosa, forming vast forests in some sections. Natural hinoki forests cover the mountainous parts of central and southern Japan (chiefly in the Kiso mountain range of Japan's main island), and of the Province of Tosa on Shikoku

[2] *Ibid.*

Island. In such areas the trees are also planted regularly, following a strict plan of reforestation. On the island of Formosa hinoki trees grow thickly in the central mountain ranges, particularly around Mt. Ari (Tainan Prefecture), Mt. Hassen (Taichun Prefecture), and Mt. Taihei (Taihoku Prefecture).

Morphologically, the hinoki tree of Japan differs slightly from that of Formosa. The former has been classified as *Chamaecyparis obtusa* (Sieb. et Zucc.) Endl., fam. *Cupressaceae*—"Hinoki" in Japanese. The Formosan tree has been classified as *Chamaecyparis obtusa* (Sieb. et Zucc.) Endl., forma *formosana* Hayata, or *Chamaecyparis taiwanensis* Masamune et Suzuki. In Japanese the Formosan tree is known as "Arisan Hinoki." Occidental literature frequently refers to the Japanese and Formosan hinoki trees by the general colloquial term "Japanese Cedar" or "Japanese Cypress."

The wood and the leaves of the hinoki tree contain an essential oil which can be isolated by steam distillation; however, the wood oil differs substantially from the leaf oil in odor, physicochemical properties and chemical composition. Of the two oils the wood oil is by far the more important as regards technical usefulness and quantity produced. Actually it is obtained not from the trunk wood, but from old stumps and roots extracted from the ground thirty to fifty years after the trees have been felled.

According to Hiraizumi,[1] production of hinoki root oil closely resembles that of sugi oil (cf. the monograph on "Oil of *Cryptomeria japonica* [L.f.] D. Don," p. 312), except that in the case of the lower boiling hinoki oil distillation can be carried out in one step, without interruption. The yield of oil ranges from 2 to 5 per cent in the old-fashioned barrel stills ("Koshiki"). In Japan, centers of production lie in the Prefecture of Kochi on Shikoku Island, and in the Prefecture of Wakayama (chiefly in the section around Mt. Koya). In the latter region the roots are now processed in modern steam stills with a steam pressure of 5 to 6 atm. Under these conditions, the yield of oil ranges from 3 to 10 per cent.

Total production of hinoki root oil in Japan at present varies from 120 to 150 metric tons per year. Prior to World War II practically all hinoki root oil came from Formosa, which then supplied from 300 to 500 metric tons yearly. However, since the war, production in Formosa has decreased to less than 200 tons per year; this decline, in turn, has greatly stimulated production in Japan, with the result that distillation of the oil has lately become quite popular in the lumber industry.

Hinoki *leaf* oil is produced by only a few distillers, and in small quanti-

---

[1] The author is greatly indebted to Dr. Teikichi Hiraizumi, Tokyo, for most of the information contained in this monograph.

ties only; the total output in Japan at present amounts to not more than about 6 metric tons per year.

Hinoki *root* oils from Japan and Formosa are so similar that more than a routine analysis is required to differentiate between the two types. In prewar years, hinoki root oil was supplied almost exclusively by Formosa. Hence most of the chemical investigations carried out by Japanese researchers were based upon Formosan oil, and the oil produced now in Japan has not yet been as thoroughly investigated as the Formosan oil. Reliable analytical methods of distinguishing between the two types of oil have not yet been developed. The color of the Japanese hinoki root oil is usually lighter than that of the Formosan oil, the latter being reddish-brown.

I. HINOKI ROOT OIL

A. Japanese Hinoki Root Oil

Physicochemical Properties.—The volatile oil obtained by steam distillation of hinoki roots is a light yellow liquid with a camphoraceous odor. An oil examined by Fritzsche Brothers, Inc., had these properties:

Specific Gravity at 15°/15°........ 0.899
Optical Rotation................. +35° 12'
Refractive Index at 20°.......... 1.4823
Acid Number.................... 0
Ester Number................... 4.9
Ester Content, Calculated as Bornyl
    Acetate..................... 1.7%
Ester Number after Acetylation.... 47.0
Solubility at 20°................. Slightly hazy in 10 vol. of 90%
    alcohol. Soluble in 0.5 vol.
    and more of 95% alcohol

The odor of the oil indicated the presence of terpineol and borneol. The odor was also reminiscent of that of certain "camphor-sassafras" fractions derived from natural camphor oil.

The properties of hinoki root oils analyzed by Schimmel & Co.[2] varied within the following limits:

Specific Gravity at 15°.............. 0.8980 to 0.9090
Optical Rotation................... +38° 54' to +43° 37'
Refractive Index at 20°............. 1.47642 to 1.47926
Acid Number...................... Up to 1.9
Ester Number..................... 9.3 to 18.7
Alcohol Content, Calculated as $C_{10}H_{18}O$
    (Acetylation in Xylene Solution,
    1 + 4).......................... 23.4 to 36.6%

[2] *Ber. Schimmel & Co.* (1928), 51.

Solubility........................ From 0.3 to 4.1 vol. of 90% alcohol are required for solution;
not soluble in 80% alcohol up
to 10 vol.

Boiling Range at 754 mm.:
160° to 170°.................... 30%
170° to 180°.................... 22%
180° to 200°.................... 12%
200° to 250°.................... 14%
250° to 285°.................... 12%
Residue........................ 10%

From these figures it appears that the root oil contains more high boiling constituents than the leaf oil.

Hirao[3] studied a hinoki root oil distilled in Tosa Province and noted these properties:

Specific Gravity at 25°/4°........... 0.8903
Specific Optical Rotation........... +40° 0'
Refractive Index at 25°............. 1.4806
Acid Number...................... 0.93
Ester Number..................... 6
Ester Number after Acetylation...... 76.62
Boiling Range at atm. pr.:
155° to 160°.................... 23.4%
160° to 175°.................... 15.3%
175° to 200°.................... 8.6%
200° to 220°.................... 16.8%
220° to 260°.................... 4.8%
260° and above................. 29.5%

Chemical Composition.—In the hinoki root oil he investigated, Hirao[4] established the presence of the following compounds:

Terpenes (about 40%)....... *d-α*-Pinene (chiefly)
Camphene ⎫
Dipentene ⎬ Small amounts
d-Limonene ⎭

Terpene Alcohols (20.46%)[5].. *d-α*-Terpineol (chiefly)
d-Borneol

Sesquiterpenes.............. Cadinene (chiefly) ⎫
⎬ About 30%
Sesquiterpene Alcohols....... Cadinol (chiefly) ⎭

[3] *J. Chem. Soc. Japan* **58** (1937), 222.
[4] *Ibid.*
[5] Calculated from the Ester Number after Actylation of the oil.

B. *Formosan Hinoki Root Oil*

Physicochemical Properties.—Tsuchihashi and Tasaki [6] examined an oil obtained in Formosa by steam distillation of old roots and stumps ("Arisan Honoki"). The oil exhibited these properties:

$$
\begin{array}{ll}
\text{Specific Gravity at } 23° \ldots & 0.8953 \\
\text{Optical Rotation at } 23° \ldots & +42° 16' \\
\text{Refractive Index at } 23° \ldots & 1.4804 \\
\text{Acid Number} \ldots & 3.23 \\
\text{Ester Number} \ldots & 8.31 \\
\text{Ester Number after Acetylation} \ldots & 94.23 \\
\end{array}
$$

Boiling Range at atm. pr.:

160° to 180°	35%
180° to 200°	16%
200° to 220°	7%
220° to 240°	12%
240° to 260°	10%
260° to 285°	13%
Residue	7%

Chemical Composition.—In the oil they investigated, Tsuchihashi and Tasaki [7] identified the following compounds:

d-α-Pinene. About 40 per cent.

d-α-Terpineol and Isoborneol. About 20 per cent of the oil consisted of terpene alcohols; 70 per cent of this amount was *d*-α-terpineol, the balance being iso-borneol.

d-Cadinene. From the sesquiterpene fraction Tsuchihashi and Tasaki isolated 13 per cent of *d*-cadinene, and called attention to the fact that the cadinene present in Japanese hinoki trunk oil is laevorotatory (Kondo [8]).

Chamaecypariol. From their oil, Tsuchihashi and Tasaki also isolated 6 per cent of a bicyclic sesquiterpene alcohol $C_{15}H_{26}O$ (b_6 145°–147°, d_{15}^{30} 0.9693, $[\alpha]_D^{30}$ −40° 44', n_D^{30} 1.5040) to which they assigned the name chamaecypariol.

Formosan hinoki root oil has become of considerable technical importance because of its high content of pinene and terpineol fractions. According to Hirao,[9] the oil has the following composition:

	Per Cent
d-α-Pinene	31
d-α-Terpineol	33
Cadinene	23
Sesquiterpene Alcohols	7

[6] *Rept. Govt. Research Inst. Formosa* I (1920), 119.
[7] *Ibid.*
[8] *J. Pharm. Soc. Japan* (1909), 1297.
[9] *J. Chem. Soc. Japan* **47** (1926), 743; **58** (1937), 222.

Another investigation of Formosan hinoki root oil is that of Nozoe and his collaborators,[10] who isolated the following compounds from the so-called "Arisan Hinoki Oil":

l-Rhodinic Acid (*l*-Citronellic Acid) $C_{10}H_{18}O_2$. B_{15} 144°–146°, α_D^{20} −6° 36′, d_4^{30} 0.9244, n_D^{20} 1.4540 (cf. Vol. II of the present work, p. 586).

Chamenol-A, $C_9H_{12}O$ or $C_{10}H_{14}O$. A new phenolic substance, b_{15} 115°–116°, α_D ±0°, d_4^{20} 0.9802, n_D^{20} 1.5182; nitroso compound m. 152°–153°, phenylurethane m. 109°–110°.

Chamenol-B, $C_9H_{12}O_2$ or $C_{10}H_{14}O_2$. A new phenolic substance, m. 41°–42°, b_{15} 122°–124°; phenylurethane m. 109°–110°, monobenzoate m. 64°–65°.

Hinokitiol, $C_{10}H_{12}O_2$. A new acidic substance, m. 51°–52°, b_{10} 140°–141°, α_D ±0°, d_4^{16} 1.0968, n_D^{16} 1.6136; Fe-complex salt ($C_{30}H_{33}O_6Fe$) m. 251°–252°, color dark red. Hinokitiol is identical with hinokitin.[11]

Nozoe [12] spent several years on the elucidation of the configuration of hinokitiol and finally arrived at the conclusion that it possesses the following structural formula:

In 1948, Erdtman and Gripenberg [13] had isolated three isomers of an acidic substance $C_{10}H_{12}O_2$ from the oil obtained from the trunk of *Thuja plicata* Don. They named these compounds α-, β- and γ-thujaplicin, m. 34°, m. 52°–52.5°, and m. 82°, respectively. Nozoe found that hinokitiol is identical with β-thujaplicin m. 52°–52.5°, and that the structural formula suggested by him for hinokitiol agrees with that proposed by Erdtman and Gripenberg for β-thujaplicin (cf. p. 331 of the present volume).

Hinokitiol has also been identified by Kawamura [14] in the oil obtained by steam distillation of the trunk wood of *Thujopsis dolabrata* Sieb. et Zucc. var. *hondai* Mak. ("Hiba" in Japanese—see the monograph on this oil, p. 323). Note that Hinokitiol has not yet been identified in the volatile oil derived from hinoki trees growing in Japan.

[10] Nozoe, *Bull. Chem. Soc. Japan* **11** (1936), 295. Iinuma, *J. Chem. Soc. Japan* **64** (1943), 742, 901. Nozoe and Katsura, *J. Pharm. Soc. Japan* **64** (1944), 181. *Yakugaku* **3**, No. 2 (1949), 174.

[11] Hirao, *J. Chem. Soc. Japan* **47** (1926), 666.

[12] Lecture before the Meeting of the Tohoku Branch of the Chemical Society of Japan, May (1949).

[13] *Nature* **161** (1948), 719.

[14] *J. Bull. Imp. Forest Expt. Sta.* (Japan) **30** (1930), 59.

Recently *l*-rhodinic acid and hinokitiol have been investigated in regard to their medicinal properties. It has been found that hinokitiol in particular possesses bactericidal and bacteriostatic action on tuberculosis bacilli *in vitro* and bacteriostatic action in slide cell cultures. In this regard hinokitiol is more powerful than the strongest of normal fatty acids, viz., capric and lauric acids, whereas *l*-rhodinic acid is less potent than these two fatty acids (Katsura).[15]

II. Hinoki Trunk Oil

Years ago Kondo [16] studied a volatile oil distilled from the trunk wood of hinoki trees growing in the Kiso district (yield 1 per cent) and noted these properties:

Specific Gravity at 23°.............. 0.9307
Specific Optical Rotation........... +11° 28′
Acid Number..................... 0
Ester Number..................... 16.8
Ester Number after Acetylation...... 39.2

Fractionation of the oil yielded:

(1) b_{20} 80°–130°, small quantity.
(2) b_{17-20} 131°–159°, 40 per cent.
(3) b_{15} 160°–170°, 36 per cent.
(4) b_{15} 171°–185°, 18 per cent.

Kondo [17] arrived at the conclusion that the chief component of fractions (2) and (3) was *l*-cadinene, b. 272°–273°, $[\alpha]_D$ −96° 33′, d_{20} 0.9165.

III. Hinoki Leaf Oil

A. Japanese Hinoki Leaf Oil

Physicochemical Properties.—The oil distilled from the leaves of the hinoki tree is a liquid of low boiling point, and with an odor reminiscent of savin or thuja oil.

Examining an oil distilled from Japanese hinoki leaves (yield 1.16 per cent), S. Uchida [18] noted these properties:

Specific Gravity at 12.5°/4°......... 0.9053
Optical Rotation.................. +41° 16′

---

[15] *Medical Time,* **3,** No. 10 (August 1948), 29.
[16] *J. Pharm. Soc. Japan* **29** (1909), 1297.
[17] *Ibid.*
[18] *J. Soc. Chem. Ind. Japan* **31** (1928), 650. Cf. *ibid., Suppl. Binding,* 159 B.

Refractive Index at 12.5°............ 1.4794
Acid Number..................... 0.60
Ester Number.................... 75.37
Ester Number after Acetylation...... 100.20

After separation of the acidic and phenolic substances, Uchida obtained the following fractions from the neutral part of his hinoki leaf oil:

b_{15}	Per Cent
45° to 85°.......	42.3
85° to 135°......	31.4
135° to 170°......	16.6
170° to 180°......	2.8

A commercial sample of hinoki leaf oil analyzed by Fritzsche Brothers, Inc., New York, exhibited these properties:

Specific Gravity at 15°/15°........ 0.898
Optical Rotation................. +39° 27'
Refractive Index at 20°........... 1.4768
Acid Number.................... 0
Ester Number................... 65.4
Ester Content, Calculated as Bornyl
  Acetate....................... 22.9%
Ester Number after Acetylation.... 116.0
Solubility at 20°................. Not completely soluble in 80% alcohol. Soluble in 0.5 vol. and more of 90% alcohol

The odor of the oil was strong, in general reminiscent of terpenes and sesquiterpenes.

Chemical Composition.—Uchida [19] isolated the following compounds from the oil:

Hinoki Acid $C_{14}H_{23}COOH$. A new crystalline acid m. 166°.

Terpenes (about 40%). Chiefly *d*-limonene and *d*-α-pinene.

Terpene Alcohols and Esters. Chiefly *d*-borneol and its acetate and nonylate. Uchida found 25 per cent of bornyl acetate and a very small amount of bornyl nonylate. The laboratories of the Takasago Chemical Industry Company,[20] on the other hand, noted that this fraction contained 12 per cent of *d*-bornyl acetate and 12 per cent of terpinyl acetate.

Cadinene. Also reported by Uchida. Small amount only.

A Sesquiterpene $C_{15}H_{24}$ (about 20%). Tricyclic and laevorotatory, containing one double bond; b. 265°–268°, $[\alpha]_D$ −15° 40′, d_4^{20} 0.9367.

[19] *Ibid.*
[20] Private communication from Dr. Teikichi Hiraizumi, Tokyo. Cf. Moroe and Hara, *J. Pharm. Soc. Japan* **71** (1951), 503. *Chem. Abstracts* **45** (1951), 9223.

A Sesquiterpene Alcohol $C_{15}H_{26}O$ (about 10%). Bicyclic, dextrorotatory, containing one double bond; b. 290°–295°, $[\alpha]_D^{20}$ +18° 0′, d_{15}^{15} 0.9607, n_D^{20} 1.5020.

A Diterpene $C_{20}H_{32}$ (about 5%). Tetracyclic and optically inactive, containing one double bond; b. 340°–343°, d_{15}^{15} 0.9632, n_D^{20} 1.5190.

B. Formosan Hinoki Leaf Oil ("Arisan Hinoki")

Physicochemical Properties.—Kafuku, Nozoe and Hata [21] steam-distilled fresh leaves of the Formosan hinoki tree and obtained 0.3 per cent of an oil with these properties:

Specific Gravity at 25°..............	0.8988
Optical Rotation at 25°..............	−5° 50′
Refractive Index at 25°..............	1.4878
Acid Number......................	0.96
Ester Number.....................	12.63
Ester Number after Acetylation.......	54.81

Chemical Composition.—After removal of the acidic constituents, the neutral part of the oil was fractionated:

b_{50}	Yield, in Per Cent	
40° to 80°...........	34.1	Terpenes
80° to 120°..........	11.4	Terpene Alcohols
120° to 140°.........	40.2	Sesquiterpenes
140° to 160°.........	9.6	Sesquiterpene Alcohols
160° to 180°.........	1.8	Diterpenes
Residue..............	0.4	

From the first fraction Kafuku, Nozoe and Hata [22] isolated a new terpene $C_{10}H_{16}$, viz., *chamene* (cf. Vol. II of the present work, p. 745). The following structural formula was suggested for chamene:

To summarize, the following compounds were isolated from the oil by Kafuku, Nozoe and Hata:

Acids (0.85% of the whole oil). Hinoki acid $C_{15}H_{24}O_2$, m. 165°–166°.

Terpenes (34% of the oil). About 50 per cent of the terpenes consisted of *d*-sabinene, 20–30 per cent of chamene, the balance of *d*-α-pinene, *p*-cymene, α-terpinene, γ-terpinene, α-thujene, and a trace of dipentene.

[21] *Bull. Chem. Soc. Japan* **6** (1931), 40, 111.
[22] *Ibid.*

Terpene Alcohols (11.6% of the whole oil). The terpene alcohol fraction consisted chiefly of *d*-terpinen-4-ol, small amounts of a laevorotatory alcohol $C_8H_{16}O$ and *l*-linalool, both for the most part in esterified form. In addition, traces of borneol were present.

(In this connection it should be noted that the chief constituents of hinoki leaf oil, viz., *d*-sabinene, *d*-chamene, and *d*-terpinen-4-ol, have never been found in Formosan hinoki *root* or *wood* oils. On the other hand, *d*-α-pinene, and α-terpineol, which form the principle constituents of the latter oils, occur in the leaf oil only in very small quantities or not at all.)

Sesquiterpenes (38% of the whole oil). This fraction consisted chiefly of a new tricyclic sesquiterpene, viz., sesquichamene (cf. Vol. II of the present work, p. 749). The balance of the fraction was *d*-cadinene.

Sesquiterpene Alcohols (8% of the oil). This fraction contained a dextrorotatory bicyclic sesquiterpene alcohol and cadinol.

Diterpenes (1% of the whole oil). Consisting chiefly of a laevorotatory tetracyclic diterpene.

Use of Hinoki Root Oil and Leaf Oil

Both hinoki leaf oil and hinoki root oil are employed for the scenting of soaps. The odor of the former is superior to that of the latter.

Hinoki root oil, by far the more important of the two, finds wide application in insecticides; but its most important use is as a mineral flotation oil in the mining industry. Large quantities of Formosan hinoki root oil were formerly employed for this purpose.

Since the root oil contains about 30 per cent of terpineol, it constitutes an excellent base for the isolation of *natural* terpineol and for the preparation of terpinyl acetate. By careful rectification, these compounds can be obtained in a high state of purity. The terpenic fractions of the root oil serve as industrial solvents, and for the manufacture of synthetic terpineol.

OIL OF *CHAMAECYPARIS LAWSONIANA* A. MURR. PARL.
("Port Orford Cedar Oil")

Chamaecyparis lawsoniana A. Murr. Parl. (syn. *Cupressus lawsoniana* A. Murr. Parl.), fam. *Cupressaceae,* the so-called "Port Orford Cedar" or "Western White Cedar," is a native of the North American Pacific Coast, but has been introduced to other parts of the world, where it is grown as an ornamental tree in parks and gardens. The leaves and terminal branches, as well as the wood, contain an essential oil which has been prepared experimentally on several occasions. For a time the oil was available in commercial quantities.

A. Leaf Oil

The oils distilled from the terminal branches (trimmings) in a lumber mill near Port Orford, Oregon, and analyzed by Fritzsche Brothers, Inc., New York, had these properties:

Specific Gravity at 15°/15°........ 0.872 to 0.915, usually above 0.900
Optical Rotation................. +33° 46′ to +43° 0′
Refractive Index at 20°........... 1.4701 to 1.4850, usually above 1.4783
Ester Content, Calculated as Bornyl
    Acetate..................... 2.9 to 11.4%, usually above 6.5%
Solubility...................... Usually soluble in 0.5 to 5.5 vol. of
                90% alcohol and more

In 1910 Schimmel & Co.[1] distilled the leaves of trees growing in Holstein (Germany), and obtained about 1 per cent of an oil with an odor reminiscent of cypress and savin oils. The properties of the oil were:

Specific Gravity at 15°............. 0.9308
Optical Rotation.................. +23° 48′
Refractive Index at 20°............ 1.48844
Acid Number..................... 3.7
Ester Number.................... 61.6
Ester Number after Acetylation...... 78.8
Solubility....................... Soluble in 0.5 vol. of 90% alcohol,
                temporarily turbid in 1 to 3 vol.

Treatment of the oil with bisulfite solution yielded small quantities of an aldehyde, the odor of which was reminiscent of lauraldehyde.

B. Wood Oil

At one time substantial quantities of essential oil were produced in lumber mills in Oregon, particularly near Marshfield, from sawdust and chips. The yield of oil averaged about 1.6 per cent.

The oil derived from the wood is a colorless or yellowish to light brown liquid, with an odor reminiscent of limonene, pinene, and borneol.

Two oils of "Port Orford Cedarwood" examined by Schimmel & Co.[2] (I), and by Thurber and Roll [3] (II) had these properties:

[1] *Ber. Schimmel & Co.*, October (1910), 134.
[2] *Ber. Schimmel & Co.* (1931), 12.
[3] *Ind. Eng. Chem.* **19** (1927), 739.

	I	II
Specific Gravity	d_{15} 0.8992	d_{20} 0.8913
Optical Rotation	$+40° 47'$	$[\alpha]_D^{20}$ $+46° 41'$
Refractive Index at 20°	1.47799	1.4760
Acid Number	0	0.19
Ester Number	23.3	19.3
Ester Number after Acetylation	80.3	83.3

Investigating their oil for its chemical composition, Thurber and Roll [4] identified the following compounds:

d-α-Pinene.................. (46%)

d-Limonene................. (3%)

d-Borneol................... (26%)

d-Cadinene.................. (21%)

l-Cadinol.................... (4%)

Some years earlier, Schorger [5] had examined a 4-year-old (rectified) oil and found that it had this composition:

d-α-Pinene.................... (60 to 61%) $[\alpha]_D$ $+51° 41'$

Dipentene...................... (6 to 7%)

l-Borneol, free.................. (11%)

Cadinene...................... (6 to 7%)

Formic and Acetic Acids, free

Formic and Capric Acids, esterified

The borneol appeared to occur in the oil partly in free form, partly esterified with formic, acetic and capric acids.

[4] *Ibid.*
[5] *Ibid.* **6** (1914), 631.

OIL OF CEDARWOOD

(Oil of Virginian Cedarwood—"Red Cedarwood Oil")

Essence de Bois de Cèdre   Aceite Esencial Cedro del Palo Ligero
Cedernholzöl   Oleum Ligni Cedri

Botany and Occurrence.—*Juniperus virginiana* L. (fam. *Cupressaceae*), the "Virginia," "Tennessee," "Eastern," or "Southern *Red* Cedar" (distinguished from the "Eastern *White* Cedar," *Thuja occidentalis* L.[1]) is a slow-growing, evergreen tree with a narrow, dense, and pyramidal crown, which, in old specimens, sometimes becomes spreading and round-topped. In the South, the red cedar attains greater height than in the North: seventy-five-year-old trees often reach a height of 60 ft. Majestic trees 5 ft. in diameter and 100 ft. tall have been reported. In years past, virgin cedar forests extended throughout Florida and Georgia, but most of them have been cut down. *Juniperus virginiana* now grows in a fairly continuous belt running approximately from the central part of Virginia, through North Carolina and the northern edge of South Carolina, into Tennessee, central Kentucky and northern Alabama. Throughout this region the tree occurs almost everywhere; it also grows scattered in certain sections of Arkansas (Ozark Mountains), southern Alabama, Mississippi, Texas and Florida.

The red cedar seems to prefer calcareous soil; it thrives on dry hillsides and in swampy land. On limey soil it develops faster, more vigorously and luxuriantly, and probably produces more essential oil than on other types of soil. The tree grows wild and prolifically, seeding itself quickly. The only planted stands are those established by the Forest Department of North Carolina for the control of soil erosion. Forest fires occur particularly among the young trees (which burn easily) and constitute the chief obstacle to rapid expansion of red cedar forests.

Most of the present cedar forests are owned by private individuals, who exploit them by felling mature trees, preserving the young ones for later years. If sufficient old trees are left standing for spontaneous reseeding, no new trees need be planted for reforestation. Some cedar forests are exploited by sawmills which purchase the right of felling the trees ("timber right") from the landowners. Cutting goes on throughout the year, particularly at periods when the farmers are not busy with their principal

---

[1] Note, however, that the "White Cedar" of the New Jersey pine barrens is really *Chamaecyparis thyoides* (L.) B.S.P.

crops. The felled logs are hauled to the nearest road with tractors or horse teams, and are then trucked to the sawmills.

The essential oil is contained chiefly in the reddish heartwood of *Juniperus virginiana* L.; the white sapwood contains very little oil. Distilling sapwood for experimental purposes, the author obtained only 0.2 per cent of an oil with a poor odor, not at all characteristic of red cedarwood.

As the tree grows older it develops more heartwood and the outer layer of sapwood becomes thinner each year. For this reason trees younger than twenty-five years should not be felled. Woodsmen distinguish between "virgin cedars," which are older trees, and "sap cedars," the younger trees. On steam distillation the wood of the former yields about 3.5 per cent of volatile oil, that of the latter less than 1 per cent. The oils distilled from the two types of trees differ considerably in regard to their odor and chemical composition. Huddle [2] noted that the oil derived from "virgin cedars" contains more high boiling constituents, and has a stronger odor than the oil from "sap cedars." The latter, on the other hand, is richer in cedrol (see below).

Production of the Oil.—Prior to 1917, practically all commercial cedarwood oil was produced by manufacturers of cedar pencil slats. For this purpose they had to use virgin timber, viz., old original growth of large trees with practically no knots and a straight, even grain. As early as 1910 most of this timber had been cut out from the forests, and the pencil slat manufacturers were forced to purchase cedar fence rails and old log cabins built by early settlers many years before with wood from virgin forests. Obviously, all the sapwood had disappeared from this old timber, which consisted entirely of red heartwood. Moreover, it had been seasoned for fifty years or more, and exposed to all kinds of weather. At the time of Rabak's investigation,[3] most cedarwood oil still came from such material (see below).

About 1917, one of the present large distillers started production of cedarwood oil, using as raw material sawdust from freshly cut cedar trees employed in the manufacture of cedar chests, closets and linings. This timber was not only freshly cut, but it was the class of timber referred to by pencil slat manufacturers as second, small growth, or "sap cedar." It was the cedar used for making cedar boards, and contained a great many knots. Because of the knots and the twisted grain, these trees were not suitable for the making of pencils; most of the trees were not more than twenty-five or thirty years old.

The pencil slat manufacturers claimed that oil from second growth cedar would be unsatisfactory for commercial purposes. As a matter of fact, the

[2] *Ind. Eng. Chem.* **28** (1936), 18.
[3] *Am. Perfumer* **23** (1929), 727.

records of essential oil houses show that for many years this type of cedarwood oil had to be sold at a discount. Gradually, however, the wood from rails and log cabins was used up, the cedar pencil slat business declined, and the oil had to be distilled more and more from sawdust of younger trees. There are still a few slats produced, but only on a small scale and, as far as the author knows, none of the mills now producing pencil slats have any equipment for distilling the oil. Their sawdust is usually mixed with dust from other wood products, and there is not enough of it to justify installation of the equipment.

To summarize: oil of cedarwood is distilled today almost exclusively from shavings and refuse obtained in the manufacture of boards and shingles for cedar chests, wardrobes, dressers and closet linings; also for wine coolers, ice buckets, pails, etc. The wood employed for this purpose comes from relatively young trees.

Total Production.—Production of the oil in the southeast varies greatly from year to year. In 1950 it amounted to about 450,000 lb., in 1951 it exceeded 500,000 lb. The latter figure represents the largest quantity produced in any previous year.

Distillation and Yield of Oil.—Since the red cedar tapers considerably with height, the felled trees are first cut into logs about 8 ft. long, this size being the most convenient for sawing boards. In order to make the waste wood suitable for distilling, it is fed into hogging machines, grinders and hammer machines, reduced to small size, and blown into the stills.

The distillery of the most important cedarwood oil producer[4] comprises sixteen galvanized iron stills, each 10 ft. high and 6 ft. wide, and each insulated with a heavy wooden jacket. The pressure in the steam generator is about 150 lb., but the live steam entering the stills is reduced to only a few pounds of pressure. Distillation of one batch of chips and dust lasts 10 to 12 hr. The condensate runs first into an oil separator where the direct, lighter-than-water, oil separates automatically from the distillation water. The latter then flows into a second, larger tank where, after cooling and settling, it separates an additional but small quantity of oil; this has a high specific gravity and dark color and is often referred to as "heavy oil" (see below).

The yield of normal oil from fresh chips and dust ranges from 2 to 2.5 per cent. The theoretical yield amounts to 3 per cent, but in actual practice this seems almost impossible to obtain. Distillers claim that long exposure of the sawdust to sunlight reduces the yield of oil, probably by resinification. Exposure of the sawdust to *moist* atmosphere also results in a lower

---

[4] The author is greatly obliged to Mr. A. L. Foster, Greensboro, N. C., for the assistance extended to him during a visit to the cedar oil producing regions.

yield of oil, probably because of fermentation. Such oil is cloudy, discolored, and lacking in the typical cedarwood character. Therefore, sawdust should be distilled as fresh as possible.

According to Huddle,[5] "virgin cedar" yields about 3.5 per cent of oil; "sap cedar" less than 1 per cent (see above). The larger the proportion of heartwood, the more oil the tree contains. Heartwood from either "sap cedar" or "virgin cedar" yields approximately the same amount of oil.

Physicochemical Properties.—The volatile oil derived by steam distillation of the wood of *Juniperus virginiana* L. is an almost colorless, somewhat viscous liquid with a soft, balsamic, and very lasting odor, characteristic of red cedarwood. Occasionally the oil is permeated with crystals of cedrol.

According to Gildemeister and Hoffmann,[6] oil of cedarwood has the following properties:

Specific Gravity at 15°.............	0.943 to 0.964
Optical Rotation...................	$-18°\ 0'$ to $-42°\ 0'$
Refractive Index at 20°............	1.50 to 1.51
Acid Number.....................	Up to 1.5
Ester Number....................	Up to 12
Ester Number after Acetylation......	26 to 68
Solubility........................	Sparingly soluble in alcohol. One volume of oil requires from 10 to 20 vol. of 90% alcohol for solution. In a few cases only 7 to 10 vol. of 90% alcohol, or up to 7 vol. of 95% alcohol are required for solution
Boiling Range at atm. pr.:	
264°–275°.....................	About 84%
275°–280°.....................	About 10%

Shipments of genuine cedarwood oils from the southeastern part of the United States, examined in recent years by Fritzsche Brothers, Inc., New York, had properties varying within these limits:

Specific Gravity at 15°/15°......	0.949 to 0.961
Optical Rotation...............	$-25°\ 27'$ to $-37°\ 15'$
Refractive Index at 20°.........	1.5030 to 1.5067
Solubility.....................	Occasionally soluble in 8 to 10 vol. of 90% alcohol; often 0.5 to 4.5 vol. of 95% alcohol are required to give a clear solution

The natural (crude) oils produced in the cedarwood sawmills usually possess a pale yellow color. To obtain clear, colorless oils, the crude oils

[5] *J. Ind. Eng. Chem.* **28** (1936), 18.
[6] "Die Ätherischen Öle," 3d Ed., Vol. II, 268.

must be rectified (redistilled). Oils rectified in recent years by Fritzsche Brothers, Inc., exhibited the following properties:

Specific Gravity at 15°/15°............ 0.938 to 0.953
Optical Rotation..................... −32° 50′ to −50° 55′
Refractive Index at 20°............... 1.5024 to 1.5052
Solubility........................... Soluble in 3 to 6 vol.
and more of 95%
alcohol

Examining the physicochemical properties of oils distilled from fresh and from old cedarwood, Rabak [7] reported these values:

	Fresh Wood	*Old Wood*
Specific Gravity at 20°............	0.9623	0.9406
Optical Rotation..................	−25° 48′	−52° 6′
Refractive Index at 20°...........	1.5050	1.5020
Acid Number.....................	1.25	0.26
Ester Number....................	2.67	0.87
Ester Number after Acetylation.....	38.6	13.03
Ester Content, Calculated as Cedryl Acetate........................	1.25%	0.47%
Total Alcohol Content, Calculated as Cedrol.........................	15.76%	5.20%
Free Alcohol Content, Calculated as Cedrol.........................	14.71%	4.80%
Combined Alcohol Content, Calculated as Cedrol.................	1.05%	0.40%
Solubility in 95% Alcohol.........	All proportions, 1 part in 5.5 vol.	

According to Rabak,[8] the specific gravity and refractive index are higher in the oil from fresh wood than in that from old wood. The much lower laevorotation of the former results from the fact that it contains a high percentage of free cedrol (which has a dextrorotation of +9° 30′) and therefore a lower percentage of the hydrocarbon, cedrene, which is strongly laevorotatory (−55°). The higher percentage of oxygenated constituents present in the oil from fresh cedarwood possibly also accounts for the greater solubility in 95 per cent alcohol.

Calculating from the ester numbers and ester numbers after acetylation of the two oils it appears that the oil from fresh cedarwood contains 14.71 per cent of free cedrol, whereas that from old cedarwood contains but 4.8 per cent. This is further borne out by the fact that 12.5 per cent of crystalline cedrol was obtained from the former, while none could be separated from the latter by the same method (see below).

[7] *Am. Perfumer* **23** (1929), 727.
[8] *Ibid.*

In general it can be said that the higher the specific gravity and the refractive index, and the lower the optical rotation of the oil, the higher is its cedrol content and the lower its cedrene content.

As regards the heavy red oil, small quantities of which separate from the stored distillation water (after separation of the main oil; see above in the section "Distillation and Yield of Oil"), it has little practical value. A sample of red oil examined by the author had these properties:

Specific Gravity at 15°.............. 0.979
Optical Rotation................... Too dark
Refractive Index at 20°............. 1.5090
Total Alcohol Content, Calculated as
    Cedrol.......................... 32.6%
Solubility at 20°.................... Soluble in 0.5 vol. and more
                   of 90% alcohol
Odor............................... Not as soft and smooth as that
                   of regular cedarwood oil,
                   but slightly stronger

Redistillation of this oil with steam yielded 42 per cent of a water-white clear oil, and a viscous dark residual oil. These two oils exhibited the following properties:

	White Oil	Residual Oil
Specific Gravity at 15°	0.952	1.008
Optical Rotation	−36° 56′	Too dark
Refractive Index at 20°	1.5041	1.5190
Total Alcohol Content, Calculated as Cedrol	11.2%	53.3%
Solubility at 20°	Cloudy in 10 vol. and more of 90% alcohol	Soluble in 7 vol. and more of 90% alcohol
Odor	Lacking in the characteristic woody note of normal cedarwood oil	Possessing a pleasant, soft cedrol note

Cedrol Content of the Oil, and Assay.—In 1895, Schimmel & Co.[9] made the statement that old cedarwood yields a semisolid oil permeated with crystals of cedrol. Schimmel & Co. expressed the belief that cedrol is not a normal constituent of the fresh wood, but is formed on aging of the wood. For years the Schimmel chemists tried to prove the presence of cedrol in cedarwood oil, but in vain. Gildemeister and Hoffmann[10] ventured the opinion that cedrol is not present in all cedarwood oils, but is formed in cedarwood chips or sawdust which, prior to distillation, had been exposed for some time to the influence of air, perhaps humid air. Special experi-

[9] *Ber. Schimmel & Co.*, April (1895), 19.
[10] "Die Ätherischen Öle," 3d Ed., Vol. II, 270.

ments, conducted by Rabak [11] in 1929, demonstrated the fallacy of this theory. Rabak proved that cedarwood oils distilled from sawdust (a commercial by-product in the processing of *fresh* cedar logs) almost invariably became semisolid with crystals of cedrol, even at room temperature. On cooling, these oils turned into a solid, buttery mass. On the contrary, oils distilled from the waste resulting from old cedar fence rails and old stumps could not be made to yield crystalline cedrol, even at low temperature (cf. "Oil of *Juniperus procera*," p. 369, below).

Rabak [12] devised a simple method for the separation and quantitative assay of cedrol in cedarwood oil; it is based upon the insolubility of cedrol in cold dilute alcohol. Details of the method will be found in Vol. I of the present work, p. 330. Under proper conditions solidification takes place with remarkable suddenness. This phenomenon is doubtless physical, and results from the extreme insolubility of cedrol in cold dilute alcohol; solidification will not take place until the distribution of the alcohol is uniform throughout the oil, or until complete emulsion with the oil is formed. In no case did oils from the fresh cedarwood fail to solidify. Several samples of oil prepared by Rabak from the sawdust of *fresh* cedar, tested by this method, gave the following results:

Sample No.	Per Cent Cedrol
1	11.2
2	11.3
3	11.3
4	13.2
5	13.7
6	13.8

The results show that cedrol was distilled over as one of the constituents of the oil throughout the distillation period of 2 hr. The final portions of the oil contained a higher percentage of cedrol than the earlier portions. The composite sample of the oils obtained from this distillation yielded 12.5 per cent of cedrol.

According to Rabak,[13] two distinct sources for the production of crystalline cedrol are available:

1. Oils distilled from the waste of fresh cedarwood afford a considerable quantity of cedrol by means of the simple and inexpensive method described above.

2. The kilns used for drying the large quantities of cedar lumber employed in the manufacture of cedar chests offer another source of supply.

[11] *Am. Perfumer* **23** (1929), 727.   [13] *Ibid.*
[12] *Ibid.*

The vapors escaping from these drying kilns, if properly concentrated and condensed, will yield large quantities of cedrol that are now entirely wasted. The kilns are frequently festooned with these crystalline substances in crude form. When lumber dried in the kilns is distilled, the oil obtained contains but little cedrol, since a large portion has been removed by the drying process. At ordinary temperatures, such oil is liquid and even at low temperature fails to deposit crystals of cedrol.

A third method of isolating cedrol is, obviously, the fractionation of cedarwood oils that contain a relatively high percentage of cedrol.

Fractionation of Cedarwood Oil.—Huddle [14] studied the conditions necessary for successful fractionation of cedarwood oil and emphasized the desirability of an inert atmosphere, a pressure sufficiently low to permit the maximum temperature of the still contents not to exceed 145° C., and selection of the refractive index as the most convenient physical property to use in the cutting of fractions. Plotting the volumes of the various fractions against their refractive indices, Huddle showed that it is possible to establish limits within which the properties of pure commercial oils should fall.

Huddle [15] also noted an apparent mutarotation, and an odor reminiscent of cedar leaf oil in the most volatile portions of the wood oil.

Analysis of Cedarwood Oil.—Because of its low price, oil of cedarwood (from *Juniperus virginiana* L.) is seldom adulterated. A careful organoleptic examination, however, is always indicated. The oil should possess a very soft, balsamic odor, characteristic of the wood; it should not have any cedar leaf character, nor the somewhat harsh note typical of the oil derived from the wood of *Juniperus mexicana* Schiede.

Determination of the physicochemical properties is advisable. Crude (nonrectified) oil of *Juniperus virginiana* usually possesses a lower optical rotation than the oil distilled from the wood of *Juniperus mexicana*.

If the alcoholic constituents have to be assayed (total alcohol content determined by acetylation and subsequent saponification, see Vol. I of this work, p. 271), it should be remembered that the relatively complex alcohols contained in cedarwood oil are not easily acetylyzed nor are their esters readily saponified. This can be best demonstrated by the following data obtained in the laboratories of Fritzsche Brothers, Inc., New York. A pure commercial cedarwood oil was acetylyzed (and then saponified), in order to determine its total alcohol content in per cent:

[14] *J. Tenn. Acad. Sci.* **13**, No. 4 (1938), 259.
[15] *Ibid.*

Saponification Period, in Hours	Acetylation Period	
	1 Hour	2 Hours
1.....................	16.4%	17.2%
2.....................	20.1%	21.3%
3.....................	22.3%	22.5%

For the assay (and isolation) of cedrol alone, the previously-described method of Rabak can be recommended. Like most assays based upon the actual separation of a constituent by physical means, the method of Rabak does not give absolutely accurate results. However, it yields comparative data, provided all experimental conditions are carefully controlled. Examination of five commercial cedarwood oils (*Juniperus virginiana* L.) in the laboratories of Fritzsche Brothers, Inc., New York, yielded crystalline cedrol in amounts ranging from 3.6 to 12.0 per cent.

Chemical Composition.—The chemical composition of the volatile oil derived from the wood of *Juniperus virginiana* L., and the structural formulas of its chief constituents, cedrene, cedrol, and cedrenol, have been investigated by numerous researchers in the course of more than a century. However, despite intensive work carried out by leading experts in terpene chemistry, among them Semmler, Treibs, Naves, Ruzicka, Plattner and their collaborators, it has not yet been possible definitely to establish undisputed structural formulas for these compounds. Several configurations have been proposed in recent years, but absolute proof of the correctness of any of these has not yet been advanced. The most recent work on the subject, at this writing, is a series of doctorate theses,[16] reporting research done under the supervision of Ruzicka and Plattner, but not yet published in the scientific press: apparently the structures suggested for cedrene, even in these most recent papers, cannot be accepted as demonstrated beyond doubt.

In 1948, Plattner[17] proposed either one of the following two azulenic formulas for cedrene:

[16] Heinrich Kläui, "Abbau der Nor-cedren-dicarbonsäure" (1947); Gerhard W. Kusserow, "Zur Kenntnis des Cedrens" (1948); Stanislaw Meyer, "Ueber die Konstitution des Cedrens, (1949), Dissertation Theses, Eidgenossische Technische Hochschule (Zürich, Switzerland).

[17] *Chimia* **2** (1948), 248. Cf. *Angew. Chemie* **61** (1949), 109.

Oil of cedarwood contains about 80 per cent of cedrene $C_{15}H_{24}$, from 3 to 14 per cent of cedrol $C_{15}H_{26}O$, and a small quantity of cedrenol $C_{15}H_{24}O$. The cedrol occurs in the oil in crystallizable and in liquid form; the two modifications are stereoisomers, but identical chemically.

Years ago Semmler and collaborators [18] were able to show that cedrene, cedrol and cedrenol are related in a simple way:

$$
\begin{array}{ccc}
\overbrace{C_{12}H_{20}} & \overbrace{C_{12}H_{20}} & \overbrace{C_{12}H_{20}} \\
| \quad | & | \quad | & | \quad | \\
C{=}CH & HO{-}C{-}CH_2 & C{=}CH \\
| & | & | \\
CH_3 & CH_3 & CH_2\cdot OH \\
\text{Cedrene} \underset{-H_2O}{\longleftarrow} & \text{Cedrol} & \text{Cedrenol}
\end{array}
$$

More recently Naves et al.[19] have demonstrated that the cedrene isolated from cedarwood oil by fractional distillation consists of a mixture of several isomers. The chief component (about 75 per cent) of these isomers is α-cedrene, which contains an endocyclic double bond and is identical with the so-called "artificial" cedrene obtained by dehydration of cedrol. Another component of the mixture of cedrene isomers is β-cedrene, which contains an exocyclic methylene group:

$$
\begin{array}{cc}
\overbrace{C_{12}H_{20}} & \overbrace{C_{12}H_{20}} \\
| \quad | & | \quad | \\
C{=}CH & C{-}CH_2 \\
| & \| \\
CH_3 & CH_2 \\
\text{α-Cedrene} & \text{β-Cedrene}
\end{array}
$$

Aside from α- and β-cedrene, the mixture of cedrene isomers contains small quantities of bicyclic sesquiterpenes similar to the cedrenes.

As regards cedrol, a tertiary sesquiterpene alcohol $C_{15}H_{26}O$, this occurs in cedarwood oil as *crystallizable* cedrol m. 86°, and as *liquid* cedrol, also called pseudocedrol. The two forms must be considered stereoisomers; Kimura [20] was able to show that liquid cedrol, on heating with potassium, or on saponification of its xanthogenate, yields crystallized cedrol m. 86°.

According to Semmler and Meyer,[21] pseudocedrol $C_{15}H_{26}O$ has these properties: b_9 147°–152°, α_D^{20} +21° 30′, n_D^{20} 1.5131. On dehydration with formic acid, pseudocedrol, like cedrol, yields cedrene.

The presence of the following compounds has been reported in cedarwood oil:

[18] *Ber.* **40** (1907), 3521; **45** (1912), 355, 786, 1384, 1553; **47** (1914), 2257.
[19] *Helv. Chim. Acta* **26** (1943), 302, 304, 305.
[20] *Ber. deut. pharm. Ges.* **20** (1910), 293.
[21] *Ber.* **45** (1912), 1384.

Cedrene. First isolated from the oil by Walter,[22] and later more thoroughly investigated by Chapoteaut,[23] Chapman and Burgess,[24] and Rousset.[25]

Semmler and collaborators [26] showed that both the cedrene contained in cedarwood oil and the cedrene obtained by dehydration of cedrol, on oxidation with potassium permanganate solution or with ozone, yield the same cedrene keto acid. This acid is liquid, but can be identified by preparation of its crystalline semicarbazone m. 162°. Moreover, on oxidation with bromine lye the keto acid in all cases yields crystalline cedrene dicarboxylic acid m. 182.5°. Therefore, the best method of identifying cedrene consists in its oxidation to cedrene keto acid, and in the oxidation of the latter to cedrene dicarboxylic acid. (For further details regarding cedrene see above, and Vol. II of the present work, p. 116.)

Oil of cedarwood contains about 80 per cent of cedrene.

Cedrol and Pseudocedrol. Cedrol, also called "Cedar Camphor," was first observed in cedarwood oil by Walter [27] more than a century ago. This tertiary sesquiterpene alcohol occurs in the oil as crystallizable cedrol m. 86°, and as pseudocedrol, the liquid stereoisomeric form of cedrol (see above, and Vol. II of this work, p. 284.)

Cedrenol. This primary sesquiterpene alcohol was first noted in the oil by Semmler and Mayer.[28] (For further details see above, and Vol. II of this work, p. 283.)

Sesquiterpenes(?). Some years ago, Glichitch and Naves [29] observed the presence of dextrorotatory, bicyclic sesquiterpenes in the last runs of cedarwood oil. More recently, Naves and co-workers [30] found that the dextrorotatory fraction (3 to 4 per cent of the oil), on repeated dehydrogenation with selenium at 290°–320°, yielded 0.32 per cent of an azulene mixture, in which S-guaiazulene could be identified.

‒ Cedarwood Oil as Adulterant, and Its Detection.

—Because of its low price and comparatively faint odor, oil of cedarwood is not infrequently used as an adulterant of more expensive oils, patchouly, vetiver, and sandalwood oils among them. In many cases cedarwood oil can be detected by its poor solubility in 90 per cent alcohol, high specific gravity, high boiling range, and pronounced laevorotation. In cases where physical tests fail, the presence of cedarwood oil can be proved chemically by submitting the suspected oil to fractionation. The cedrene fraction b. 263°–264°, or b_{12} 123°–124° is then oxidized with potassium permanganate solution to cedrene keto acid $C_{15}H_{24}O_3$, b_{10} 205°–215°, which can be identified by preparation of its semicarbazone m. 162°. Further oxidation of the

[22] *Liebigs Ann.* **39** (1841), 247. *Ann. chim.* [3], **1** (1841), 498.
[23] *Bull. soc. chim.* [2], **37** (1882), 303.
[24] *Proc. Chem. Soc.* (1896), 140.
[25] *Bull. soc. chim.* [3], **17** (1897), 485.
[26] *Ber.* **45** (1912), 355, 791, 1389, 1556.
[27] *Liebigs Ann.* **39** (1841), 247.
[28] *Ber.* **45** (1912), 786.
[29] *Chimie & industrie,* Numéro Spécial, **19** (1928), 482.
[30] *Helv. Chim. Acta* **26** (1943), 302, 324.

cedrene keto acid with alkaline bromine solution yields crystalline cedrene dicarboxylic acid m. 182.5° (see above, "Chemical Composition").

Use.—Oil of cedarwood is used widely in perfumery, and for the scenting of soaps, technical preparations, room sprays, disinfectants and similar products. It is an excellent odor fixative.

For clearing microscope sections a selected rectified oil of cedarwood should be used having a refractive index about 1.504 at 20°. For use with immersion lenses a specially prepared viscous oil having a refractive index of exactly 1.515 at 18° is required.

⸰ OIL OF RED CEDAR LEAVES

The term "Cedar Leaf Oil" would appear to imply that the oil in question is distilled from the leaves of the red cedar tree, *Juniperus virginiana* L. (fam. *Cupressaceae*). This, however, is not the case; the leaves of the red cedar are not used for the isolation of their essential oil. The commercial term "Cedar Leaf Oil" actually refers to the oil distilled from the leaves of the *white* cedar, *Thuja occidentalis* L. (fam. *Cupressaceae*), cf. the monograph on "Oil of Thuja," p. 325 of the present volume.

Oil from the leaves of the *red* cedar, *Juniperus virginiana* L., has been distilled only occasionally. In an experiment carried out by Fritzsche Brothers, Inc.,[31] New York, in 1894, the yield of oil was 0.2 per cent. Similar experiments were undertaken later by Hanson and Babcock.[32]

Physicochemical Properties.—The following properties were observed on these experimental oils:

```
Specific Gravity at 15°............... 0.887 to 0.900
Optical Rotation.................... +59° 25'
Saponification Number.............. 10.9
Ester Number after Acetylation....... 39.1
Solubility......................... Insoluble in 10 vol.
                                      of 80% alcohol
```

The oils had a pleasant, somewhat sweetish odor. On fractionation the bulk of the oil distilled below 180°.

Several commercial oils of cedar leaves described by Gildemeister and

[31] Cf. *Ber. Schimmel & Co.*, April (1894), 56.
[32] *J. Am. Chem. Soc.* **28** (1906), 1201.

Hoffmann [33] exhibited laevorotation and were probably derived from the leaves of *Thuja occidentalis* L. (see above).

Chemical Composition.—In a true red cedar leaf oil, Schimmel & Co.[34] identified the following compounds:

α-Pinene. In the lowest boiling fractions. Characterized by means of the nitroso-chloride.

d-Limonene. Identified by preparation of the tetrabromide m. 104°–105°.

Borneol. M. 203°–204°. Present in the oil partly free, partly esterified [with iso-valeric acid(?)].

Cadinene. In the highest boiling fractions.

Use.—As was mentioned above, the oil from the leaves of the *red* cedar is not produced on a commercial scale.

OIL OF TEXAN CEDARWOOD

Botany, Habitat, and Range.—*Juniperus mexicana* Schiede (fam. *Cupressaceae*), the so-called "Texas Cedar" is a small to medium sized tree, growing up to 20 ft. in height. Its trunk and branches are irregular in shape and usually crooked; hence the timber cannot be used for sawing into boards for closet linings, chests, and other furniture. Moreover, on exposure to the atmosphere the wood easily develops cracks.

The tree occurs in a wide range, from central and western Texas, through Mexico, as far south as Guatemala. It grows at altitudes of 700 to 2,500 ft., usually on rough and rocky limestone hills, but prefers deep sand with a thin top soil. This type of land has little value, except for grazing of cattle. Because of the poor soil and a dearth of rainfall, the cedar trees grow very slowly, developing much heartwood and only little sapwood. This fact offers a considerable advantage as regards distillation of the essential oil, which is contained in the heartwood only. According to Pool,[1] the whole area in Texas, where *Juniperus mexicana* Schiede grows, now comprises about three million acres, leaving sufficient cedar trees for many years to come.

[33] "Die Ätherischen Öle," 3d Ed., Vol. II, 274.
[34] *Ber. Schimmel & Co.*, April (1894), 56; April (1898), 14.
[1] *Chemurgic Digest* **7**, No. 7 (1948), 7.

The essential oil derived by distillation of the heartwood has been on the market intermittently since about 1929, when the first distillery was started in Rock Springs, Texas. In the beginning the oil was shipped in the crude state, without being refined, but recently a large distillery located on the Guadeloupe River, about three miles north of New Braunsfels in Texas, has begun to produce the oil with more modern methods. The industry prospered for a time, and from 1945 to 1948 about 150,000 lb. of oil were produced yearly by three distilleries in Texas. Lately, however, production has declined for several reasons, among them the fact that the Texan oil cannot easily compete with the regular cedarwood oil derived in the southeastern states from *Juniperus virginiana* L. The Texan oil is distilled from wood of trees that have to be cut specifically for this purpose, whereas the oil of the species *virginiana* is a low priced by-product, distilled from waste sawdust and shavings in the operation of large timber mills.

Nevertheless, the Texan oil will be discussed here, because during and after World War II large quantities reached the market, and production can be increased again, whenever demand and prices warrant it. Moreover, the Texan oil is an excellent source for the isolation of cedrol.

Distillation and Yield of Oil.—According to Pool,[2] the timber is usually cut by Mexican laborers on a contract basis, by the cord, and is stacked in the cut-over area to dry. When dry, the wood grinds and distills better than when green. Usually the wood is seasoned for 90 days, but will not suffer when left outdoors for a year or two.

When ready for use, the wood is reduced by means of wood hogs and hammer mills to chips of 6-mesh size; these are conveyed into stills of 7 by 10 ft. holding 5,000 lb. of grindings. Distillation of one charge requires about 6 hr., and results in a high-grade oil. Albers [3] mentions two stills in a distillery with a combined capacity of 21,000 lb. of comminuted wood ($\frac{1}{16}$-mesh). In this distillery 16 hr. are required to exhaust the charge in the stills.

The yield of crude oil varies between 1.8 and 2.3 per cent. Rectification of the crude oil entails a loss of 15 to 20 per cent. If left for some time in the rectification still, the "tailings" (residue) become waxy or crystalline.

Physicochemical Properties.—Crude Texan cedarwood oil is a reddish to brown colored, somewhat viscous liquid with an odor characteristic of cedarwood, but not as soft as that of the oil derived from the wood of *Juniperus virginiana* L. Compared with the latter, the oil from Texas exhibits a higher laevorotation, and a higher cedrol content. Because of their

[2] *Ibid.*
[3] Cf. Windemuth, *Pharm. Arch.* **16**, No. 2 (1945), 17.

higher cedrol content, good Texan oils usually have a high specific gravity, a property always desirable in cedarwood oils.

The above-mentioned large distillery near New Braunsfels in Texas has tried to market its oil in several grades, viz., crude (natural) oil, white (rectified) oil, liquid pseudocedrol, crystalline cedrol, and (residual) cedarwood tar. The various grades are obtained by fractionation of the crude (natural) oil *in vacuo* in an atmosphere of nitrogen.

Samples and shipments of the different qualities analyzed by Fritzsche Brothers, Inc., New York, had these properties:

Specific Gravity at 15°/15°...... 0.945 to 0.978
Optical Rotation............... −33° 54′ to −62° 3′
Refractive Index at 20°......... 1.5029 to 1.5084
Solubility..................... Usually soluble in 8 to 10 vol.
                               of 90% alcohol

These limits are rather wide because many of the samples analyzed represented fractions of the crude oil (see above). The Scientific Section of the Essential Oil Association of the U. S. A. recommended the following limits for the best commercial grades of this oil:

Specific Gravity at 15°/15°...... 0.950 to 0.960
Optical Rotation............... −35° 0′ to −50° 0′
Refractive Index at 20°......... 1.5040 to 1.5070
Solubility..................... Soluble in all proportions of
                               95% alcohol

Chemical Composition.—The volatile oil derived by steam distillation of the wood of *Juniperus mexicana* Schiede contains approximately the same constituents as the oil of *Juniperus virginiana* L., but in different proportions. As was pointed out above, the cedrol content is higher in the Texan oil.

Investigating the chemical composition of oil of *Juniperus mexicana* Schiede, Windemuth [4] found that it contains *cedrene, cedrol* and probably *pseudocedrol* (cf. the monograph on "Oil of Red Cedarwood" from *Juniperus virginiana* L.—section "Chemical Composition").

Use.—Crude cedarwood oil from Texas, and its various fractions, are used for the scenting of soaps and numerous technical preparations, among them room sprays, deodorants, insecticides, moth-proof clothing bags, floor polishes, janitor's supplies, lubricating greases, etc.

[4] *Ibid.*

OIL OF *JUNIPERUS PROCERA* HOCHST.
(Oil of East African Cedarwood)

The East African cedar, *Juniperus procera* Hochst. (fam. *Cupressaceae*), grows over wide ranges of East Africa, particularly in Abyssinia, Usambara, Kenya, and Tanganyika. In some sections it forms extended forests. The tree prefers altitudes ranging from 1,500 to 3,000 m. The wood of *Juniperus procera* Hochst. closely resembles that of *Juniperus virginiana* L., the North American red cedar.

Distilling shavings and comminuted pencil slats derived from the wood of the East African cedar tree, Schimmel & Co.[1] obtained 3.2 and 3.24 per cent, respectively, of essential oil. Macculloch[2] reported a yield of 2 per cent of oil from fresh wood shavings. More recently, Beckley[3] obtained 0.96 to 2.57 per cent of oil from wood shavings. The older the shavings, the lower was the yield of oil. Fresh shavings contained 1.42 per cent, two-year-old shavings 0.28 per cent, and seven-year-old shavings 0.02 per cent of oil. After eleven years the shavings yielded only traces of oil.

Physicochemical Properties.—The oil derived from the wood of *Juniperus procera* Hochst. is a liquid, or a semisolid mass permeated with crystals. The odor of the oil resembles that of cedarwood and vetiver root. The color of the oil ranges from light yellow to reddish-brown.

Gildemeister and Hoffmann[4] reported the following properties for East African cedarwood oil:

Specific Gravity at 15°.............	0.968 to 0.988
Optical Rotation..................	−16° 0′ to −38° 30′
Refractive Index at 20°...........	1.480 to 1.509
Acid Number.....................	1 to 15
Ester Number....................	1 to 9
Ester Number after Acetylation.....	70
Ester Number after Cold Formylation	87.5 to 92.75 [5]
Alcohol Content, Calculated as Cedrol	36.27 to 38.55%
Solubility........................	Soluble in 60 vol. of 70% alcohol, in 1.6 vol. of 80% alcohol, in 0.5 to 5 vol. of 90% alcohol

The oils distilled by Beckley[6] exhibited these properties:

Specific Gravity at 15.5°...........	0.9453
Optical Rotation..................	−47° 53′ to −63° 48′

[1] *Ber. Schimmel & Co.,* October (1911), 105.
[2] *J. Soc. Chem. Ind.* **38** (1919), 364T.
[3] *East African Agr. J.* **2** (1936), 127. Through *Ber. Schimmel & Co* (1938), 12.
[4] "Die Ätherischen Öle," 3d Ed., Vol. II, 274.   [6] *East African Agr. J.* **2** (1936), 127.
[5] Chiris, *Parfums France* **4** (1926), 22.

(*Top*) Production of cedarwood oil in the southeastern part of the United States. Storage of cedar logs in a mill yard near Birmingham, Alabama. (*Below*) A small cedar sawmill in the forest. (*Right*) Inside view of a large cedarwood distillery in Greensboro, North Carolina. *Photos Fritzsche Brothers, Inc., New York.*

(*Left*) A branch of *Juniperus communis* with berries. (*Right*) Gin (Steinhäger) production in Austria. Juniper oil is obtained as a by-product in the alcoholic distillation of fermented juniper berries. *Photos Fritzsche Brothers, Inc., New York.* (*Below*) Juniper bushes (*Juniperus communis*) growing near Csepel, Buckaerdö, Com. Pest, Hungary. *Photo Dr. Jules de Bittera, Budapest, Hungary.*

Refractive Index.................... 1.4999 to 1.5141
Acid Number..................... 0.56 to 1.12
Ester Number.................... 0.94 to 5.66

Schimmel & Co.[7] removed the crystals from an oil by filtration and found that the liquid oil had the following properties:

Specific Gravity at 15°............. 1.0289
Optical Rotation.................. −32° 30′
Refractive Index at 20°............ 1.51011
Acid Number..................... 27.06
Ester Number.................... 7.93
Ester Number after Acetylation..... 89.6
Solubility....................... Soluble in 2 vol. and more of 80% alcohol; soluble in 0.5 vol. of 90% alcohol

Chemical Composition.—The only constituent actually identified in the oil is *cedrol* (Schimmel & Co.). Beckley noted that the first fraction of a light colored oil had an odor reminiscent of pinene, whereas the corresponding fraction of a normal reddish-brown oil exhibited an odor of limonene. The same author found that the wood of young trees yielded oils with the largest amounts of cedrol (23 to 76 per cent). The cedrol from the oil of dried wood did not crystallize as readily as that from the oil of fresh wood. Macculloch noted that the amount of cedrol present in the oil depended on the interval between the time when the wood was disintegrated and the time when it was distilled. If the disintegrated wood had been exposed for some weeks to a hot sun, the oil obtained on distillation cooled to a mass of cedrol crystals. If not so exposed, but distilled a few days after disintegration, the oil contained only 38 per cent of cedrol.

Use.—According to the author's knowledge, only small quantities of the oil have been produced. The oil could be used similarly to that derived from the wood of the North American red cedar.

[7] *Ber. Schimmel & Co.,* October (1911), 105.

OIL OF JUNIPER BERRIES

Essence de Genièvre   *Aceite Esencial Bayas de Enebro*
Wacholderbeeröl   *Oleum Juniperi*

Botany, Habitat, and Range.—*Juniperus communis* L. (fam. *Cupressaceae*), the common juniper, is a shrub or tree attaining a height of 3 m. or more, and a trunk diameter of 25 to 30 cm. It grows wild in many parts of Europe and Asia, ranging as far east as the western Himalaya Mountains and northeastern Asia. In North America, the bush or tree occurs south to Pennsylvania, and west to Illinois, New Mexico, and northern California. *Juniperus communis* L. is a very variable species with several geographical varieties and some garden forms; the typical upright form (var. *erecta* Pursh) is common in Europe, and occasionally found in the northeastern parts of North America.[1] The most common North American variety, however, is *Juniperus communis* var. *depressa* Pursh, a low shrub rarely exceeding 1.5 m. in height. The "berries"[2] of the latter variety are inferior to those of the variety *erecta*, having a turpentine-like odor and taste. Nevertheless, since the medicinal properties of both varieties appear to be equal, berries of the variety *depressa* were accepted as official in the National Formulary, during World War II, when supplies of berries from var. *erecta* could not be shipped from Europe.

In general, the var. *erecta* grows in scattered stands, or together with other bushes. It thrives on sunny heaths and clearings in pine forests and mountain slopes exposed to the warm sun. Occasionally the trees form almost impenetrable patches, covering as many as 70 hectares.

Juniperus communis L. is a dioecious plant, with the male reproductive organs on one individual, the female on another. The same tree bears green (unripe) one-year-old berries, and blue (ripe) two-year-old berries. The berries contain from 0.5 to 2.0 per cent of essential oil, which can be isolated by steam distillation. Ripe (blue) berries yield more essential oil than unripe (green) ones. The quality and yield of the oil depend greatly upon the geographical origin of the berries.

Collection of the Berries.—Juniper berries are collected in a simple way. Harvesters carefully beat the branches of the bush with sticks, until the ripe (two-year-old) berries drop into baskets, or upon sheets placed beneath the bush. Green (one-year-old) berries remain on the branches and

---

[1] A. Rehder, "Manual of Cultivated Trees and Shrubs Hardy in North America," New York, The Macmillan Company (1949), 62.
[2] They are not berries in the botanical sense.

may be collected the following year. In the late afternoon, the harvested material is transported to the nearest village, where the berries are sifted, winnowed, and spread out in a thin layer on floors for drying in the sun or under a shed. Care must be taken to prevent fermentation, which easily takes place if the fresh berries are kept in sacks. Any berries damaged by fermentation are sold at a discount, because they possess an inferior flavor and poor appearance.

Quality, Producing Regions and Export of the Berries.—The appearance, flavor, and essential oil content of the berries depend a great deal upon their geographical origin, and upon local conditions—among them climate, soil, altitude, and exposure to the sun. Trees growing at elevated altitudes and in warm sunny places produce the best berries. Those from Italy have always been considered of best quality; Hungarian berries follow next.

(*a*) *Italian Berries.*—Italy is by far the largest producer of juniper berries. The berries are large, deep blue, rich in essential oil, and of excellent flavor. Harvest usually takes place from August 20 to September 10. Total production per year varies greatly depending upon the demand; in normal years it averages 3,500 to 4,000 metric tons.[3] Prior to World War II, the bulk of this quantity went to Germany.

The producing regions are in the Apennines, particularly in Tuscany, with Florence as center. The tree grows especially well at altitudes ranging from 600 to 1,200 m., on the warm hillsides and mountain slopes of the famed "Chianti Region," near the villages of San Donato, Pocchi Ponzi, and Castellina. Another section in Italy, which produces, however, a somewhat inferior quality of berries, embraces the eastern part of Venezia, and Istria (now partly Yugoslavian territory). The juniper trees here grow at altitudes from 200 to 700 m. These berries exhibit a somewhat reddish tint, and are not as blue as those from the Apennines.

The Italian berries are usually offered in four grades:

1. Large, hand-picked berries, sold to the trade in cellophane-wrapped, 1-lb. lots, and retailed through groceries to households for cooking and home use.

2. The next smaller size, graded in machines. Sold in sacks for general kitchen use, particularly for the making of preserves.

3. Also machine-graded, these serve for various industrial purposes, for the flavoring of sauces, making of preserves, and for distillation of alcoholic beverages. Their price averages one-half of that of the No. 1 berries. Occasionally this grade of berry is sold in powdered form.

4. The smallest berries, machine-graded, used primarily for the distilla-

[3] *Ber. Schimmel & Co.* (1939), 88.

tion of essential oil. Their price is usually only one-third of that prevailing for grade No. 1.

(b) *Hungarian Berries.*—The Hungarian berries follow the Italian in regard to quality and quantity produced. In fact, certain sections of Hungary grow juniper berries equal in appearance and flavor to the Italian. Production in Hungary fluctuates greatly from year to year, depending upon the general demand and production in Italy; it may reach as much as 1,000 metric tons per year. In 1937, for example, 470 tons of juniper berries were harvested in Hungary. Of this quantity, 322.8 tons were exported to Germany, 40.9 tons to other countries, while 106.3 tons were processed or stored in Hungary.[4]

[In this connection it should be mentioned that in Hungary, and even more so in Czechoslovakia and Yugoslavia, large quantities of juniper berries are used domestically for distillation of "Borovička," a very popular alcoholic beverage of the gin type. In Germany, Austria, and Switzerland, it is called "Steinhäger." This spirit is nothing but an alcoholic distillate of fermented juniper berries, containing from 40 to 50 per cent of alcohol. Slovaks are particularly fond of this strongly flavored beverage.]

Prior to World War I, Hungary was a very large producer of juniper berries, exporting yearly 70 to 80 railroad cars of berries. The bulk of these came from the northern Carpathian Mountains, which were then a part of Hungary. Most of the references found in the older literature on Hungarian juniper berries deal with those collected in this area. These berries are relatively small and of low sugar content. The northern Carpathian Mountains are now part of Czechoslovakia; hence the berries must be classified as Czechoslovakian.

In present-day Hungary the juniper tree grows abundantly in the northern mountain ranges, particularly near Börzsöny, Cserhát, Mátra and Bükk; in the Trans-Danubian sections, principally in the forests of Bakony, north of Balaton Lake; and in the sand hills between the rivers Danube and Tisza, particularly near Kecskemét. Here the soil consists of white, loose sand, which develops a typical sand dune vegetation (*Gypsophila paniculata, Alkanna tinctoria,* etc.). In this area the juniper tree often forms large, almost impenetrable stands.

The berries produced today in Hungary, particularly in the driftsand region between the Danube and the Tisza, are larger than those from the northern Carpathian Mountains, and attain a diameter of 7 mm. and more. Most berries from Hungary measure about 6 to 7 mm. in diameter. One liter of berries weighs from 350 to 400 g. The best Hungarian berries com-

[4] *Ibid.* (1938), 110.

pare very well with those from Tuscany. Their flavor is mild and rich, with none of the undesirable turpentine off-note so characteristic of low-grade berries.

(*c*) *Czechoslovakian Berries.*—Like Hungary, Czechoslovakia is potentially a very large producer of juniper berries. Actual production, however, fluctuates greatly from year to year, depending upon world markets and economic and political conditions. Most of the berries originate from the northern Carpathian Mountains (see above); they are relatively small and of low sugar content.

(*d*) *Yugoslavian Berries.*—The quality of Yugoslavian berries depends upon local conditions. Those from Istria and adjacent sections in Dalmatia, for example, resemble the Italian berries, but usually exhibit a reddish, rather than a dark-blue, tint. Much depends upon the altitude. In Istria and Dalmatia the juniper tree grows at altitudes ranging from 200 to 700 m.

(*e*) *Tyrolean Berries.*—Here again, geographical location and climate play an important role as regards appearance and aroma of the berries. Trees growing in the warm, sunny parts of the southern Tyrol produce much better berries than trees growing in the colder, rainy, and misty northern sections. The berries from the northern Tyrol often exhibit an odor and flavor reminiscent of the leaves of *Pinus mugo* Turra, the "Dwarf" or "Mountain" Pine, and other pinaceous trees. Nevertheless, substantial quantities of juniper berries are collected in the Tyrol (partly Austrian, partly Italian), but are used chiefly for the local distillation of "Steinhäger" (see above).

(*f*) *Berries from North-European Countries.*—Juniper berries from Germany, Scandinavia, Poland, and Russia usually are of such poor aroma, and contain so little essential oil, that they cannot be used for distillation.

(*g*) *North American Berries.*—During World War II the United States was completely cut off from the former sources of juniper berries in Europe, and many efforts were made to use North American berries (i.e., from var. *depressa* Pursh) for the distillation of the essential oil. Numerous experiments were made with berries from different regions (New England, Pennsylvania, the southeastern states, California, Mexico, etc.), but only in a few cases was it possible to obtain distillates, the odor and flavor of which approximated those of the imported berries. In most instances the essential oil of the domestic material had a disagreeable, turpentine-like off-note. Moreover, collection of the berries from wild-growing trees in the United States is far too costly to compete with production abroad. In order to establish a domestic juniper berry industry in the United States or Mexico, it would be necessary to import selected strains of *Juniperus communis* L., var. *erecta* Pursh from Italy, and to plant them experimentally under varied conditions of soil, climate and altitude. (The juniper tree was cultivated in Europe as far back as 1560;[5] today only wild-growing plants are exploited.)

Chemical Composition of the Berries.—Investigating the chemical composition of juniper berries, Casparis and Freund[6] found that they contain 8 per cent of resin (chiefly resin acids; phenols and esters absent), essential oil, 0.36 per cent of "juniperin" (probably a mixture of a tannin with a sugar or sugars), a mixed glyceride of λ-isostearic acid (?) and 15-hydroxy-pentadecanoic acid m. 84° (acetyl derivative m. 59°), *l*-maleic acid, invert sugar, and potassium salts.

Adulteration of the Berries.—Years ago juniper berries from the Tyrol were occasionally adulterated with the small berries collected from *Juniperus communis* var. *nana* Loud., the so-called "Dwarf" or "Mountain" juniper, a prostrate, spreading shrub growing prolifically on dry, sunny slopes in the Tyrolean Mountains, at altitudes up to 2,500 m. This bush invades pastures; but being an abode for mice and rats, it is avoided by cattle, and represents a great nuisance to the dairy farmer. Because of its small size, and the high altitudes at which this bush grows, collection of the berries is now much too costly to make adulteration of true juniper berries with berries from var. *nana* profitable.

Another adulterant of juniper berries, formerly used quite extensively, is the berry of *Juniperus oxycedrus* L., the so-called "Prickly Juniper." This shrub grows wild and profusely in Spain, Italy (particularly in eastern Venezia and Istria), Dalmatia, Hungary and other countries where *Juniperus communis* L. also thrives. The berries of the species *oxycedrus* have a reddish color, and are larger than those of the species *communis*. The former possess a characteristic turpentine-like note, which is very undesirable in flavors. Years ago, genuine juniper berries were often adulterated with those of *oxycedrus*, particularly in Trieste and Leghorn, the principal shipping ports for juniper berries in Italy. Today official standards for the berries are so strict that *oxycedrus* berries can no longer be used for the purpose of adulteration. Besides, collection of the *oxycedrus* berries is now just as expensive as that of the true juniper berries.

Distillation and Yield of Oil.—The essential oil of juniper berries now being offered on the market originates in either of the two following ways:

1. The bulk of today's juniper berry oil is a by-product in the distillation of the above-mentioned alcoholic "Borovička" ("Brinjevec" in Slovenian) beverages popular in Slavic countries, and "Steinhäger" liquors well known in Germany and Austria. These beverages are produced in numer-

---

[5] A. Rehder, "Manual of Cultivated Trees and Shrubs Hardy in North America," New York, The Macmillan Company (1949), 62.
[6] *Pharm. Acta Helv.* **13** (1938), 307. Through *Chem. Abstracts* **34** (1940), 849.

ous small and medium-sized distilleries, particularly in Czechoslovakia, Yugoslavia, Hungary, and the Tyrol. For this purpose the berries of *Juniperus communis* L. are crushed, immersed in warm water and fermented. After completion of the fermentation process, the mass is pumped into a still provided with a stirring device and a short rectification column, and is distilled with constant stirring. The distillate consists of a mixture of water, alcohol, and essential oil. This crude distillate is then rectified until an alcoholic liquor containing from 40 to 50 per cent of alcohol is obtained. Being only slightly soluble in 50 per cent alcohol, most of the essential oil contained in the distillate separates in the receiver as a distinct layer, and must be removed. Small and medium-sized distilleries sell their juniper oil, obtained as by-product, to the larger distilleries, which bulk the numerous small lots, and usually submit the bulking to final rectification. The type of oil thus obtained constitutes the large part of commercial juniper oil, particularly that offered on the American market.

Depending upon the quality of the berries, and the method of fermentation and rectification employed, 1,000 kg. of juniper berries yield from 16 to 18 liters of alcoholic beverage (containing 50 per cent of alcohol), and from 5 to 6 kg. of essential oil.

In judging the quality of this oil, it should be kept in mind that during distillation the essential oil separating in the receiver is actually submitted to extraction with an aqueous-alcoholic medium containing 40 to 50 per cent of alcohol. Certain constituents of the oil, and particularly the more easily soluble, oxygenated (and, incidentally, most valuable) odoriferous components will go into the solution. In fact, the finished alcoholic beverage owes its characteristic flavor to the constituents which have been extracted from the oil. The essential oil, on the other hand, will be partly deprived of these oxygenated components, and will consist chiefly of terpenes insoluble in 40 to 50 per cent alcohol.

2. The best quality of juniper berry oil is obtained by regular distillation of the berries, without any previous alcoholic fermentation. Depending upon the quality and origin of the berries, the yield of oil in this case ranges from 0.8 to 1.6 per cent. Italian and good Hungarian berries give the best yield, those from cold, northern countries the lowest yield.

Juniper berry oils obtained by regular distillation exhibit the full and rich aroma characteristic of the berries; they have a deeper and milder odor and flavor than the oils obtained as by-product in the alcoholic distillation of the berries. The latter oils can often be recognized by their terpene-like odor.

Obviously the oils obtained by regular distillation of the berries must fetch a considerably higher price than the by-product oils. To offset the higher cost of production in the regular distillation of the berries, some essential oil houses in Europe submit the residual berries (after distillation) to repeated extraction with warm water. By concentrating the aqueous extracts *in vacuo*, a syrup of 40° to 42° Bé., and consisting chiefly of invert sugar, will be obtained. The yield, calculated upon the berries, varies between 30 and 38 per cent. This concentrate is the well known *Succus juniperi*, a product formerly used widely as a diuretic and sudorific in European pharmacy.

Other producers submit the residual berries (after regular distillation) to fermentation and alcoholic distillation, because they still contain very small quantities of essential oil. However, any alcoholic distillate of berries already exhausted by steam distillation will obviously be of poor quality.

Physicochemical Properties.—The volatile oil derived from the berries of *Juniperus communis* L. is a mobile, colorless or light yellow-greenish liquid with a peculiar odor characteristic of the berries. The flavor is somewhat burning and bitter. On aging, the oil becomes more viscous, the specific gravity increases, and the odor assumes a note reminiscent of oxidized turpentine oils or other essential oils containing a high percentage of terpenes.

The physicochemical properties of a juniper berry oil are of help chiefly in detecting gross adulteration. They vary too widely—depending upon origin of the berries, method of distillation and age of the oil—to be of much help in judging quality. For this purpose, therefore, careful organoleptic tests must be resorted to. As regards odor and flavor, the best oils are those obtained from Tuscan berries by regular distillation.

Genuine juniper berry oils imported by Fritzsche Brothers, Inc., New York, from various parts of Europe (Italy, Hungary, Czechoslovakia, Yugoslavia and the Tyrol) had properties varying within these limits:

Specific Gravity at 25°/25°...... 0.860 to 0.875, usually between 0.862 and 0.868
Optical Rotation............... −7° 45′ to −13° 6′, occasionally as low as −5° 46′
Refractive Index at 20°......... 1.4780 to 1.4819, occasionally as low as 1.4758
Saponification Number.......... 2.8 to 8.4
Solubility..................... Sometimes soluble in 0.5 vol. of 95% alcohol. Usually opalescent to cloudy in 95% alcohol up to 10 vol.

These shipments included oils obtained as by-products in the alcoholic distillation of the berries, and oils derived by regular steam distillation of the berries.

The following properties are those of pure oils collected by the author in various parts of Europe, when surveying the production of juniper berry oil. These oils were by-products in the alcoholic distillation of berries:

	Czechoslovakia	*Yugoslavia*	*Hungary*
Specific Gravity at 25°.......	0.863 to 0.870	0.862 to 0.870	0.859
Optical Rotation............	−8° 6′ to −9° 36′	−10° 30′ to −11° 52′	−9° 32′
Refractive Index at 20°......	1.4795 to 1.4818	1.4778 to 1.4827	1.4763
Acid Number..............	1.3 to 1.5	1.3 to 1.5	1.4
Ester Number.............	3.3 to 5.1	4.2 to 6.1	3.3
Ester Number after Acetylation.....................	25.2 to 29.9	24.3 to 34.5	19.6
Solubility in 95% Alcohol, at 25°	From clearly soluble to slightly opalescent in 0.5 vol., cloudy with more. A few oils insoluble in alcohol		

As regards the oils obtained by regular distillation of the berries (without alcohol), the following properties are noted by Gildemeister and Hoffmann,[7] for oils distilled by Schimmel & Co.:

Specific Gravity at 15°..............	0.867 to 0.882
Optical Rotation.................	Usually laevorotatory up to −13°; seldom optically inactive. Occasionally slightly dextrorotatory (cf. below)
Refractive Index at 20°.............	1.472 to 1.484
Acid Number.....................	Up to 3
Ester Number.....................	1 to 12
Ester Number after Acetylation......	19 to 31
Solubility........................	Sparingly soluble in alcohol, particularly in dilute alcohol. For solution, from 5 to 10 vol. of 90% alcohol are required. Many oils are not clearly soluble in 90% alcohol. Freshly distilled oils are usually clearly soluble in 90% alcohol, older oils in most cases not without turbidity

Boiling Range:

160° to 165°.....................	4 to 5%
165° to 170°.....................	12 to 26%
170° to 175°.....................	11 to 16%
175° to 180°.....................	7 to 12%
180° to 190°.....................	7 to 10%
190° to 200°.....................	4 to 6%
Above 200°......................	38 to 44%

Two oils derived by regular distillation of juniper berries in Carniola (Yugoslavia), and collected by the author, exhibited these values:

	I	*II*
Specific Gravity at 25°.............	0.868	0.859
Optical Rotation.................	−6° 30′	−3° 30′
Refractive Index at 20°.............	1.4801	1.4759
Acid Number.....................	1.4	1.4
Ester Number....................	5.1	3.3

[7] "Die Ätherischen Öle," 3d Ed., Vol. II, 257.

	I	II
Ester Number after Acetylation......	31.7	28.9
Solubility in 95% Alcohol...........	Clearly soluble in 0.5 vol., cloudy with more	

Oils produced under the author's supervision in Seillans (Var), France by regular distillation of juniper berries imported from Tuscany, had these properties:

Specific Gravity at 25°.........	0.865 to 0.872
Optical Rotation..............	−3° 34′ to −9° 20′
Refractive Index at 20°........	1.4790 to 1.4842
Saponification Number.........	4.6 to 4.8
Solubility in 95% Alcohol......	Soluble in 0.5 vol.; opalescent to cloudy with more alcohol

The values cited below afford a fairly good example of the properties of oils obtained by regular distillation of the berries (I), and those of an oil derived as by-product in alcoholic distillation (II). Both oils originated from Hungary:

	I	II
Specific Gravity at 25°.............	0.860	0.859
Optical Rotation...................	−7° 37′	−11° 2′
Refractive Index at 20°............	1.4780	1.4770
Acid Number.....................	0.6	0.7
Ester Number....................	3.6	5.1
Ester Number after Acetylation......	18.1	14.0
Solubility in 95% Alcohol..........	Soluble in 1 vol. and more	Soluble in 0.5 vol.; faintly opalescent with more

As far as the optical rotation of juniper berry oil is concerned, the oils usually exhibit laevorotation. In fact, the National Formulary [8] specifies a rotation (at 25°) of 0° to −15°. Nevertheless, slight dextrorotation may occasionally be encountered in genuine oils, particularly those from Italy. Gildemeister and Hoffmann (see above) mention that some juniper berry oils of unquestionable purity are slightly dextrorotatory. The present author, himself, had occasion to examine dextrorotatory oils from Italy. Palazzo and Alinari [9] analyzed numerous Italian juniper berry oils and found in most cases laevorotation (up to −18°, even −20°), but occasionally slight dextrorotation (+2° to +3°) in oils obtained by regular distillation. Pronounced dextrorotation, however, must be viewed with suspicion because it may indicate the presence of an oil distilled from leaves (needles) of the juniper plant. Jermstadt,[10] for example, examined six Norwegian

[8] Ninth Edition, 282.
[9] *Ann. R. Istituto sup. forest. naz.* **6** (1921), 1.
[10] *Norg. Apotekerforen. Tids.* (1928), No. 5 and 6.

"Juniper Berry Oils," and reported optical rotations ranging from $+33° 20'$ to $+41°$. However, it should be mentioned that the Norwegian Pharmacopoeia defines as "Juniper Berry Oil" an oil distilled from the berries *and young shoots* of the juniper plant. Such oils exhibit an off-odor characteristic of juniper leaves.

As can be judged from the tables of physicochemical properties, oil of juniper berries is only slightly soluble in 90 per cent alcohol, occasionally not clearly soluble even in 95 per cent alcohol. The National Formulary [11] requires that the oil dissolve in 4 vol. of alcohol with either cloudiness or turbidity. On dilution to 10 vol., the solution should show no separation of oily globules after standing for 12 hr.

Freshly distilled oils are usually clearly soluble in 90 per cent alcohol, but on aging the oils lose most of their solubility, becoming soluble only with turbidity. Oils partly deterpenated (by fractionation or extraction with dilute alcohol) are particularly liable to undergo a decrease in solubility (Gildemeister and Hoffmann).

During World War II the imported juniper berry oil was no longer available in the United States and distillers were therefore forced to use the North American berries (see the discussion under "North American Berries," p. 373). Oils distilled by Fritzsche Brothers, Inc., New York, from domestic juniper berries had properties varying within these limits:

Specific Gravity at 25°/25° . . . . . . 0.833 to 0.852
Optical Rotation . . . . −9° 25' to −21° 0'
Refractive Index at 20° . . . . 1.4758 to 1.4801
Acid Number . . . . Up to 2.9
Saponification Number . . . . 1.9 to 15.8
Solubility . . . . Sometimes soluble in 0.5 to 10 vol. of 95% alcohol. Usually opalescent to cloudy in 95% alcohol up to 10 vol.

Because the odor and flavor of these domestic oils were much inferior to the European product, the use of these domestic berries was immediately discontinued as soon as imports from Europe again were available.

Chemical Composition.—The chemical composition of the volatile oil derived from the berries of *Juniperus communis* L. was investigated more than a century ago by Zaubzer,[12] Buchner,[13] Blanchet,[14] Dumas,[15] and

---

[11] Ninth Edition, 282.
[12] *Repert. f. d. Pharm.* **22** (1825), 415. Cf. Gildemeister and Hoffmann, "Die Ätherischen Öle," 3d Ed., Vol. II, 260.
[13] *Repert. f. d. Pharm.* **22** (1825), 425. Cf. Gildemeister and Hoffmann, "Die Ätherischen Öle," 3d Ed., Vol. II, 260.
[14] *Liebigs Ann.* **7** (1833), 167.
[15] *Ibid.* **15** (1835), 159.

Soubeiran and Capitaine,[16] but their work brought few concrete results. We owe our present knowledge of the composition of the oil chiefly to the later investigations carried out by Wallach,[17] Schimmel & Co.,[18] Haensel,[19] Palazzo and Alinari,[20] and Casparis and Freund,[21] who reported the presence of the following compounds in the oil:

α-Pinene. Identified in the fraction b. 156°–159° by means of the nitrosochloride m. 109°–110° and the nitrolbenzylamine m. 123°–124° (Wallach, and Schimmel & Co.). β-Pinene is not present in this fraction (Haensel).

Camphene. In the fraction b. 161°. Characterized by hydration to borneol and isoborneol (Schimmel & Co.).

Junene(?). According to Palazzo and Alinari, juniper oil derived from *Italian* berries contains no pinene or camphene, but a hydrocarbon, probably olefinic, b_{13} 60°–65°, d_{15} 0.8378, α_D^{16} +18° 56'. The specific gravity of this compound was lower than that of pinene and camphene.

More recently Casparis and Freund isolated a hydrocarbon $C_{10}H_{16}$, b. 164°–166°, d_4^{20} 0.8242, α_4^{20} +19° 36', which they named "Junene" (cf. Vol. II of the present work, p. 746). It had strongly diuretic properties. The juniper berry oils investigated by Casparis and Freund contained α-pinene, camphene, and cadinene.

1-Terpinen-4-ol. To isolate the oxygenated compounds, Schimmel & Co. extracted the oil repeatedly with 70 per cent alcohol, and after removal of the solvent by distillation, obtained an oil of pleasant juniper odor; d_{15} 0.9300; α_D −3° 44'; ester number 21.8; ester number after acetylation 136; alcohol content, calculated as $C_{10}H_{18}O$, 41.65%; alcohol content, determined as $C_{10}H_{18}O$ in the oil after dilution with xylene, 56.2%. (Details concerning 1-terpinen-4-ol will be found in Vol. II of this work, p. 198.)

Other Alcohols(?). Treating the fraction b_8 95°–130° of the oil with phthalic anhydride, Schimmel & Co. isolated very small quantities of an alcohol mixture b. 218°–226°, b_8 105°–110°, d_{15} 0.9476, α_D −4° 30', n_D^{22} 1.48248; its odor was reminiscent of geraniol and borneol.

Submitting the higher boiling fractions of a juniper berry oil to treatment with phthalic anhydride, Haensel isolated small quantities of a primary alcohol $C_{10}H_{18}O$.

Unidentified Compounds(?). According to Schimmel & Co., the fraction b_8 72°–88° contains small quantities of compounds with a particularly characteristic odor.

Cadinene. Identified in the fraction b. 260°–275° by means of the dihydrochloride m. 118° (Schimmel & Co.).

Crystalline Compounds(?). On standing for a prolonged period in a cool place, the last runs of juniper berry oil separate crystals which, after repeated recrystalliza-

[16] *Ibid.* **34** (1840), 324.

[17] *Ibid.* **227** (1885), 288.

[18] *Ber. Schimmel & Co.,* April (1890), 43; October (1895), 46; October (1909), 120; October (1910), 128.

[19] *Chem. Zentr.* (1908), II, 1437.

[20] *Atti congresso naz. chim. pura applicata* (1923), 309. *Ber. Schimmel & Co.* (1925), 90.

[21] *Pharm. Acta Helv.* **14** (1939), 1.

tion from alcohol, melt at 165°–166° (Schimmel & Co.). The older literature (see above) refers to these crystals as "juniper camphor," "juniper stearoptene" or "juniper hydrate."

Use.—Juniper berry oil is used widely in essences for the flavoring of beverages and liqueurs, particularly of the gin and sloe gin type. Several European liquors, "Steinhäger" among them, owe their characteristic flavor chiefly to the presence of juniper berry oil.

The oil has been known for a long time as a diuretic. Because of its local irritating effect on inflamed organs, however, great care must be exercised in its dosage.

Suggested Additional Literature

B. Augustin, "Die Ungarischen Wacholderbeeren," *Riechstoff Ind.* **7** (1932), 170.

OIL OF *JUNIPERUS OXYCEDRUS* L.

Juniperus oxycedrus L. (fam. *Cupressaceae*) is a common shrub or small tree growing wild in stony places and on barren hillsides of Mediterranean and Near East countries, from Spain and North Africa as far east as the Caucasus and Iran. In some sections it occurs at altitudes up to 3,000 ft. The numerous "berries"[1] are red-brown, much larger than those of *Juniperus communis* L., but of inferior odor and flavor. The odor recalls turpentine oil. The woody parts of the tree serve for the empyreumatic distillation of cade oil, which is produced chiefly in Spain (see below).

A. Berry Oil

According to Gildemeister and Hoffmann,[2] steam distillation of the berries of *Juniperus oxycedrus* L. yields from 1.3 to 1.5 per cent of an essential oil, with a specific gravity of 0.839 to 0.854 at 15°, and an optical rotation of −4° 40′ to −8° 30′. The oil is not clearly soluble in alcohol.

Palazzo and Alinari[3] reported that an oil derived from Istrian berries

---

[1] They are not berries in the botanical sense.
[2] "Die Ätherischen Öle," 3d Ed., Vol. II, 265.
[3] *Atti congresso naz. chim. pura applicata* (1923), 314. *Ber. Schimmel & Co.* (1925), 42.

by steam distillation contained pinene (probably) and an olefinic terpene of the myrcene type (d_{15} 0.8025).

The berry oil is not produced on a commercial scale.

B. Leaf Oil

Steam-distilling leaves and terminal branchlets of *Juniperus oxycedrus* L. in the Crimean Peninsula, Rutovski and Vinogradova [4] obtained 0.01 per cent of an essential oil with an odor reminiscent of fir needle oils. The oil had these properties:

Specific Gravity at 20°/20°...... 0.9720
Optical Rotation............... +16° 19′
Refractive Index at 20°........ 1.4956
Acid Number.................. 2.0
Ester Number................. 50.68
Solubility................... Soluble in 0.5 vol.
of 90% alcohol

The leaf oil is not produced on a commercial scale.

C. Steam-Distilled Wood Oil

The essential oil derived from the woody part of the branches by steam distillation was first described by Huerre,[5] who reported these properties:

Specific Gravity at 15°....... 0.925 to 0.927
Optical Rotation at 20°...... −31° 25′
Solubility.................. Soluble in 12 vol. of
90% alcohol
Boiling Range at 760 mm..... 260°–300° (73 per cent
of the oil distills be-
tween 260° and 280°)

Huerre [6] found that the oil contains an average of 21.11 per cent of *l-cadinene*. The maximum cadinene content observed by Huerre was 30.59 per cent.

Gattefossé and Igolen [7] steam-distilled comminuted heartwood of *Juniperus oxycedrus* L., originating from Morocco, and obtained an oil of balsamic, turpentine-like odor. The properties were:

Specific Gravity at 15°....... 0.9476
Optical Rotation............ −21° 4′
Refractive Index at 20°...... 1.5145
Ketone Content, Calculated as
$C_{15}H_{22}O$ (Hot Oximation).. 13.6%

[4] *Riechstoff Ind.* (1926), 216.
[5] *J. pharm. chim.* [7], **12** (1915), 273.
[6] *Ibid.* [7], **23** (1921), 81.
[7] *Ind. parfum.* **4** (1949), 111.

Sontag[8] submitted this type of oil to a closer investigation. Steam-distilling the wood of *Juniperus oxycedrus* L., he obtained 1.5 per cent of an amber-colored, viscous essential oil, with these properties:

Specific Gravity at 15°........................ 0.9632
Optical Rotation at 16°........................ −28° 34′
Refractive Index at 20°........................ 1.5125
Acid Number................................... 0.84
Ester Number.................................. 6.31
Ester Number after Acetylation................. 58.92
Ester Number after Formylation................ 94
Ketone Content, Calculated as $C_{15}H_{24}O$.......... 6.54%
Aldehyde Content (Bisulfite Method)............ About 0.3%
Acid and Phenol Content (Determined with 3% NaOH sol.)................................ About 1%

Sontag[9] reported the presence of the following compounds in the essential oil derived by steam distillation of the wood:

Sesquiterpenes (70%).............. *l*-β-Caryophyllene
                                   l-Cadinene (large quantities)
                                   Cedrene (smaller quantities)

Sesquiterpene Alcohols (5 to 10%)... Pseudocedrol (more than 50%)
                                     Two sesquiterpene alcohols (not identified)

Ketones and Aldehydes (3 to 4%)... Carvone(?)
                                    A ketone (identified with that of vetiver)
                                    Three ketones (isolated, but not identified)

Phenols (0.3%).................... *p*-Cresol (traces)

Acids (0.7%)

The essential oil derived by steam distillation of the wood of *Juniperus oxycedrus* L. was also investigated by Mousseron, Granger and Ronayroux,[10] who arrived at results differing from those of Sontag (see above). These authors reported the following composition:

l-Cadinol. About 40 per cent of the essential oil (cf. Vol. II of the present work, p. 277).

d-Cadinene. For properties see Vol. II, p. 93.

A Sesquiterpene $C_{15}H_{24}$. Less abundant than *d*-cadinene; it had these properties: b_{20} 132°, d_{25} 0.9112, $[\alpha]_{546}$ −27° 0′, $[\alpha]_{579}$ −23° 37′, n_D^{25} 1.50167. Reduction of this sesquiterpene gave a hydrocarbon $C_{15}H_{28}$, b_{20} 130°, d_{25} 0.8969, $[\alpha]_{546}$ −2° 5′, $[\alpha]_{579}$ −1° 38′, n_D^{25} 1.48830.

A Sesquiterpene Alcohol $C_{15}H_{26}O$. Mousseron et al. also isolated from the essential oil 5 per cent of a sesquiterpene alcohol $C_{15}H_{26}O$, isomeric with cadinol; it had these properties: m. 118°–119°, $[\alpha]_{546}$ −103° 30′, $[\alpha]_{579}$ −89° 12′ (2.85 per cent sol. in benzene).

[8] *Rev. marques parfums France* **17** (1939), 5.   [10] *Compt. rend.* **208** (1939), 1411.
[9] *Ibid.*

The steam-distilled type of wood oil (essential oil) is not produced on a commercial scale.

D. *Empyreumatic Wood Oil*
(Oil of Cade)

Empyreumatic (destructive) distillation of the wood of *Juniperus oxycedrus* L. yields the so-called oil of cade, known in pharmacy also as "Juniper Tar" or *Pix juniperi*. Huerre [11] has pointed out that in the process of empyreumatic distillation the oil contained in the wood distills over as volatile (essential) oil, *and* as partly decomposed (empyreumatic) oil. The former acts as a solvent for the latter, which consists of heavier tar-like substances. In other words, the cade oil of commerce is a mixture or solution of essential oil, and partly decomposed empyreumatic oil. Often, on prolonged standing of a lot, a part of the tar-like portion separates from the solution, forming a deposit (see below).

Oil of cade is produced chiefly in Spain, particularly in the province of Malaga, centers of production being Tolox and picturesque Ronda. The best quality of cade oil originates from this section, which enjoys a warm, distinctly Mediterranean, climate. A different type of oil comes from the province of Cuenca; in fact, the physicochemical properties of the oil from Cuenca differ so widely from those of the Malaga type of oil that Spanish producers are inclined to assume it originates from a different plant species. The problem has never been thoroughly investigated, because the places in the hills where the oil is produced are so primitive and so difficult of access that city people hesitate to visit them.

Prior to the outbreak of the Spanish Civil War in 1936, Spain produced an average of 150 metric tons of cade oil per year. More recently, production has declined to about 60 tons annually, owing principally to reduced demand on the world market.

Prior to distillation, wood from the trunk, branches, and roots of *Juniperus oxycedrus* L. is cut into pieces; these pieces are stacked on a concave slab, from the center of which a pipe leads downward (descending distillation). An iron pot above the slab is heated by means of burning wood coal. The heat thus created forces the essential oil from the wood, at the same time causing some decomposition of the oil. The end product is thus a complex of the essential oil, its own decomposition products, and additional pyrogenous substances distilled from the wood itself. The yield of oil averages 1.2 to 1.3 per cent.

Physicochemical Properties.—Oil of cade or "Juniper Tar" is a dark red-brown, clear, viscous liquid with a strong empyreumatic, tar-like odor, and a warm, bitter taste.

[11] *J. pharm. chim.* [9], **23** (1941), 441. Cf. *ibid.* [7], **19** (1919), 33, 65.

Reliable exporters in Spain submit the lots arriving from the producing regions to careful inspection, which includes determination of the specific gravity, moisture content and solubility in benzene. A test for the presence (absence!) of rosin is always included, because field distillers or intermediaries occasionally adulterate the oil with rosin. A procedure for this test will be found in Vol. I of the present work, p. 334.

As was mentioned above, on prolonged standing, oil of cade often separates a very dark, tar-like deposit on the bottom of the container. The quantity of this deposit (which is practically insoluble in petroleum ether) appears to depend upon the moisture content of the oil, being in direct proportion to it. Many drums of cade oil arriving in the United States contain a heavy black deposit, which the American essential oil importers usually separate before offering the clear oil on the market. The samples of cade oil described below, were drawn by Fritzsche Brothers, Inc., New York, for the purpose of analysis, from the *clear* part of the drum contents.

The specific gravity of these oils determined on numerous shipments from Spain has varied between 0.959 and 1.005 at 25°/25°. The test for rosin was found to be negative in all shipments of genuine grade oil.

Oil of cade is very slightly soluble in water, soluble in 9 vol. of 95 per cent alcohol, and only partially soluble in petroleum ether.

For further tests the reader should consult the United States Pharmacopoeia and other official standard works.

To offer a light-colored cade oil to consumers who cannot use the natural dark oil, some essential oil houses rectify the crude oil *in vacuo*. The properties of several lots of rectified cade oil prepared by Fritzsche Brothers, Inc., New York, have varied within the following limits:

Specific Gravity at 25°/25°........ 0.952 to 0.961
Optical Rotation................. +4° 17' to +4° 40'
Refractive Index at 20°.......... 1.5110 to 1.5200
Solubility....................... Soluble in 5 vol. of 95%
                                  alcohol and more

Chemical Composition.—It has been known for a long time that cade oil contains *cadinene* (a sesquiterpene $C_{15}H_{24}$, b. 273°–275°), *hydrocarbons* b. 210°–400°, and phenols, among them *creosol, pyrocatechol* derivatives, *guaiacol,* and its ethyl and propyl derivatives.

In 1939, Mousseron, Granger and Ronayroux [12] submitted the empyreumatic oil, obtained by destructive distillation of the wood of *Juniperus oxycedrus* L. (oil of cade), to a close investigation, also examining the essential oil derived by steam distillation of the wood (see above). Mousseron and his collaborators found that in regard to chemical composition

12 *Compt. rend.* **208** (1939), 1411.

the essential oil closely resembles the *neutral* portion of cade oil. Mousseron et al. reported the presence of the following compounds in oil of cade:

d-Cadinene. (Cf. Vol. II of the present work, p. 93.)

A Sesquiterpene $C_{15}H_{24}$. Less abundant than *d*-cadinene. Regarding the properties of this sesquiterpene, see the findings of Mousseron et al. described above, in the section on the chemical composition of the *essential* oil from the wood.

l-Cadinol. (Cf. Vol. II of the present work, p. 277.) The empyreumatic oil contains only 10 per cent of *l*-cadinol, whereas the essential oil contains about 40 per cent (see above).

Dimethylnaphthalene. Present only in the empyreumatic oil, but not in the essential oil. Regenerated from its picrate m. 105°, the compound was a liquid b_{20} 133°, d_{25} 0.9993, n_D^{25} 1.60004.

Use.—Oil of cade is widely employed in the treatment of chronic eczema and other skin diseases. The native population of Mediterranean countries have used the oil since early times for the healing of cutaneous diseases of domestic animals.

The oil is used also in medicinal soaps, to which it imparts not only a strong odor, but also therapeutic properties.

Suggested Additional Literature

L. Danzel, *"Juniperus oxycedrus* Tar ('Oil of Cade') in Human Pharmacy, Zoöpharmacy, and Phytopharmacy," *Produits Pharm.* 2 (1947), 251. *Chem. Abstracts* **41** (1947), 7677.

OIL OF SAVIN

Essence de Sabin   *Aceite Esencial Sabino*   *Sadebaumöl*
Oleum Sabinae

Botany and Habitat.—*Juniperus sabina* L. (fam. *Cupressaceae*) is a shrub or small tree attaining a height of as much as 5 m., and growing wild in the mountains of central and southern Europe. On steam distillation the ends of the branches and the attached leaves yield an essential oil that is used in certain pharmaceutical preparations. The true savin oil must not be confused with that occasionally distilled in southern France from related *Juniperus* species, notably *J. phoenicea* L. and *J. thurifera* L. var. *gallica* De Coincy. The physicochemical properties and chemical composition of the oils derived from these latter species and varieties differ substantially from those of the true savin oil.

Chief producing regions of savin oil are in the Tyrol, particularly in the Oetz, Puster, and Virgen Valleys, and around the Hoch Tauern Mountains. In Tyrolean sagas it is said that the plant was introduced to the Tyrol by returning Crusaders. In Switzerland the bush has been practically exterminated because it has been found that it acts as host to a fungus which destroys pear trees. In the Tyrol permission to cut the bushes is granted by the government without charge. The peasants gather the distillation material throughout the year, whenever they are not busy with other work, and even in the winter, provided the slopes are free of snow. For cutting, the collectors use short, curved knives. After three to four years the bushes grow again to full height.

Prior to distillation the branches are reduced to short lengths. Distillation of one charge requires 12 to 15 hr. The yield of oil ranges from 1.5 to 1.6 per cent, but may be higher under favorable conditions.

Physicochemical Properties.—Oil of savin is a colorless to slightly yellow liquid of sharp, somewhat disagreeable odor and pungent, camphoraceous taste.

According to Gildemeister and Hoffmann,[1] the physicochemical properties of savin oil vary within these limits:

Specific Gravity at 15°. . . . . 0.907 to 0.930
Optical Rotation. . . . . +38° 0' to +62° 0'
Refractive Index at 20°. . . . . 1.473 to 1.480
Acid Number. Up to 3
Ester Number. 91 to 138
Ester Number after Acetylation. . . . . 127 to 154
Solubility. . . . . Soluble in 0.5 and more vol. of 90% alcohol. Soluble in 3.5 to 15 vol., usually in 6 to 8 vol., of 80% alcohol, but not always clearly soluble

Shipments of pure savin oils from the Tyrol examined by Fritzsche Brothers, Inc., New York, exhibited properties ranging within the following limits:

Specific Gravity at 25°/25°. . . . . 0.905 to 0.917
Optical Rotation. . . . . +57° 16' to +62° 53'
Refractive Index at 20°. . . . . 1.4718 to 1.4740
Ester Number. 117.6 to 138.0
Ester Number after Acetylation. . . . . 144.8 to 157.7
Solubility. . . . . Soluble in 0.5 vol. of 90% alcohol and more. Often soluble in 5 to 6.5 vol. of 80% alcohol and more; sometimes with slight turbidity

[1] "Die Ätherischen Öle," 3d Ed., Vol. II, 276.

Two genuine savin oils procured by the author while surveying essential oil production in the Tyrol had these properties:

	Oil from the Virgen Valley	Oil from the Oetz Valley
Specific Gravity at 15°..............	0.928	0.913
Optical Rotation..................	+64° 30'	+59° 40'
Refractive Index at 20°...........	1.4722	1.4726
Ester Number....................	126.8	117.5
Ester Number after Acetylation....	181.6	156.2
Solubility........................	Soluble in 0.5 vol. and more of 90% alcohol	Soluble in 0.5 vol. and more of 90% alcohol
Boiling Range:		
Up to 165°......................	2.0%	1.60%
165° to 170°....................	1.5%	3.20%
170° to 175°....................	3.5%	6.40%
175° to 180°....................	5.0%	14.40%
180° to 185°....................	7.0%	5.60%
185° to 190°....................	7.5%	5.60%
190° to 195°....................	5.0%	4.6%
195° to 200°....................	10.5%	7.0%
200° to 210°....................	13.0%	6.0%
210° to 220°....................	8.0%	11.6%
220° to 230°....................	23.0%	9.2%
230° to 240°....................	11.5%	17.2%
240° and above (decomposition products and residue).........	2.5%	7.6%

Years ago Fromm,[2] and Semmler [3] observed that, upon repeated fractionation of the oil, from 25 to 30 per cent of the oil distills over below 175°. The importance of the boiling range in evaluating the purity of a savin oil was stressed more recently by Manceau, Revol and Vernet [4] who found that in the case of a genuine savin oil only a small quantity distills below 170°–180°. If more than 25 to 30 per cent of the oil distills over below 170°–180°, the oil in question is probably not a true savin oil (*Juniperus sabina* L.) but adulterated with the French type of savin oil (*Juniperus phoenicea* L.) or with turpentine oil.

Chemical Composition.—The chemical composition of savin oil has been investigated by Wallach,[5] Schimmel & Co.,[6] Fromm,[7] Semmler,[8] Elze,[9] and

[2] *Ber.* **33** (1900), 1192.

[3] *Ibid.*, 1463.

[4] *Bull. sci. pharmacol.* **43** (1936), 14.   *Chem. Zentr.* (1936), II, 1261.

[5] *Liebigs Ann.* **238** (1887), 82.

[6] *Ber. Schimmel & Co.*, October (1895), 40; April (1900), 40; October (1900), 59; April (1903), 71; October (1907), 80; April (1908), 84; April (1911), 101.

[7] *Ber.* **31** (1898), 2025; **33** (1900), 1192, 1210.

[8] *Ber.* **33** (1900), 1463.

[9] *Chem. Ztg.* **34** (1910), 767.

Agnew and Croad,[10] who reported the presence of the following compounds in the oil:

n-Decyl Aldehyde. In the foreruns of the oil Elze identified small quantities of *n*-decanal.

α-Pinene. Very small quantities only; in the fraction b. 160° (Agnew and Croad).

d- and *l*-Sabinene. Examining the fraction b. 162°–165° Semmler first noted the presence of *d*-sabinene in the oil. Later Agnew and Croad found that the oil which they investigated contained *l*-sabinene (cf. Vol. II of the present work, p. 64).

α-Terpinene. In the fraction b. 170°–180°; identified by Schimmel & Co.,[11] who prepared the nitrosite m. 156°.

d-Sabinol. The chief constituent; present in the fraction b. 210°–213°. This alcohol $C_{10}H_{16}O$, b$_3$ 77°–78°, was first isolated from the oil by Fromm, and named sabinol (cf. Vol. II, p. 230).

d-Sabinyl Acetate. Sabinol occurs in the oil partly free, partly esterified, the most important ester being the acetate. Sabinyl acetate b$_3$ 81°–83°, d$_{15}$ 0.972, has a high optical rotation, viz., $α_D$ +79° (Elze).

An Aldehyde(?). In the fraction boiling above 222°, Schimmel & Co.[12] observed a compound b$_{20}$ 127°–129°, d$_{16}$ 0.9163, $α_D$ +11° 40′, which reacted with bisulfite solution and possessed an odor similar to cuminaldehyde. The substance in question was probably an aldehyde, because it formed a phenylhydrazone m. 40°–45°, and an oxime m. 85°.

Citronellol. Identified by Schimmel & Co.[13] in the fraction b. 220°–227°.

Geraniol. Identified by Elze in the last runs of a savin oil.

Dihydrocuminyl Alcohol. Also observed by Elze in the last runs of the oil. Identified by means of its naphthylurethane m. 146°–147°.

Cadinene. In the highest boiling fractions of the oil Wallach noted the presence of cadinene.

The distillation waters of the oil contain *methyl alcohol, furfural* and *diacetyl* (Schimmel & Co.[14]).

Use.—Formerly oil of savin was used as an antirheumatic, vermifuge and emmenagogue but, because of its toxicity and irritating effects, the oil has lost much of its former importance.

SUGGESTED ADDITIONAL LITERATURE

E. Belani, "Tyrolean Pine Needle Oils," *Deut. Parfümerieztg.* **27** (1941), 264. *Ber. Schimmel & Co.* (1942–43), 58.

[10] *Analyst* **37** (1912), 295. Cf. Henderson et al., *J. Chem. Soc.* **95** (1908), 289, 1465.
[11] *Ber. Schimmel & Co.*, April (1911), 101.
[12] *Ibid.*, April (1900), 40.
[13] *Ibid.*, October (1907), 80.
[14] *Ibid.*, October (1900), 59; April (1903), 71.

BOTANICAL CLASSIFICATION OF ESSENTIAL OIL PLANTS

by

Theodor Philipp Haas, Ph.D.

In the Prefaces to Volumes III, IV, V, and VI it has been pointed out that the essential oils described in this series are grouped within the botanical families of the plants from which the oils are derived. However, the plant families themselves, in these volumes, do not follow any definite taxonomic system, but rather considerations of utility and facility. To satisfy botanists and botanically inclined chemists, therefore, it seems desirable to include here a table of the various essential oils arranged according to a recognized taxonomic system. This may appear a bold undertaking since modern botanists differ widely upon certain points of their science, which many consider an art as well as a science.

The following table lists the families and genera of those plants from which the oils described in Volumes III, IV, V, and VI of this series are derived.[1] With the exception of the *Gramineae,* this table is arranged according to A. Engler's "Syllabus der Pflanzenfamilien," 11th Ed., revised by L. Diels, and published in Berlin in 1936. The arrangement of the *Gramineae* employed in the table follows the more recently published "Die natürlichen Pflanzenfamilien," Vol. 14e, 2nd Ed., by A. Engler and K. Prantl, revised by R. Pilger, and published in Leipzig in 1940.

The taxonomic system of Engler has been used here because it is the only such system that has been worked out completely (for which reason it is also used by most herbaria). Engler's classification embraces 320 families of the higher flowering plants (the subdivision *Angiospermae*). It would be difficult to say how many of these families contain plants yielding essential oils—their number is certainly very high. However, only some 49 families (including 153 genera, without their synonyms) yield commercially or scientifically important oils.[2] To this number must be added the class *Coniferae* from among the subdivision *Gymnospermae,* the former consisting of 4 families with 15 genera. Moreover, there must also be included the genus *Evernia* from among the subclass *Ascolichenes* (which does not belong to the seed plants).

In addition there are several genera (*Fusanus, Umbellularia, Hardwickia, Myrocarpus, Mosla, Pycnanthemum, Saussurea, Tanacetum*) not found in the "Syllabus der Pflanzenfamilien"; they occur in the "Index Kewensis." In our table these additional genera are placed after those noted in the "Syllabus," but within their proper families. Otherwise, the sequence of families and genera follows the "Syllabus" throughout, and where there is a question of synonyms, priority has been given to the "Syllabus."

In the table below, the figures following each family and genus entry designate the volumes and pages of the present series where monographs devoted to the oils of that family and genus may be found. The names in parentheses are synonyms, in large part recorded in the "Index Kewensis" and frequently used in the literature. In our table, generic names are occasionally repeated as synonyms, with the pages cited, in order to make it possible to find them in the series under the synonymous name.

The standard reference work for plant illustrations is the "Index Londonensis" published by Kew Gardens; this covers material to 1941. It must be emphasized that this source does not carry illustrations, but is simply an index to them.

---

[1] To simplify the table, names of subclasses and orders have been omitted.

[2] Eight among the *Monocotyledones,* 41 among the *Dicotyledones.* According to George Neville Jones (*Sci. Monthly,* May 1951), the approximate known number of genera and species among the living *Angiospermae* is, for the *Monocotyledones,* 3,000 genera, with 50,000 species, and for the *Dicotyledones,* 9,500 genera, with 200,000 species. The *Coniferae* include 50 genera, with 550 species.

Division: *EUMYCETES (THALLOPHYTA)*
　Subclass: *ASCOLICHENES*
　　Family: *Usneaceae* (Vol. VI)
　　　Genus: *Evernia,* pp. 179–191

Division: *EMBRYOPHYTA SIPHONOGAMA* (SEED PLANTS)
　Subdivision: *GYMNOSPERMAE*
　　Class: *CONIFERAE*
　　　Family: *Podocarpaceae* (Vol. VI)
　　　　Genus: *Dacrydium,* pp. 195–197
　　　Family: *Pinaceae* (Vol. VI)
　　　　Genera: *Picea,* pp. 201–210; 217–222
　　　　　　　Tsuga, pp. 203–210
　　　　　　　Pseudotsuga, pp. 210–214
　　　　　　　Abies, pp. 214–234
　　　　　　　Cedrus, pp. 234–239
　　　　　　　Pinus, pp. 239–308
　　　Family: *Taxodiaceae* (Vol. VI)
　　　　Genera: *Sciadopitys,* pp. 311–312
　　　　　　　Cryptomeria, pp. 312–317
　　　Family: *Cupressaceae* (Vol. VI)
　　　　Genera: *Callitropsis,* pp. 321–323
　　　　　　　Thujopsis, pp. 323–325
　　　　　　　Thuja, pp. 325–332
　　　　　　　Cupressus, pp. 332–341
　　　　　　　Chamaecyparis, pp. 341–352
　　　　　　　Juniperus, pp. 353–389
　Subdivision: *ANGIOSPERMAE*
　　Class: *MONOCOTYLEDONES*
　　　Family: *Gramineae* (Vol. IV)
　　　　Genera: *Elyonurus* (*Elionurus, Lygeum*), pp. 153–155
　　　　　　　Vetiveria (*Anatherum, Andropogon*), pp. 156–180
　　　　　　　Cymbopogon (*Andropogon*), pp. 5–148
　　　　　　　Andropogon (*Cymbopogon, Amphilophis*), pp. 148–153
　　　Family: *Cyperaceae* (Vol. VI)
　　　　Genus: *Cyperus,* pp. 125–126
　　　Family: *Palmae* (Vol. VI)
　　　　Genus: *Cocos,* p. 121
　　　Family: *Araceae* (Vol. VI)
　　　　Genus: *Acorus,* pp. 109–117

Family: *Liliaceae* (Vol. VI)
Genera: *Allium,* pp. 67–71
Lilium, pp. 73–74
Hyacinthus, pp. 71–73
Convallaria, p. 75
Family: *Amaryllidaceae* (Vol. V)
Genera: *Narcissus,* pp. 348–352
Polyanthes, pp. 343–348
Family: *Iridaceae* (Vol. VI)
Genera: *Crocus,* p. 105
Iris, pp. 79–105
Family: *Zingiberaceae* (Vol. V)
Genera: *Hedychium,* pp. 131–132
Kaempferia, pp. 130–131
Curcuma, pp. 120–126
Alpinia, pp. 127–130
Zingiber, pp. 105–120
Aframomum (Amomum), pp. 103–105
Amomum, pp. 101–103
Elettaria, pp. 85–100
Class: *DICOTYLEDONES*
Family: *Piperaceae* (Vol. V)
Genus: *Piper,* pp. 135–161
Family: *Betulaceae* (Vol. VI)
Genus: *Betula,* pp. 11–20
Family: *Moraceae* (Vol. VI)
Genus: *Humulus,* pp. 129–142
Family: *Santalaceae* (Vol. V)
Genera: *Osyris,* pp. 193–194
Santalum, pp. 173–187; 191–192
Fusanus (Eucarya, Santalum), pp. 187–191
Family: *Aristolochiaceae* (Vol. VI)
Genus: *Asarum,* pp. 145–148
Family: *Chenopodiaceae* (Vol. VI)
Genus: *Chenopodium,* pp. 151–161
Family: *Caryophyllaceae* (Vol. V)
Genus: *Dianthus,* pp. 411–413
Family: *Ranunculaceae* (Vol. VI)
Genus: *Nigella,* p. 165
Family: *Magnoliaceae* (Vol. V)
Genera: *Magnolia,* pp. 382–383
Michelia, pp. 379–382
Illicium, pp. 361–379
Family: *Anonaceae* (Vol. V)
Genus: *Cananga (Canangium),* pp. 267–316
Family: *Myristicaceae* (Vol. V)
Genus: *Myristica,* pp. 59–81

Family: *Lauraceae* (Vol. IV)
  Genera: *Cinnamomum,* pp. 213–328
        Ocotea, pp. 199–203
        Sassafras, pp. 193–198
        Cryptocarya (Cryptocaria), pp. 211–213
        Laurus, pp. 204–207
        Umbellularia, pp. 207–210
        Aniba (Ocotea), pp. 183–193

Family: *Cruciferae* (Vol. VI)
  Genera: *Cochlearia (Armoracia),* pp. 63–64
        Brassica, pp. 55–62
        Raphanus, pp. 62–63

Family: *Resedaceae* (Vol. V)
  Genus: *Reseda,* pp. 401–403

Family: *Saxifragaceae* (Vol. V)
  Genus: *Philadelphus,* pp. 407–408

Family: *Hamamelidaceae* (Vol. V)
  Genera: *Hamamelis,* p. 255
        Liquidambar, pp. 243–254

Family: *Rosaceae* (Vol. V)
  Genera: *Spiraea,* p. 56
        Rosa, pp. 3–48
        Prunus, pp. 48–56

Family: *Leguminosae* (Vol. V)
  Genera: *Acacia,* pp. 227–237
        Copaifera, pp. 203–211
        Myroxylon, pp. 212–225
        Lupinus, pp. 239–240
        Genista, p. 239
        Spartium, pp. 237–239
        Wistaria, p. 240
        Hardwickia (Oxystigma), pp. 211–212
        Myrocarpus, pp. 225–227

Family: *Geraniaceae* (Vol. IV)
  Genera: *Geranium,* pp. 734–737
        Pelargonium, pp. 671–734

Family: *Zygophyllaceae* (Vol. V)
  Genus: *Bulnesia,* pp. 197–200

Family: *Rutaceae* (Vol. III)
  Genera: *Xanthoxylum,* pp. 376–378
        Ruta, pp. 378–385
        Pilocarpus, pp. 374–375
        Cusparia (Galipea), p. 363
        Boronia, pp. 364–367
        Barosma, pp. 368–372
        Amyris, pp. 385–391
        Clausena, pp. 372–374
        Citrus, pp. 5–359

Family: *Burseraceae* (Vol. IV)
  Genera: *Boswellia,* pp. 352–356
        Bursera, pp. 331–344
        Commiphora, pp. 344–352
        Canarium, pp. 357–360

Family: *Euphorbiaceae* (Vol. VI)
  Genus: *Croton,* pp. 169–170

Family: *Anacardiaceae* (Vol. V)
  Genera: *Pistacia,* pp. 169–170
        Schinus, pp. 165–168

Family: *Tiliaceae* (Vol. V)
  Genus: *Tilia,* p. 421

Family: *Malvaceae* (Vol. VI)
  Genus: *Abelmoschus* (*Hibiscus*), pp. 173–175

Family: *Dipterocarpaceae* (Vol. V)
  Genera: *Dryobalanops,* pp. 261–263
        Dipterocarpus, pp. 259–261

Family: *Cistaceae* (Vol. VI)
  Genus: *Cistus,* pp. 45–52

Family: *Violaceae* (Vol. V)
  Genus: *Viola,* pp. 391–398

Family: *Myrtaceae* (Vol. IV)
  Genera: *Myrtus,* pp. 363–369
        Pimenta (*Myrtus, Eugenia*), pp. 370–396
        Eugenia (*Caryophyllus*), pp. 396–437
        Leptospermum, pp. 526–529
        Melaleuca, pp. 529–548
        Eucalyptus, pp. 437–525

Family: *Umbelliferae* (Vol. IV)
  Genera: *Coriandrum,* pp. 602–615
        Cuminum, pp. 615–619
        Apium, pp. 591–602
        Petroselinum, pp. 656–663
        Carum, pp. 551–552; 573–584
        Pimpinella, pp. 563–570
        Foeniculum, pp. 634–645
        Anethum, pp. 619–634
        Oenanthe (*Phellandrium*), pp. 666–668
        Levisticum, pp. 649–654
        Angelica (*Archangelica*), pp. 553–563
        Ferula, pp. 570–572; 645–648; 665–666
        Peucedanum (*Imperatoria*), pp. 654–655
        Daucus, pp. 585–590
        Crithmum, pp. 663–665

Family: *Ericaceae* (Vol. VI)
  Genus: *Gaultheria,* pp. 3–7

Family: *Primulaceae* (Vol. V)
  Genus: *Cyclamen,* p. 417

Family: *Oleaceae* (Vol. V)
  Genera: *Syringa,* pp. 338–339
          Jasminum, pp. 319–338
Family: *Verbenaceae* (Vol. VI)
  Genus: *Lippia (Aloysia),* pp. 37–41
Family: *Labiatae* (Vol. III)
  Genera: *Rosmarinus,* pp. 695–710
          Lavandula, pp. 440–519
          Nepeta, pp. 434–436
          Salvia, pp. 710–738
          Monarda, pp. 527–535
          Melissa, pp. 395–399
          Hedeoma, pp. 583–586
          Satureia, pp. 739–744
          Hyssopus, pp. 436–440
          Origanum, pp. 525; 539–541; 542–545
          Majorana (Origanum), pp. 519–524
          Thymus, pp. 525–526; 744–763
          Mentha, pp. 576–583; 586–687
          Perilla, pp. 687–691
          Pogostemon, pp. 552–575
          Ocimum, pp. 399–433
          Mosla (Orthodon), pp. 545–552
          Pycnanthemum, pp. 691–695
          Coridothymus (Thymus), pp. 535–539; 541–542
Family: *Myoporaceae* (Vol. V)
  Genus: *Eremophila,* pp. 192–193
Family: *Rubiaceae* (Vol. V)
  Genera: *Gardenia,* pp. 355–356
          Leptactina, pp. 356–357
Family: *Caprifoliaceae* (Vol. V)
  Genus: *Lonicera,* p. 387
Family: *Valerianaceae* (Vol. VI)
  Genus: *Valeriana (Patrinia),* pp. 23–34
Family: *Compositae* (Vol. V)
  Genera: *Solidago,* pp. 464–467
          Erigeron, pp. 456–459
          Blumea, pp. 431–433
          Helichrysum, pp. 467–472
          Inula, pp. 453–456
          Tagetes, pp. 477–480
          Santolina, pp. 475–477
          Anthemis, pp. 433–437
          Achillea, pp. 425–426; 472–475
          Matricaria, pp. 438–445
          Artemisia, pp. 428–431; 451–453; 459–463; 485–496
          Arnica, pp. 426–428
          Saussurea (Aplotaxis, Aucklandia), pp. 446–451
          Tanacetum, pp. 480–485

INDEX

Numbers in *italics* indicate main entries; in the case of a plant species, they indicate references to monographs (or sections of monographs) dealing with the *oil* of the species.

Wherever possible, synonymous names for chemical compounds have been brought together under one main heading, such heading being in each case that employed in Vol. II of this series. Cross-references are made from the several synonyms. Thus, in the text, *Eudesmol* may also be called *Cryptomeradol* and *Machilol*. In this index, the latter names have been cross-referred to *Eudesmol*. The researcher interested in tracing the occurrence of any specific chemical compound in various oils should find this system helpful.

Abelmoschus moschatus, 173
Abies alba, 201, 202, *222*, 224
Abies alba—cone oil, *228*
Abies alba—leaf (needle) oil, *224*
Abies balsamea, 212, *231*, 232
Abies balsamifera, 231
Abies douglasii, 210
Abies excelsa, 224
Abies mayriana, 217, *219*, 220
Abies mucronata, 210
Abies pectinata, 224
Abies picea, 224
Abies sachalinensis, 217, *219*, 220, 221
Abies sibirica, 214
Abietene, 279
Acetaldehyde, 97, 161
Acetic acid, 18, 27, 31, 34, 39, 52, 74, 140, 146, 175, 189, 212, 271, 329, 336, 338, 352
Acetone, 18, 161, 235
Acetophenone, 48, 50, 51, 96, 98
Acetovanillone, 96
Acetoveratrone, 96, 98
Acorone, 116
Acoroxide, 116
Acorus calamus, 109
Aka-todo-matsu, 217
Albicaulene, 282
Allicin (allylsulfinyl-allyl sulfide), 67, 68
Alliin, 67, 68
Alliinase, 68
Allium cepa, 70
Allium sativum, 67
Allyl cyanide, 56, 57, 58, 59, 60
Allyl disulfide oxide, 69
Allyl isothiocyanate (allyl mustard oil), 55, 56, 57, 58, 59, 60, 63, 64
Allyl mustard oil, *see* Allyl isothiocyanate
Allylpropyl disulfide, 69
Allyl sulfenic acid, 68
Allyl sulfide, 67
Allylsulfinyl-allyl sulfide, *see* Allicin

Allyl thiocyanate, 56, 71
Aloysia citriodora, 37
Ambergris, 48
Ambrette seed oil, *173*
Ambrettolic acid, 175
Ambrettolide, 175
α-Amino acrylic acid, 68
Ammonia, 68, 161
Androl, 234
Anethole, 299
Anisaldehyde, 244, 250
Ansérine vermifuge, essence d', 151
Ao-todo-matsu, 217
Apple cider, 60
Araceae oils, 107
Araucaria cookii, 321
Araucaria oil, *321*
Arborvitae, eastern, 325
Arborvitae, false, *323*
Aristolochiaceae oils, 143
Aristolochia reticulata, 145 fn.
Aristolochia serpentaria, 145 fn.
Armoracia lapathifolia, 63
Asaronaldehyde (2,4,5-trimethoxybenzaldehyde), 114, 115, 148
Asarone (1,2,5-trimethoxy-4-propenylbenzene), 114, 115, 147
Asarum canadense, 145
Asarum europaeum, 147
Ascaridole, 151, 153, 154, 157, 158, 159, 160
Ascaridole glycol, 161
Atlantone, 237
α-Atlantone, 236, 237
γ-Atlantone, 236, 237
Atranol, 186, 188
Atranorin, 184, 186, 187, 188
Aurantine, 279
Azulene, 115, 146, 209, 250

Baldrianöl, 23
Balm of Gilead tree, 231
Balsam, Canada, *232*, 233

399

INDEX, VOLUMES I–VI

This Collective Index represents a careful revision and compilation of the individual indexes to each of the six volumes of the series "The Essential Oils."

Numbers in *italics* indicate main entries; in the case of plant species, they indicate references to monographs (or sections of monographs) dealing with the essential oil of the species. Roman numerals indicate specific volumes of the series.

Wherever possible, synonymous names for chemical compounds have been brought together under one main heading, such heading being in each case that employed in Vol. II of this series. Cross-references are made from the several synonyms. Thus, *n-Decylaldehyde*, in various volumes, may be called *Capraldehyde, Capric aldehyde*, or *Decanal*. In the present index, the last three names have been cross-referred to *n-Decylaldehyde*.

In the course of compiling this index, some inconsistencies of nomenclature were observed in the text; these have been noted and corrected. In very large part such inconsistencies may be traced to the original literature quoted by the authors of this series. This is particularly the case with the *older* chemical literature, where consistency in nomenclature is not always to be found.

Abbe refractometer, I, 244
Abelmoschus moschatus, VI, *173*
Abies alba, VI, 201, 202, *222*, 224
 —cone oil, VI, *228*
 —leaf (needle) oil, VI, *224*
Abies balsamea, VI, 212, *231*, 232
Abies balsamifera, VI, *231*
Abies douglasii, VI, *210*
Abies excelsa, VI, *224*
Abies mayriana, VI, 217, *219*, 220
Abies mucronata, VI, *210*
Abies pectinata, VI, *224*
Abies picea, VI, *224*
Abies sachalinensis, VI, 217, *219*, 220, *221*
Abies sibirica, VI, *214*
Abietene, VI, 279
Abietic acid, I, 37, 63; IV, 149; V, 246
Absinthe, essence d', V, *487*
Absinthin, V, 488
Absinthol, III, 717
Absolute flower oils—production (*see also individual flower oils*), I, 196, 199, 211, 217
Absolutes of *chassis* (*see also individual flower oils*), I, 197
Absolutes of *enfleurage* (*see also individual flower oils*), I, 196
Absynthole, V, 494
Acacia cavenia, V, 227, 228, 231, *232*
Acacia dealbata, V, *234*
Acacia decurrens var. *dealbata,* V, *234*
Acacia farnesiana, V, *227*, 232
Acacia floribunda, V, 234, 235
Acacia flower oil—production (*see also individual Acacia species*), I, 188

Acetal—b.p. (*Table*), I, 385
Acetaldehyde, I, 54, 62; II, *308*, 309, 332, 807; III, 127, 531, 616; IV, 304, 306, 569, 583; VI, 97, 161
 —b.p. (*Table*), I, 382
Aceteugenol, *see* Eugenol acetate
Acetic acid, II, 201, 375, 377, 378, 379, 407, 559, *561*, 565, 618, 620, 621, 623, 624, 626, 628, 630, 632, 794; III, 87, 106, 118, 126, 194, 200, 201, 241, 243, 284, 328, 356, 376, 419, 423, 436, 467, 468, 469, 503, 526, 529, 534, 585, 616, 633, 657, 672, 681, 694, 743; IV, 135, 140, 147, 150, 206, 303, 305, 348, 589, 590, 612, 648, 652, 655, 703, 727; V, 71, 78, 79, 237, 309, 403, 469, 470, 474; VI, 18, 27, 31, 34, 39, 52, 74, 140, 146, 175, 189, 212, 271, 329, 336, 338, 352
 —b.p. (*Table*), I, 386
Acetic anhydride—b.p. (*Table*), I, 387
Acetic ether, *see* Ethyl acetate
Acetins as adulterants, I, 338
Acetoacetic acid, I, 54, 55
Acetone (dimethyl ketone), I, 53 ff., 62; II, 170, 176, 259, 332, 341, *373*, 382, 384, 403, 458, 480; III, 529, 620; IV, 43; V, 309, 474; VI, 18, 161, 235
 —b.p. (*Table*), I, 382
Acétone anisique, V, 375
Acetophenone (acetylbenzene; hypnone; methyl phenyl ketone), II, *474*; VI, 48, 50, 51, 96, 98
 —b.p. (*Table*), I, 396
Acetovanillone, VI, 96
Acetoveratrone, VI, 96, 98

411